NEUROFEEDBACK AND SELF-REGULATION IN ADHD

Second Edition

WERNER VAN DEN BERGH, M.D.

www.bmedpress.com

BMED PRESS
health+care+science

For additional information about this book:

BMED Press LLC

5402 S. Staples St., STE 200

Corpus Christi, Tx 78411

(817) 400 – 1639

www.bmedpress.com

customer-service@bmedpress.com

ISBN: 978-0-9827498-6-9 (Softcover)

ISBN: 978-0-9827498-7-6 (Ebook)

A special thanks to Stephanie Clark for her translation of the first edition of this book.

CONTENTS

NEUROFEEDBACK AND SELF-REGULATION IN ADHD

A Non-Drug Therapy that Fosters Vigilance and Self-Regulation

INTRODUCTION TO THE NEW EDITION

ADHD (ATTENTION DEFICIT Hyperactivity Disorder) is the most common psychiatric disorder in children, with a prevalence of 5% according to DSM-5 (American Psychiatric Association, 2013). ADHD is caused by a disruption of the functioning of certain neural networks in the brain. ADHD is hereditary in more than half of the cases, with 30% of those affected having a least one parent with ADHD. Additionally, 30-50% of children with ADHD have significant difficulties that persist into adulthood, and they have an 80% chance of having at least one child with ADHD. It is necessary to note that ADHD has neurobiological origins; therefore, it is not caused by shortcomings in upbringing or by the increased expectations and demands of modern society.

ADHD is frequently comorbid with other behavioral disorders (Barkley, 2006), including sleep disorders (30 to 56%); oppositional defiant disorder (40 to 80%); conduct disorder (20 to 56%), as a precursor of antisocial personality disorder (20%); anxiety disorders (10 to 40%); depression (30%); bipolar disorder (6 to10%); substance use disorders (15 to 50%); tic disorders (10 to 15% for simple tic, less than 2% for Tourette's disorder); and specific learning disorders, such as dyslexia (20%), premenstrual dysphoric disorder, borderline personality disorder, autism spectrum disorders, and non-verbal learning disorders. A number of studies have shown (Cumyn, 2009) that more than 50% of adults with ADHD have a comorbid behavioral disorder.

Similar to most psychiatric disorders, ADHD is diagnosed using subjective behavioral ratings. This subjectivity often leads to persistent doubts concerning the validity of the diagnosis and its neurobiological causes. Over the last fifteen years, independent research groups published a steady stream of articles on the value of using QEEG (quantitative electroencephalogram) in the diagnosis of ADHD. This prompted the American Academy of Paediatrics, in their 2004 guidelines on ADHD, to describe QEEG as a valuable diagnostic tool that can improve our understanding of the fundamental neurophysiological disruption. To the present day, this new and important tool for objective diagnosis has been underused in clinical practice. In 2013, the U.S. Food and Drug Administration allowed marketing of the NEBA (Neuropsychiatric EEG-based Assessment Aid) System, which can assist in the assessment of ADHD in 6 to 17 years old children and adolescents.

Brain imaging studies (single photon emission computed tomography [SPECT], positron emission tomography [PET], and functional magnetic resonance imaging [fMRI]) of people with ADHD have provided growing evidence about the underlying neuroanatomical correspondences, especially at a functional anatomic level. A limitation of these imaging methods is that they provide no information on the temporal neurodynamics. EEG (electroencephalogram) analysis evaluates neuronal functional processes that last for just milliseconds, and it is therefore more suited for this purpose. Although QEEG can confirm an ADHD diagnosis in the form of statistically distinct or deviant EEG patterns, fundamental EEG research can provide a greater insight into what is amiss in the regulation of brain function and can enable a better understanding of the ways in which dysfunctions in behavioral regulation arise.

A great deal of published literature describes only the behavioral characteristics of ADHD. While these studies are frequently sufficient to guide a diagnosis, a strong need for more objective parameters rather than subjective behavioral descriptions remains. A deeper insight into the underlying dynamics can help us understand the essential nature of ADHD. We shall further discuss a deficiency in self-regulation as the origin of vigilance dysfunction, both of which are the fundamental underlying problems in ADHD. All too often, the simplified formulas that arise from a purely descriptive viewpoint of ADHD lead to the prescription of simplified solutions. These include mostly tips on the successful handling of behavioral difficulties, such as instructions that enable children to remain seated longer to complete homework.

That attention is a complex dynamic self-regulating system that is often overlooked. In ADHD, problems exist at far deeper levels than the superficial behavioral problems. Inadequate self-regulation is fundamentally responsible for the problems with vigilance, attention, and the consequent behavioral difficulties. More importantly, new developments in recent years help us understand that traditional concepts, such as response inhibition, have become obsolete at the neural level while new insights into more basic neural processes are being discovered. The principles of cognitive behavioral therapy (CBT), attention training, and cognitive self-instruction methods frequently fall short because the basic underlying neurobiological difficulties are not being considered. Meta-analytic results indicate that claims regarding the academic, behavioral, and cognitive benefits associated with the extant cognitive training programs are unsupported in ADHD (Rapport, 2013). Behavior therapy has its foundations in simplified behavioral models, such as Pavlov's classical conditioning model, which disregards that Pavlov himself stated that the degree of conditioning depends on individual variations in a dog's temperament. Even Watson (1909), the father of behaviorism and instrumental (operant) conditioning, in his prebehaviorist period wrote, "This gives us a key to what all animals of a particular species naturally do – i.e., the acts which they perform without training, tuition, or social contact with their fellow animals. It teaches the psychologist, too, the way to go about the animal's education – i.e., gives him a notion of the problems, which the structural peculiarities of the animal will *permit* him to learn… We must know the avenues through which we may appeal to him." ADHD is a syndrome with a reduced susceptibility to behavioral conditioning. These fundamental aspects of ADHD should be kept in mind during the diagnosis and treatment. We must first understand the causes of behavioral symptoms, and we must not allow ourselves to think that the symptoms are the problem. ADHD symptoms are the expression of poor self-regulation, and self-regulation is the key to effective behavioral change.

To build a practical understanding of self-regulation, we will consider the organization of the electrical activity of the brain. These include not only the empirical static differences expressed in the QEEG pattern, but also the recently uncovered dynamic changes in the electrophysiology of ADHD. These dynamic electrophysiological abnormalities provide increased insight into the system dysfunction that underlies ADHD and brings into focus a neuropsychological perspective of disturbed self-regulation in ADHD. The weaknesses of the clinical diagnostic system have led to the criticisms of ADHD diagnosis as subjective and have initiated a search of objective markers of this disease.

In this book, we examine deeply and systematically the patterns and emergence of electrical activity as well as the nature of the neural dysfunction in ADHD to arrive at a better understanding of ADHD and of the way in which effective treatment can address problems with state regulation. Effective treatment focuses on the improvement in self-regulation with a substantial contribution of both neurofeedback therapy and medication. As a treatment, neurofeedback therapy trains individuals to normalize the abnormal EEG pattern that reflects deviant brain activity specific to ADHD. Neurofeedback training not only modulates a particular EEG-pattern, but also encourages a broader reorganization of the EEG with consequent behavioral organization.

Neurofeedback originated in the late 1960s when Sterman described its accidental discovery following a treatment for epilepsy. In 1976, Joel Lubar reported its first application to the treatment of ADHD. Controlled studies were not available until 1995, and the first randomized controlled studies with follow up assessments for up to 2 years were published only in 2004. In the1980s, the first theoretical model emerged to explain how neurofeedback works. This was followed by a succession of published studies that investigated the application of neurofeedback to ADHD during the 1990s. As a result of these positive developments, neurofeedback became more connected to the objective and measurable QEEG instead of being based solely on clinical observations. Both neurofeedback and QEEG remained almost purely empirical and without a solid theoretical base. In the sixties, a functional dynamic model was developed to offer a theoretical framework for empirical EEG research on psychiatric problems (Bente, 1964; Ulrich 1994). A parallel stream of research studied the influence of psycho-pharmaceuticals on the EEG. This provided a framework to study and understand how methylphenidate medication (brand names: Ritalin SR™, Ritalin™, Concerta™) works. Traditional QEEG was limited to stationary power spectrum analysis and phase/coherence analysis. More recently, EEG amplitude envelop spectrum analysis as well as analysis of the EEG phase resets made it possible to study non-stationary aspects of the EEG and its temporal structure, which gave rise to important insights into metastability and self-organization. These more recent developments can be connected to Bente's early EEG vigilance model. On the other hand, since the start of this century, fMRI rest-state functional connectivity studies along with the application of the EEG to ADHD have contributed to the knowledge of large-scale brain networks. This knowledge can be transferred to the new methods of 3-D EEG source reconstruction, such as (s)LORETA. Moreover, new event-related potential methods allow us to study self-regulation.

There is a great need to advance our understanding of neurofeedback's mechanism of action, and this book aims to integrate available data from different research areas. It is vital that the theoretical models, formed out of the still growing studies on neurofeedback self-regulation mechanisms in ADHD in which precisely self-regulation is disturbed, find their way into clinical application. Thorough background knowledge of neurofeedback is not an optional extravagance for the neurofeedback therapist. The commercialization of this method frequently leads to inadequate therapist training, which lacks proper training or supervision, although it provides 'sufficient' simplified background guidance. These commercial neurofeedback training methods use exciting video games with simplified, standardized operating instructions, and they promote these games for the most divergent symptoms. Because of varying degrees of therapist incompetence, neurofeedback therapy is ineffective in many of these cases. These factors discredit the neurofeedback in some scientific and clinical circles. Hence, the fact that knowledgeably applied neurofeedback can be a highly effective treatment failed to gain widespread public acceptance. Even when an EEG neurofeedback training protocol seems to be rather simplistic at first sight, the critical elements to make it successful are often related to small but important details about how to instruct the patient, how to avoid rewarding artefacts, how to determine the thresholds, how to keep a patient motivated, how to monitor changes in EEG in different frequency bands and locations, and the like. These small but important details are related to the deeper backgrounds, which are discussed in this book. Even when not utilizing QEEG tools for diagnostic purposes and when not applying neurofeedback, these new insights are also helpful for a better understanding of ADHD and of the ways in which clinical ADHD situations should be handled. A deeper understanding of the brain's dynamics at systems' level can help us improve the assessment and treatment.

Since the first edition of this book in 2010, many new developments have taken place. We review a series of new randomized controlled clinical studies and new meta-analysis studies of neurofeedback in ADHD. Additionally, we offer new insights into the neurophysiological underpinnings of self-regulation and vigilance, which are the central problem in ADHD. Self-regulation is also the essential working mechanism of neurofeedback. Therefore, we replaced 'state regulation' by 'self-regulation' in the title of this book. State regulation refers to the ability to adapt brain states to changing environments and indeed, it is disturbed in ADHD. Self-regulation is a more comprehensive concept, which also includes state regulation. Self-regulation implies that the whole brain works as a system, which organizes itself and where agency is not the initiator but the outcome of the whole system. It also implies a combination of bottom-up and top-down processes, which culminate in executive functioning, reinforced learning, and preferred behavioral options, which all together give rise to decision-making guided by long-term goals with motivation. The cortical EEG oscillations drive these processes. Neurofeedback uses these self-regulation processes with the goal to improve self-regulation through its application to the treatment of ADHD, as neurofeedback in ADHD not only addresses the EEG oscillations involved in self-regulation deficits, but also serves as a self-regulation treatment. New insights into ADHD from the viewpoint of large-scale brain networks, which have been discovered only during this century, will also be discussed.

It is critical to acknowledge that, especially in neurosciences, it is important not only to gather facts, but also to interpret them with theoretical models. Since the models approximate the reality, they are by definition false. To paraphrase the statement from statistician George Box that all models are wrong but some are useful, the utility of any model comes from its capacity to explain neural dynamics and cognitive function and to suggest further avenues of research to test and develop the model. Finally, one of the greatest sins in analyzing the electrophysiological data is to assume that there is a single correct signal analysis method. While one can certainly make mistakes in the application of a method, there is little to be gained from 'analytic chauvinism.' The complexity of the data extracted from electrophysiological methods indicates that a single analytic approach is insufficient. Deepening our knowledge of the data and their different models will help us discover intriguing insights along with pitfalls and limitations. This should help us apply electrophysiological assessments and treatments efficiently and cautiously.

CHAPTER 1
Vigilance and Self-Regulation in ADHD

THE TERM ADHD (attention deficit disorder with or without hyperactivity) officially came into use only with its official introduction to the handbook of the American Psychiatric Association, the DSM-IV in 1994. Previously, the terms 'hyperkinetic syndrome' or 'minimal brain dysfunction' (MBD) were used, and in 1980, the term ADD was introduced in DSM-III.

Consequently, the emphasis shifted decisively to the presence of attentional disturbances in ADHD. Canadian psychologist Virginia Douglas (1972) inspired this change, which emphasized problematic self-regulation of attention as the fundamental problem. Disturbed self-regulation expresses itself through difficulties of planning, organization, self-control, and the maintenance of a measured, adaptive level of alertness. Within this schema, sleep regulation problems were also described, which were incidentally adopted in 1980 as one of the diagnostic criteria (hyperactivity during sleep). In later sanctioned guidelines, this last element would be dropped not because it did not occur frequently, but because it was regarded as insufficiently specific. Douglas also emphasized that ADHD children are guided to a much greater degree by the immediate results of their behavior rather than by the likely long-term consequences.

Since the introduction of the ADHD concept, a variant form without hyperactivity, which describes ADHD individuals as rather passive dreamers, has also been acknowledged. Even now, this form is still frequently overlooked because people with this variant are less disruptive (within their environment) and often encounter learning and self-image difficulties only at a later age (9-14) compared to those with hyperactivity. It has long been recognized that hyperactivity in adulthood often decreases or becomes expressed as inner unrest. This lies at the root of the old idea that hyperkinetic syndrome disappears in adulthood. Difficulties with attention and organization are stressed more often now. Increasingly, we have come to realize that for at least half of the children, these problems with attention and organization will survive into adulthood. The change in nomenclature from 'subtypes' to 'presentations' in DSM-5 (2013) reflects increasing evidence that symptoms within individuals are often fluid across their lifespan rather than stable.

Attention difficulties were recognized as the fundamental problem only after Douglas emphasized that the root cause of the disorder lies in the brain and not in the character of the child with ADHD. Moreover, after Douglas highlighted the role of attention, the interest in the disorder among psychiatrists and scientists has greatly increased. Later, Virginia Douglas commented that she personally would have preferred to call the disorder a 'disturbance of self-regulation.' Since the 1970s, she demonstrated in a number of studies that the nature of the attention deficits in ADHD is tied to task complexity. For example, reaction times are too slow in simple or stimulus-poor tasks while they are too quick in complex or stimulus-rich tasks. This can be measured clearly with computerized attention tasks. Both reaction time anomalies improve after the administration of Ritalin. These observations led Douglas to characterize ADHD as an inadequate 'self-regulation,' which negatively affects the appropriate investment, apportioning, organization, and maintenance of attention. Moreover, inadequate 'self-regulation' contributes to the development of impulsive behaviour and a strong tendency to seek immediate gratification. Her studies revealed that Ritalin works to improve not just attention, but also self-regulation. For example, 'working memory' has been found to improve along with 'divergent thinking ability' (i.e., creative 'fan-like' associations along lines of thought) and mental flexibility.

The American psychologist Russell Barkley (1994) further developed the self-regulation model in 1990. He defined self-regulation or, alternately, self-control as any self-directed action that adjusts the individual's response to an event and produces a net change in the long-term consequences of that behavior to the long-term advantage of the individual. An adjustable level of self-control allows for the flexible adaptation of behavior to the changing demands of daily tasks. If self-control is insufficient, immediate external factors rather than foreseeable long-term consequences determine the behavior.

Together with other factors, this contributes to impairments in working memory and problems with self-control of motivation, working memory, attention, and emotion. Impaired self-control explains the development of problems in ADHD, especially the lack of perseverance to long-term goals and the deficits in internal supervision. The definition of ADHD developed by Barkley implicates inadequate 'executive functions' that are associated with the frontal cerebral cortex and contribute to the disruption of self-regulation. The term 'executive functions' generally encompasses working memory, including, among other things, the sense of time, behavioral anticipation from previous experience that forms a base for planning and execution), self-talk (including self instruction), self-regulation of emotion, motivation, alertness, and the ability to analyze and recombine a problem to create a novel solution (reconstitution). Executive functions may be defined as 'neurocognitive processes that maintain an appropriate problem-solving set to attain a later goal' (Willcutt, 2005). There is good evidence of impairment in various executive function measures amongst groups of children with ADHD. However, executive function deficits are not specific to ADHD: they occur in children with other conditions and are not uncommon in children with no disorders. Conversely, children can meet criteria for ADHD diagnosis and not show impairment in executive functions.

Because of this disturbance in self-regulation, ADHD behavior lacks sufficient internal guidance, and others often judge it as chaotic, reactive, and ill considered. Thought and action, knowledge and performance, past, future, and the moment are all distinguished from one another. ADHD does not disrupt knowledge of a correct action; instead, it affects the actual behavioral performance and optimal timing of that knowledge at the appropriate moments. These factors convey the impression that ADHD is a disorder of 'will power' or motivation, which greatly contributes to misunderstanding and irritation from others. Normally, adaptive self-controlled behavior is governed less by immediate demands and more by long-term consequences (predicted based on experience). People with ADHD have a sort of time 'blindness', so that the individual functions, for the most part, from moment to moment. This clouded time perception is linked to a diminished ability to hold the order of events in working memory. We have the impression that free will is curtailed; although, in a way, it could be argued that someone with ADHD is freer and less enslaved by time. We all think back nostalgically to the innocence of childhood when our behavior was free from time's dictates. However, as adults, we must let time co-rule our behavior if we are to adapt and survive in the society. This impoverished sense of time explains why someone with ADHD cannot tolerate delay and is frequently impatient. This also partly explains the procrastination behaviors and the unsuccessful attempts to teach time management to someone with ADHD. Regardless of how well someone with ADHD learns these techniques, it often does not lead to behavioral changes (i.e., improved time awareness).

The executive functions associated with frontal brain areas start to develop clearly only at around 6 years of age. This explains why it is very difficult to diagnose ADHD before age six. Moreover, it can explain why both executive functions, which remain problematic after hyperactivity, and situationally linked attentional difficulties diminish in adulthood. Considering that the prevailing diagnostic criteria were developed with children and adolescents between the ages of 6 to 18, they often offer little support for diagnostic decisions in adulthood. Therefore, it is useful to investigate working memory's (planning and strategy use) perception, organization of time, internal speech (following instructions), self control of emotions and motivation, goal directed creativity, and perseverance in the assessment of both adults and children.

Virginia Douglas and Russell Barkley received great recognition for shaping the understanding of ADHD as a disorder of self-regulation. However, their approach does not sufficiently account for the neurodynamics, as they do not question the origins of the 'self' that self-regulates; instead, they seem to assume unduly that 'self' corresponds to our 'I' that controls everything. The self-regulation model postulated by Douglas was among the first to shift focus from specific cognitive deficits, such as sustained attention, response inhibition, or working memory, to processes that may influence all of these constructs. A recent formulation of Douglas' model (2008) suggests that complex effortful (or adaptive) control processes contribute to efficient attention and inhibition. Effortful control is conceptually related to self-regulation and executive functions, and it is thought to modulate other cognitive processes implicated in ADHD, including working memory, self-monitoring, and planning. Although this model provides an interesting and plausible alternative to the cognitive deficit models of ADHD, empirical examination of regulatory deficits has proven difficult, given their complexity and poor operationalization.

More recently, studies have highlighted the importance of 'state regulation' in ADHD because attention problems are certainly partly attributable to an erratic capacity to maintain an optimal and stable state of alertness, specifically, state regulation is not as internally steered while it is too strongly dependent on external factors (van der Meere, 2001). Weak state regulation has been studied in many young children, shedding light on possible later life malfunctions in attentional self-regulation. Small children with lax self-regulation demonstrate difficulty in stabilizing their alertness (in attentional terms: a fluctuating and frequently suboptimal alertness level) and an unregulated sleep wake cycle. State regulation can therefore be described as a task adaptive behavior related to biologically based (versus psychologically based) motivation. The management or evaluation mechanism in this model is however lacking a clear description and operationalization of the self-monitoring and adaptive control processes. Thus, ADHD may involve deficits in self-monitoring and adaptive control, both of which are necessary for effective self-regulation but have been difficult to study.

Self-regulation has been implicated in prominent theories of ADHD (Douglas, 1999; Sergeant, 2000), and it is gaining research attention, as single core deficit models (cognition; motivation) are increasingly viewed as insufficient to understand this heterogeneous disorder. However, empirical studies of self-regulation have proven difficult due to the complexity of this construct and the relative lack of reliable and valid measures of the relevant processes. Fortunately, over the past several years, extensive research has been conducted on the neurophysiological correlates of self-regulation. Cognitive neuroscience research has identified a reliable electrophysiological index of performance monitoring, the error-related negativity (ERN or Ne) (Falkenstein, 1991), and the no-go P3 anteriorization (Fallgätter, 2004), which are generated in the dorsal anterior cingulate cortex, a brain structure involved in self-monitoring and behavioral regulation and in the pathophysiology of ADHD. These neurophysiological indices provide a window into the understanding of the regulatory processes that may be broadly important in ADHD yet have previously been challenging to operationalize. Additionally, the right inferior frontal gyrus is playing a role in what has been traditionally called response inhibition. Newer insights however pinpoint the underlying attentional dysfunctions and dysfunctional context monitoring as a more basic neural substrate for this executive function. Besides the dorsal anterior cingulate and the right inferior frontal gyrus, the ventromedial prefrontal cortex is playing an important role in self-regulation by attributing value to selected actions. Intrinsic motivational values of actions are related to the 'self,' which probably for this reason also has its neural substrate in the ventromedial prefrontal cortex.

Self-regulation is also important to regulate vigilance. In 1923, Henry Head developed a doctrine of 'vigilance,' which he regarded as a neurologically based activity that determines the complexity and 'level' of organic and psychological response. Head was inspired by the disintegration ideas of the great 19th century British neurologist Hughlings Jackson. 'Vigilance' came into operation whenever any instance of human behavior occurred; thus, it could be associated with extremely varied behavior results, which Head failed to explain adequately. Mackworth (1950), commissioned by the Royal Air Force in 1948 to address the observed decline in radar operator performance, devised the 'vigilance tasks.' Subsequently, in 1950, the British Medical Research Council published Mackworth's monograph entitled 'Researches in the measurement of human performance,' attracting widespread notice. As every psychologist will know, the terms 'vigilance situation,' 'vigilance task,' and 'vigilance test' almost, if not entirely, replaced the original use of 'vigilance' as direct nervous activity. This represented far more than just a change in terminology. 'Situations,' 'tasks,' and 'tests,' used by Mackworth and many others in the rather wider sense, all raise direct and definable experimental problems, whereas 'vigilance' in its simple and generalised form does not. A 'situation' and a 'task' are things that can be characterized, produced, and controlled within limits. A 'test' is something that can be produced and reproduced. The word 'vigilance' was used (and still is widely used) as adjective to qualify classes of situations, tasks, and tests and not as a noun to define a theoretical activity directly. Thus, speaking of vigilance tasks, situations, and tests brings the vigilance topic into the field of experiment while at the same time, it revives some of the old problems of 'attention' and 'vigilance' regarded as generalized activities that are often determined in part by immediate stimuli and in many instances by more remote conditions or by events within the psychological or neurological response systems. Perhaps an even more influential movement in research are the classic studies of the brain stem reticular formation by Moruzzi and Magoun (1949) in which they characterized 'attention' and 'vigilance' as a cortical activation or arousal system, respectively; these studies also helped bring back into vigorous discussion views reminiscent of 'attention' prior to, and of 'vigilance' in, the 1920's. What has actually happened is that experiment has shown that Head's old concept of vigilance was not entirely wrong but only insufficiently formulated. The psychological past constantly, so to speak, returns, but always in new forms. To understand and value current practice, it is necessary to know something of that past but never be wholly ruled by it. Nevertheless, the concept of 'vigilance,' as used today, usually refers to Mackworth's experimental concept. The good news is that in the 1960s, the German psychiatrist Bente (1969) rediscovered Head's concept of vigilance and, inspired by the neo-Jacksonian French psychiatrist Henri Ey (1938), developed a framework to translate these ideas into EEG patterns. His work was further elaborated by his collaborator Ulrich (1994, 2013), but their ideas did not spread to the larger neuroscience community. Even their successors, such as Hegerl (2008), who used Bente's vigilance model, still see vigilance as a synonym for arousal, limiting the scope to the same simple level as the traditional arousal model, which is still used by many neurofeedback practitioners. The good news however is that recent work by Leech and Sharp (2014) in the UK has developed the 'Arousal, Balance and Breadth of Attention Model,' emphasizing the important role of the dorsal posterior cingulate in interaction with the central executive network and the dorsal attention network, where functional metastability is the most important characteristic. Leech and Sharp do not seem to be aware that their model is very similar to Head's concept of vigilance, which was also born in the UK; nevertheless, their work has been substantiated by recent neuroscience research.

Sleep deprivation in people without ADHD could be used as a model for ADHD. One night or more of insufficient sleep weakens attention and thus the complex organization of behavior. In this case, momentary stimuli in the outside world rather than internal planning reflexively determine the behavior. An analogy that comes to mind is a pile of unorganized paper on a desk that needs attention. Similarly, people who are sleep deprived or with ADHD will muddle through without making clear decisions and will address the paperwork with equal urgency instead of employing classification and prioritization schemes.

Cognitive neuroscience researchers use neurophysiological indices of error processing to examine the components of self-regulation and related factors. This approach may fill an important gap in the regulatory deficit models of ADHD by providing methods to parse the aspects of self-monitoring and adaptive control. At a neurophysiological level, self-regulation must involve the integrated functioning of structures that serve high-level cognition, such as the prefrontal cortices, and structures that serve motivation, such as the limbic system (Pennington, 2005). Adaptive control is considered an important part of self-regulation, involving the frontal systems of the brain, including the prefrontal cortex, the anterior cingulate cortex, and the basal ganglia (Holroyd & Coles, 2002). Executive function systems are thought to regulate the most global aspects of human behavior, such as planning and decision-making, particularly when a task is novel or difficult. Importantly, deficits in regulation of cognition, emotion, or behavior may depend on an individual's ability to determine when adaptive control is required.

Although not classified among the core symptoms of ADHD in DSM-III, DSM-IV, and DSM-5, deviations in affect as well as poor motivation were considered primary clinical symptoms in earlier classifications of childhood ADHD (Clements, 1966), and they are still a major part of childhood ADHD today. It has also been recognized that ADHD in adulthood often includes emotional over-reactivity, mood swings, and irritability (Wender, 2001) and that mood disorders are often seen as comorbidity in ADHD in adults. New fMRI studies of the large-scale brain networks have also shown that besides the default mode network, the central executive network, the attention networks, the salience network, and the motivation/affect networks are dysregulated in ADHD.

Summary

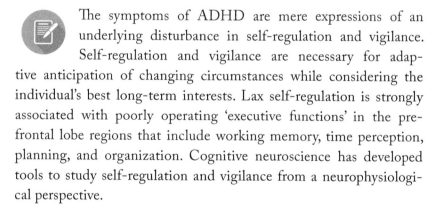The symptoms of ADHD are mere expressions of an underlying disturbance in self-regulation and vigilance. Self-regulation and vigilance are necessary for adaptive anticipation of changing circumstances while considering the individual's best long-term interests. Lax self-regulation is strongly associated with poorly operating 'executive functions' in the prefrontal lobe regions that include working memory, time perception, planning, and organization. Cognitive neuroscience has developed tools to study self-regulation and vigilance from a neurophysiological perspective.

CHAPTER 2
Large-Scale Brain Networks/Systems and Their Involvement in ADHD

ADHD HAS LONG been thought to reflect dysfunction of prefrontal-striatal circuitry while largely ignoring the involvement of other circuits. Recent advances in systems neuroscience-based approaches to brain dysfunction enable the development of models of ADHD pathophysiology that encompass a number of different large-scale 'resting state' networks. What has only recently been appreciated is that large-scale neural systems exhibit synchronous intrinsic fluctuations at rates 10-100 times slower compared to the usual EEG frequencies. These fluctuations persist during tasks, rest, wakefulness, and sleep, and their correlations reflect the underlying connectivity of the brain's functional units. In other words, task-based imaging is no longer the only means of identifying neural networks because intrinsic relationships are continuously encoded in the spontaneous activity of the brain, and these can be most easily appreciated during rest. The growing work on the role of brain oscillations in coordinating activity within and between neural networks is consistent with such hypotheses that localize neuropsychological impairments at the circuit level of function rather than within specific individual brain regions. Converging lines of evidence support the hypothesis that ADHD results from dysregulated or aberrant interactions within and among large-scale neural systems.

2.1 Large-Scale Brain Networks

2.1.1 Default Mode Network (DMN)

Traditionally, and certainly in the first decade after fMRI has been introduced to study brain function, studies of brain function have focused on task-evoked responses. However, Berger who discovered the EEG in the 1920's wrote, 'Mental work adds only a small increment to the cortical work, which is going on continuously and not only in the waking state.' Only since 2001, fMRI studies have been targeting the intrinsic activity of brain networks involving information processing to interpret, respond to, and predict environmental demands. Raichle (2001) named this activity 'dark energy.' In the earlier fMRI studies, investigators looked only at cognitive task scans without resting state scans to identify areas involved in performing the tasks. Raichle started to look at the resting state scans without the task scans. What immediately caught his attention was the fact that regardless of the task under investigation, activity decreases were clearly present and almost always included the posterior cingulate and the adjacent precuneus. When self-referential mental activity was present, the anterior medial prefrontal cortex was also involved.

A major step forward was the discovery that this large-scale network organization, including but not limited to the DMN, could be revealed by studying the patterns of spatial coherence in the spontaneous fluctuations over time of the fMRI blood-oxygen dependent (BOLD) signal. By selecting a 'seed' in a region of interest (ROI), one is able to detect the functional anatomy of an intrinsic network by looking at correlated infra-slow fluctuations of the BOLD signal. In this way, other intrinsic networks were discovered, including the ventral and dorsal attention network, the frontoparietal control network, the salience network, the motivation network, and others. Even when these latter networks become active only during active tasks, their basic coherence remains intact when there are no tasks ready to be activated.

The DMN contains two hubs, the anterior medial PFC (aMPFC) and posterior cingulate cortex (PCC), and two subcomponent systems, the dorsomedial prefrontal cortex (dMPFC) subsystem and the medial temporal lobe (MTL) subsystem. In a model that combines task-based and resting state data, Andrews-Hanna (2010) established that the dMPFC subsystem is activated when subjects perform self-referential cognitive processes anchored in the present while the MTL subsystem is preferentially activated by cognitions regarding projecting oneself into the future.

2.1.2 Dorsal Attention Network (DAN)

At the same time as the DMN was identified, Corbetta proposed a two-component model for top-down and bottom-up attentional control (Corbetta and Shulman, 2002;

Corbetta, 2008). Top-down influences involve a DAN comprising the superior parietal lobe, intraparietal sulcus, and frontal eye fields. On the other hand, the VAN conveys bottom-up influences, mediating changes in attentional focus and two-way transitions between the default and executive networks.

The DAN system includes regions in the frontal eye fields, ventral premotor cortex, superior parietal lobule, intraparietal sulcus, and motion-sensitive middle temporal area (MT+). This system tracks performance on tasks involving search and detection. Specifically, activity in the dorsal attention system increases at the onset of search displays, maintains activity while awaiting a target, and further increases activity when targets are detected (Corbetta and Shulman, 2002). The DAN system is anticorrelated with the DMN system and conveys top-down (goal-driven) influences in attentional focus (Corbetta and Shulman, 2002; Corbetta, 2008).

2.1.3 Ventral Attention Network (VAN)

On the other hand, the VAN conveys bottom-up (stimulus-driven) influences, mediating the changes in attentional focus and two-way transitions between the default and executive networks. The VAN is strongly lateralized to the right and comprises the temporo-parietal junction (TPJ) (supramarginal and superior temporal gyri) and the middle and inferior frontal gyri. As with the default network, the metabolic activity of the VAN decreases during focused states, and it becomes transiently activated during attentional reorientation. Dorsal and ventral attention networks interact to keep the focus of attention guided by ongoing expectations while maintaining the responsiveness to potentially important but unattended sensory information.

The role of the VAN during task performance, attentional reorienting, and goal-directed behavior remains enigmatic because its temporal dynamics and link to behavior are still poorly understood. One hypothesis is that the VAN works as a circuit breaker that interrupts ongoing cognitive activity by modulating dorsal network selection when an unexpected behaviorally relevant event is at hand (Corbetta, 2008). However, it is not clear where the reorienting signal initiates and whether the interaction between the two systems occurs directly or through connections with sensory areas. Although reorienting to behaviorally relevant events is critical for survival, reorienting to irrelevant stimuli may interfere with task performance. Hence, during demanding cognitive engagement, it may be advantageous to impose an attentional filter that restricts VAN activation, protecting the ongoing focus of attention from distractors. When attention is focused, the ventral network is suppressed to prevent reorienting to distracting events. The source of the filtering signal may be the dorsal network or other parts of prefrontal cortex (such as the anterior cingulate and anterior insula) either directly or indirectly via subcortical loops.

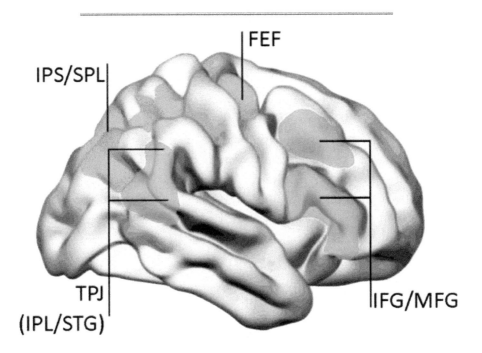

Figure 1. Dorsal and Ventral Attention Network (Corbetta and Shulman, 2002).

While originally conceptualized as a system for redirecting attention from one object to another, recent evidence suggests a more general role for the VAN in switching between networks, which may explain recent evidence of its involvement in functions such as social cognition. An intriguing development in the last few years is that activation of right TPJ, the posterior core of the ventral attention network, has been reported during the 'theory of mind' (ToM) cognition, i.e., reasoning about other people's mental states. Colocalization of the right TPJ for attention reorientation and ToM might reflect cognitive processes that are present in both paradigms. For example, both reorienting and ToM paradigms often involve breaches of expectation (e.g., invalid cues or false-belief stories), which appear to modulate the ventral network. Decety and Lamm (2007) suggested that many aspects of social cognition involve a comparison of 'internal predictions with actual external events,' explaining the ubiquitous presence of right TPJ activity. Another possibility along these lines is that TPJ activity during ToM tasks reflects signals linked to shifts in eye gaze or perception or imagery of gaze. Several studies have shown that posterior STS is activated during the perception of gaze shifts. Finally, in ToM experiments, subjects continually shift between a simulation or judgment of the other person's mind or viewpoint and processing of perceptual evidence from their own viewpoint that supports the simulation or judgment.

Interestingly, the most rostral part of the right TPJ (rostral part of the inferior parietal lobule and superior temporal sulcus), together with the most caudal part of the right inferior frontal gyrus, is a part of the mirror neuron system, which plays a role in intuitive pre-reflective social introspection. On the other hand, the most rostral part of the inferior parietal lobule and superior temporal sulcus are parts of the reflective mentalizing ToM system. Interestingly, the right inferior frontal gyrus is also a part of the ventral attention system.

2.1.4 Frontoparietal Control Network (FPCN)

Vincent (2008) reported a detailed spatial characterization of a third system - the frontoparietal control system - that is anatomically interposed between the DMN and DAN. Thus, the frontoparietal control system may be uniquely positioned to integrate information coming from the other two systems and to adjudicate between potentially competing inner- versus outer-directed processes.

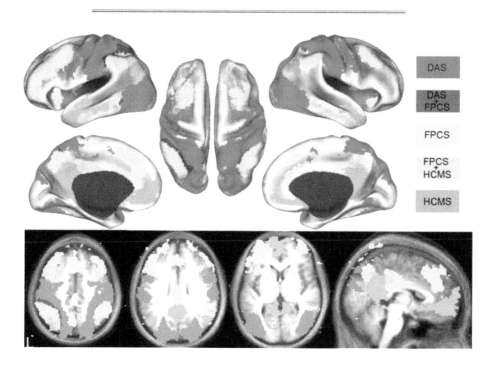

Figure 2. Interposition of the frontoparietal control system between the hippocampal memory system (DMN) and the dorsal attention network (Vincent, 2008)

Vincent's motivation to undertake this exploration emerged based on the extensive literature that suggests executive control systems guide decision-making by integrating information from the external environment with stored internal representations. Tasks that require simultaneous consideration of multiple interdependent contingencies or conflicting stimulus-response mappings and the process of integrating working memory with attentional resource allocation engage a similar system that includes anterior cingulate, lateral parietal, and prefrontal cortex. The anterior prefrontal cortex (aPFC, Brodmann area 10), in particular, is most responsive during tasks that demand integrating the outcomes of multiple cognitive operations in the pursuit of a higher behavioral goal. Koechlin and Hyafil (2007) noted that lateral prefrontal regions select and maintain the task sets governing ongoing action, whereas the frontopolar cortex (aPFC) enables previously selected task sets to be maintained in a pending state for subsequent automatic retrieval and execution on completion of the ongoing one, which suggests that the aPFC is at the apex of the cognitive control hierarchy (see also Badre and D'Esposito, 2007). Further, there is a reason to believe that this area of the brain is greatly expanded in humans relative to macaques and apes. For these reasons, the aPFC was selected for the initial functional connectivity analyses of a potential cognitive control system. Vincent reported the frontoparietal control system to include the anterior prefrontal, dorsolateral prefrontal, dorsomedial superior frontal/anterior cingulate, anterior inferior parietal lobule, and anterior insular cortex. This constellation of regions is commonly engaged by tasks that require controlled processing of information. Task paradigms eliciting controlled processing related to the simultaneous consideration of multiple interdependent contingencies, conflicting stimulus-response mappings, and integrating working memory with attentional resource allocation commonly engage the frontoparietal control system. Previous research has defined the roles for regions within the frontoparietal control system. Anterior cingulate cortex commonly increases activity after the commission of errors (Carter, 1998; Dosenbach, 2006), which is consistent with a role of this region in conflict monitoring during task performance (Botvinick, 2004). The anterior cingulate cortex has also been implicated in the instantiation of action sets, as it transiently responds at the start of task blocks (Dosenbach, 2006). This result is consistent with observation that lesions in or around anterior cingulate cortex lead to impaired initiation of voluntary actions (Cohen, 1999). The aIPL often increases activity during tasks involving working memory, and it may serve as a temporary storage buffer. The aPFC has been associated with the coordination of information processing and information transfer between multiple brain regions during the performance of concurrent tasks (Koechlin, 1999; Ramnani and Owen, 2004).

2.1.5 Salience Network (SN); Cingulo-Opercular network

Seeley (2007) split the frontoparietal control system into two parts, one associated with 'salience' (including dorsal anterior cingulate dACC and orbital fronto-insular AI cortex) and the other associated with 'executive control' (including dorsolateral frontal and parietal cortex). Dosenbach (2007) also examined functional correlations within a region in or near the presently described frontoparietal system and distinguished between cingulo-opercular and frontoparietal networks as well. One challenge in studying brain networks is that they can be defined differently by different groups. Some people consider the salience network to be the same as the cingulo-opercular network. Others suggest that they are two different networks with different functions set closely together in the brain.

The AI (anterior insula) and dACC are part of a functional circuit involved in both attention as well as interoceptive and affective processes. Recent research has also suggested that a key function of this network is to identify the most homeostatically relevant stimulus among several internal and extrapersonal stimuli to guide behavior.

The salience network was initially defined by Seeley (2007) as a set of regions that encode emotional and cognitive processes that are personally relevant, whereas the ventral attention network has been implicated in bottom-up/stimulus-driven attention (Corbetta, 2008). Although these proposed roles of salience vs. ventral attention networks are not identical, the high degree of spatial overlap between the two putative networks as well the observation that regions within the salience network, such as the dACC, respond robustly during salient sensory stimulation suggest that the salience and ventral attention networks are highly functionally inter-related. Alternatively, they can be considered a single bilateral network.

The aINS and dACC are considered to be the core of the salience network (Menon and Uddin, 2010), and they are also among the regions that are commonly activated in many types of task fMRI, including pain studies. The SN also includes two key subcortical structures, the amygdala and the substantia nigra/ventral tegmental area (SuN/VTA), which are important for detecting emotional and reward saliency.

2.1.6 Motivational (Reward) / Affective (Limbic) Network

The medial orbitofrontal cortex (value attribution), anterior cingulate and anterior insula (saliency), amygdala and ventral striatum have been described as the motivational network. There is a strong overlap with the salience network.

Key components of the affective network include hippocampus, parahippocampal gyrus, amygdala, orbitofrontal cortex, medial frontal cortex, nucleus accumbens (ventral striatum), subgenual anterior cingulate cortex, and anterior insula. One could say that reward and motivation are one aspect of the affective states.

2.2 Electrophysiological Signatures of Large-Scale Brain Networks

Very low frequency EEG oscillations (VLF, 0.02–0.2 Hz; Vanhatalo, 2004) are similar to baseline slow hemodynamic oscillations (0.01–0.08 Hz), displaying decreased amplitude in ADHD (Zang, 2007). Several authors have characterized the EEG activity related to the default network based on topographic distributions of low-frequency oscillations that have been found to activate–deactivate between rest and task conditions (Helps, 2008, 2009). In ADHD subjects, power in VLF oscillations is reduced compared to controls, and deactivation in rest-to-task transitions is weaker (Helps, 2010). Furthermore, in low-rating ADHD subjects, this deactivation is stronger than in high-rating ADHD subjects, and it is also stronger in the medial prefrontal cortex and in temporal regions (Broyd, 2011). In a magneto-encephalography study, adults with ADHD exhibited broadband deficits in medial prefrontal cortices (MPFC) but not in other DMN regions compared to adults without ADHD (Wilson, 2013). It has also been demonstrated that the oscillations of the amplitude strength of all traditional EEG frequency bands at Fz are in a fixed phase delay with the infra slow BOLD oscillations (Palva and Palva, 2012).

Sadaghiani (2012) established that the differentiation of three important functional brain networks by virtue of different intrinsic connectivity is paralleled by distinct electrophysiological signatures. While all networks show selective associations with alpha oscillations, these differ in sign (DAN, SN) and in property, power versus phase locking (SN, FPCN). The likely reason for these associations is not direct and biophysical, but indirect and functional. Different aspects of a single oscillation band may be related to different functions of these networks. The relationship involving alpha oscillations in tonic (intrinsically maintained) alertness (SN, alpha synchronization, which is modulated by SN but has its source in posterior DMN); their long-range phase locking in phasic (externally triggered) alertness, which supports phasic aspects of cognitive executive control (FPCN); and their focal desynchronization in top-down guided selective attention (DAN) is hierarchical. Bottom-up (salience) as well as top-down modulation can recruit executive control.

Active processing in early (lower level of cortical hierarchy) sensory regions is associated with decreased alpha amplitudes and attenuated synchronization (Bollimunta, 2008, 2011) whereas in attentional, executive, and higher-level sensory regions, alpha amplitude (Mo, 2011) and synchronization (von Stein, 2000) correlate positively with task-related neuronal processing and local cortical excitability. During visual working memory maintenance, alpha-band amplitudes load-dependently strengthened in frontoparietal regions together with beta- and gamma-band amplitudes, despite being load-dependently suppressed in the visual regions (Palva, 2011). Since frontal and parietal regions are thought to underlie attentional and central executive functions in visual working memory, as indexed by fMRI as well as lesion studies, the frontoparietal localization of the positive memory-load dependence of alpha-band oscillations implies an attentional functionality in visual working memory retention. Intriguingly, alpha-band power has recently been shown to increase after video game training on dual task performance that required enhanced attentional switching (Maclin, 2011). This result is in line with observation of a positive correlation of alpha oscillations with BOLD signal (Sadaghiani, 2010) in the inferior frontal, insular, and cingulate cortices that play a key role in this cognitive function (Dosenbach, 2008). A phase reset of ongoing alpha oscillations in frontal and parietal sites could thus play a role in coordinating the large-scale frontoparietal networks during visual working memory encoding and attention.

An accumulating body of evidence emphasizes a direct involvement of alpha oscillations in the mechanisms of top-down modulation, attention, and consciousness. Neural correlates of consciousness (NCC) are widely recognized to involve neuronal coalitions and synchronous assemblies, recurrent processing, and the frontoparietal network. One conceptual model of NCC is the 'global neuronal workspace' (GNW) (Baars, 1988) in which sensory information enters awareness following an interaction between the sensory and frontoparietal network. Palva (2007) proposed a framework in which a subset of neurons that are engaged in oscillations belong to the NCC through an alpha frequency band synchronized sensori-fronto-parietal network that defines the GNW. This framework is based on the following six lines of evidence: (i) top-down modulation can be mediated by alpha frequency band phase interactions, and thus alpha rhythmicity could contribute to recurrent processing and top-down amplification; (ii) alpha frequency band oscillations can phase lock between widely separated cortical regions and thus form functional large-scale networks; (iii) enhanced alpha frequency band synchrony in the frontoparietal network is associated with the execution of cognitive tasks; (iv) alpha, beta, and gamma frequency band oscillations coexist and are colocalized during stimulus processing and task execution; (v) a oscillations can be synchronized with theta, beta, and gamma oscillations in response to cognitive demands, which appears to be essential for the coordination and communication in multiband networks; and (vi) perception and action can proceed in discrete 'snapshots' involving alpha frequency band periodicity. Frontoparietal alpha synchrony should be found during focused attention and working memory as well as during conscious perception, cognition, and action, but it should not phase lock to the stimulus processing when the stimuli are subliminal, unattended, or not consciously perceived for other reasons (Palva, 2007). Alpha frequency band oscillations that are not phase locked to the synchronous frontoparietal network do not belong to the GNW and thereby might have different functional roles, such as idling or inhibition.

Recent advances in combining cortical source reconstruction and data-driven interaction analysis approaches have paved the way for mapping the anatomical and topological structures of synchronized cortical networks from M/EEG data (Palva, 2010). Inter-areal phase synchrony in alpha-, beta-, and gamma-bands is memory load-dependently enhanced during visual working memory maintenance. Load-dependent alpha synchronization was observed in frontoparietal, cingulate, and insular cortices concurrently with synchronization in the beta- and gamma-band networks. Importantly, the hubs of the visual working memory retention period of alpha-band network were more frontal compared to those of the beta- and gamma-band networks, suggesting that the alpha-band interactions underlie higher-level attentional functions compared to the beta- or gamma-band interactions. Network hubs were also observed in the insula, cingulate, and orbitofrontal structures that have been suggested to play a role in task-set maintenance (Dosenbach, 2008) or tonic alertness (Sadaghiani, 2010). It is notable; however, that the synchrony in the cingulo-opercular system was not restricted to any of the frequency bands but seemed to involve equally alpha-, beta-, and gamma-band networks. Finally, it was also observed that the memory load-dependent plateau in the strength of phase synchrony in alpha and beta bands predicted the individual VWM capacity, which indicates a direct representational or attentional role of these frequency bands.

Importantly, a recent TMS–EEG study showed that neuronal activity in frontoparietal regions may directly control the alpha amplitude in sensory cortex and demonstrated that the alpha-band amplitude is causally related to perception (Capotosto, 2009). Palva (2010) suggested that inter-areal alpha-band phase interactions in the frontoparietal regions might underlie the top-down modulation of local oscillation amplitudes in sensory regions. Possible loci for the interaction between frontal attentional/executive and sensory representational activities could be the regions that are high in the sensory processing hierarchy. One such interesting area is the posterior parietal cortex that is strongly and memory-load dependently phase synchronized with frontal regions and yet shows local alpha-band amplitude suppression below baseline levels during memory retention and a negative correlation of amplitude with memory-load. Mazaheri's findings confirmed that phasic frontal theta synchronization induces parieto-occipital sensory alpha desynchronization after a visual cue stimulus, which forewarns a visual imperative stimulus (Mazaheri, 2010).

A sliding window analysis of simultaneous EEG–fMRI data has been performed to examine whether temporal variations in coupling among three major networks (DMN, DAN, SN) are associated with temporal variations in mental state, as assessed by the amplitude of alpha and theta oscillations in the EEG (Chang, 2013). Alpha power (and theta power in an inverse direction) covaried with the spatial extent of anticorrelation between DMN and DAN, with higher alpha power associated with larger anticorrelation extent. States of higher vigilance have previously been linked to increased anticorrelation between DMN and DAN. Elevated power in the alpha band has been suggested to correspond to a state of alertness and undirected readiness distinct from focused attention that may facilitate faster and more accurate task performance (Sadaghiani, 2010). Increased alpha (and increased activity in the salience network) may thus correspond to epochs of more frequent switching, which is consistent with the increases in anticorrelations observed here. Strong correlations between alpha power and dorsal anterior cingulate are also present. Interestingly, while the coupling across most cortical regions decreased as a function of alpha, the average connectivity among the thalamus ROI of the salience network (which appears to lie in primarily in the mediodorsal nucleus), the anterior insula, and several other regions of the salience network tended to increase, supporting the association between spontaneous alpha fluctuations and salience network activity. These findings support the idea that the salience networks act as a 'switch' between the respective endogenous and exogenous functions of these networks, which lead to the triple core network model (Menon, 2011).

2.3 Triple Core Network Model

Three intrinsic connectivity networks are particularly important for understanding higher cognitive function and dysfunction in fundamental ways, hence the use of the term 'core' neurocognitive networks. Menon (2011) proposed a model of aberrant saliency mapping and cognitive dysfunction, where dysfunctional interactions among the DMN, FPCN, and SN can provide new insights into several mental disorders, such as schizophrenia, depression, anxiety, bipolar disorder, borderline personality disorder, dementia, autism, and ADHD. Indeed, studies of psychopathology are now increasingly focused on understanding the ways in which disturbances in distributed brain areas that operate within large-scale systems contribute to cognitive and affective dysfunction. It has become increasingly apparent that the original goal of mapping dysfunctional cognitive and psychological processes associated with psychiatric disorders onto individual brain areas is now widely considered implausible.

Emerging evidence suggests that SN, and most notably the right AI, is an integral hub in mediating dynamic interactions between large-scale brain networks involved in externally oriented attention and internally oriented self-related mental processes. These discoveries point to a model in which the SN plays an important role in saliency detection, attentional capture enhanced by error signals, and dynamic cognitive control.

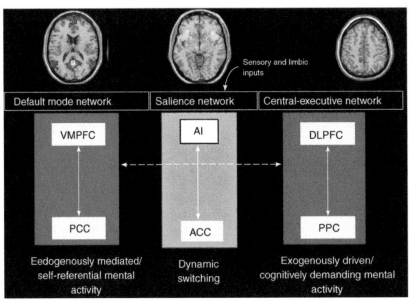

Figure 3. Triple Core Model where the SN is processing sensory and limbic input and serves to initiate dynamic switching between DMN and FPCN to regulate behavior and homeostatic state (Trends in Cognitive Sciences, Bressler and Menon, 2010)

The SN switching mechanisms help focus attention on external stimuli, as a result of which they take on added significance or saliency. Several processes are fundamental to attention: automatic bottom–up filtering of stimuli, competitive selection, working memory, and top–down sensitivity control. Filtering and amplification of specific stimuli can in principle occur at multiple levels in the hierarchy of ascending neural pathways that bring stimuli from the external world to the primary and secondary sensory cortex. At each level, filters enhance responses to stimuli that are infrequent in space or time or are of learned or instinctive biological importance. Once a stimulus activates the AI, it will have preferential access to the brain's attentional and working memory resources. The analysis of combined EEG and fMRI data provides additional insights into the role of the SN in attentional control (Menon, 2010). The spatio-temporal dynamics underlying this process has four distinct stages. *Stage 1* About 150 ms post-stimulus, primary sensory areas detect a deviant stimulus, as indexed by the mismatch negativity (MMN) component of the evoked potential. *Stage 2* This 'bottom–up' MMN signal is transmitted to other brain regions, notably the AI and the ACC. *Stage 3* About 200–300 ms post-stimulus, the AI and ACC generate a 'top–down' control signal, as indexed by the N2b/P3a component of the evoked potential. This signal is simultaneously transmitted to primary sensory areas as well as other neocortical regions. *Stage 4* About 300–400 ms poststimulus, neocortical regions, notably the premotor cortex and temporo-parietal areas (ventral attention network), respond to the attentional shift with a signal that is indexed by the time-average P3b evoked potential. *Stage 5* The ACC facilitates response selection and motor response via its links to the midcingulate cortex, supplementary motor cortex, and other motor areas. As part of a functionally coupled network, the right AI and ACC help integrate bottom–up (AI) attention switching with top–down (ACC and associated dorsomedial prefrontal cortex) control and biasing of sensory input. This dynamic process, which is central to attention, enables an organism to sift through many different incoming sensory stimuli and adjust gain for task-relevant stimuli.

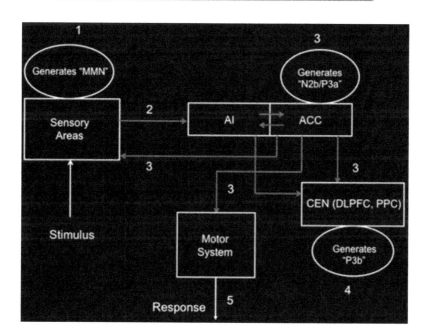

Figure 4. Stage 1–5 in the spatio-temporal dynamics of attentional control (Menon, 2010).

2.4 Large-Scale Brain Systems in ADHD

2.4.1 Large-Scale Brain Systems Models in ADHD

ADHD has long been thought to reflect dysfunction of prefrontal-striatal circuitry, largely ignoring the involvement of other circuits. Recent advances in systems neuroscience-based approaches to brain dysfunction enable the development of models of ADHD pathophysiology that encompass a number of different large-scale 'resting state' networks.

In ADHD, it is assumed that ineffective salience processing results in DMN interferences during goal-directed activity (daydreaming) and in DAN and FPCN inferences during reflective cognitive activity (distractibility). The reason why the SN is less active is likely related to the hypoactive (hypodopaminergic) motivational network (which overlaps with the salience network) in ADHD. When ADHD subjects are very motivated, the triple core network is functioning well, in a similar way as after taking Ritalin, but in order to get them motivated, they need an important and immediate reward (Liddle, 2011).

Sonuga-Barke and Castellanos (2007) suggested that ADHD could be considered a default network disorder. They reasoned that the default network in ADHD might be refractory to regulation by other neural systems, thus producing intrusions or disruptions of ongoing cognition and behavior, which would manifest itself as periodic lapses in on-task performance, a hallmark of ADHD. Decreased default network coherence has been found in ADHD and decreased default network suppression has been related to increased intra-individual variability in a small sample of children with ADHD. Interferences with less anticorrelation between the default network and cognitive control networks underpin ADHD attentional lapses.

An interesting result has been obtained by comparing healthy young subjects scanned after rested wakefulness and after 24 hours of full sleep deprivation (De Havas, 2012). Sleep deprivation produced an increase in intra-subject variability of reaction times and degraded attentional performance. These were paralleled by decreases in default network functional connectivity and weaker anticorrelation between the default network and anti-correlated regions.

Sonuga-Barke's (2003) proposal of a dual-pathway (executive system and motivation system) pathophysiology in ADHD is also in line with the triple core model. In his model, delayed aversion is a core feature of an ineffective motivational network in which an alteration of reward mechanisms is involved and which would be involved particularly in the hyperactive, impulsive subtype of ADHD.

The ventral attentional network, closely related to circuits referred to as the salience network, is involved in monitoring salient stimuli, i.e., behaviorally relevant stimuli, and in interrupting ongoing activity when appropriate. The dorsal attentional network is less active in ADHD during performance of executive tasks.

2.4.2 Within and Between Network Disconnectivity in ADHD

Castellanos (2008) described a lower rest state functional connectivity between the posterior cingulate and precuneus on the one hand and the dorsal anterior cingulate and anteromedial prefrontal cortex on the other. Sun (2012) also described a lower anticorrelation between the dorsal anterior cingulate on the one hand and the posterior cingulate and dorsomedial prefrontal cortex on the other. A lower connectivity between the anteromedial prefrontal cortex and the posterior cingulate, both DMN areas, has also been described in ADHD adults (Castellanos, 2008; Mattfeld, 2014). Choi (2013) described a lower connectivity between the anteromedial prefrontal cortex and the precuneus, as well as between the SN on the one hand and the DMN and FPCN on the other. Uddin (2008) applied a network homogeneity approach and showed ADHD-related reductions only in the posterior DMN (posterior cingulate). Tomasi and Volkow (2012) described an increased connectivity between the orbitofrontal cortex (OFC) and the anterior cingulate. Dopamine neurons in the ventral tegmental area project to ventral striatum, caudate, and OFC, modulating the neuronal activity in these brain regions. Dopamine changes the efficacy of other neurotransmitter signals in the brain, apparently by reducing spontaneous background activity; thus, lower dopaminergic function in ADHD might cause increased spontaneous activity as well as increased short-range functional connectivity. This hypothesis is consistent with higher amplitude of low-frequency fluctuations in lateral OFC and higher rest state functional connectivity of the anterior cingulate with OFC/insula and inferior frontal cortices previously reported for ADHD children. In the same study, Tomasi and Volkow described a lower functional connectivity between OFC and superior parietal lobule (DAN). A weaker functional connectivity of the OFC/insula and ventral striatum with posterior parietal regions has been reported for ADHD children rather than for normal children, which is also consistent with the dopaminergic modulation of parietal activity and with prior reports of decreased functional connectivity between striatal and posterior cortical regions in ADHD. The connectivity of superior parietal cortex (BA7) with DAN regions and with OFC/insula and temporal networks (middle and inferior temporal cortex) were lower.

Connectivity between DAN and DMN and between DAN and OFC was lower. In conclusion, here, the authors document higher short-range functional connectivity in reward-motivation network regions encompassing ventral striatum and orbitofrontal cortex and lower long-range functional connectivity in attention (superior parietal lobule) and default-mode (precuneus) network regions for ADHD children than for control subjects. It may be noteworthy that Barry (2011) demonstrated theta hypercoherence in short distance and alpha hypocoherence in long distance locations in ADHD. Interestingly, similar findings with structural connectivity (diffusion tensor imaging of white matter integrity) have been described in other studies (Cao, 2013) in which the ADHD group showed decreased structural connectivity in the prefrontal-dominant circuitry and increased connectivity in the orbitofrontal-striatal circuitry. These changes correlated significantly with the inattention and hyperactivity/impulsivity symptoms, respectively. Intriguingly, a smaller volume of the right medial orbitofrontal cortex has been described in ADHD boys (Boes, 2009), which correlated with non-planning impulsivity when contingencies were projected in the distant future or were of uncertain probability.

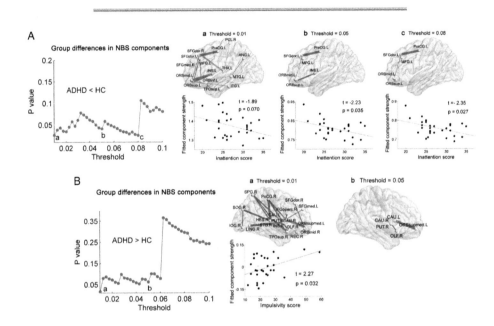

Figure 5. Decreased structural connectivity (blue), which correlated with inattention and increased structural connectivity (red), which in turn correlated with impulsivity (Cao, 2013).

The ADHD group in Tomasi and Volkow's study also had a decreased connectivity between corticostriatal and parietal networks that might underlie the impairment in attention and the decreased motivation to sustain attention as well as the impaired inhibition of the default mode networks in ADHD.

McCarthy (2013) described a lower functional connectivity within DAN, VAN, and FPCN, and an increased connectivity within the DMN and motivational network (affective ACC, OFC, amygdala, ventral striatum, AI, and hippocampus) in ADHD adults.

2.4.3 Affective Network Disconnectivity in ADHD

Although not classified among the core symptoms of ADHD in DSM-III, DSM-IV, and DSM-5, deviations in affect were considered as a primary clinical symptom in earlier classifications of childhood ADHD (Clements, 1966). In adult ADHD, besides the traditional core symptoms, Wender (2001) described also mood swings, irritability, and emotional overreactivity as core symptoms, occurring in 30-70% of adults with ADHD. ADHD children with affect dysregulation often display uncontrolled outbursts of emotion, rapid and exaggerated changes in mood (emotional lability), and increased frustration with unexpected emotional challenges. Additionally, affect dysregulation in childhood has been associated with subsequent psychopathology, poor psychosocial functioning, and decreased quality of life in ADHD well into adulthood. Affective disorders are highly comorbid with adult ADHD. In the dual pathway model of ADHD (Sonuga-Barke, 2003), it has been suggested that each circuit contributes separately to the clinical phenotype of ADHD.

Tomasi and Volkow's (2012) findings of increased connectivity between OFC and the anterior cingulate and Cao's (2013) findings of increased structural connectivity between OFC and the caudate nucleus discussed in the previous section are also relevant here. Three recent seed-based RS-fMRI studies of ADHD, one conducted in the adult cohort and the other two in the child cohort, have examined the components of the intrinsic affective network. Hyperconnectivity of the superior parietal lobe and cerebellum to the anterior cingulate cortex was found in adults diagnosed with ADHD in childhood but not in healthy comparison adults (McCarthy, 2013). However, affective network hypoconnectivity was found in medication naïve children with ADHD but not in healthy comparison children (Posner, 2013). Specifically, decreased connectivity of the ventral striatum with the orbitofrontal cortex, hippocampus, and anterior prefrontal cortex was observed. Decreased connectivity between left ventral striatum and left orbitofrontal cortex correlated with symptoms of emotional lability. A weaker connection between the orbitofrontal cortex and the ventral striatum diminishes the regulatory control of the orbitofrontal cortex over the ventral striatum, resulting in heightened emotional lability. The medial orbitofrontal gyrus and striatum have reciprocal interconnections that subserve the inhibitory functions and reward processing. The third study (Hulvershorn, 2014) found hyperconnectivity between the amygdala and subgenual anterior cingulate cortex in a subpopulation of ADHD children with high emotional lability. The divergent findings of both hyperconnectivity and hypoconnectivity within the affective network, although shown by using different seeds, suggest that the intrinsic affective connectivity network in ADHD could be less integrated or even disorganized.

To complement the prior seed-based findings of the affective network in ADHD, Ho (2015) adopted a data-driven approach (ICA) to measure the functional connectivity within the affective network in ADHD children. This approach is independent of the seed definition and automatically removes motion and physiological noise. Increased bilateral amygdala connectivity (particularly with frontal areas) and decreased left orbitofrontal connectivity within the affective network have been found. The hyperconnectivity at the left amygdala within the affective network was associated with increased aggressiveness and conduct problems as well as decline in global functioning in children with ADHD. The divergent patterns of hypoconnectivity of the orbitofrontal cortex and hyperconnectivity of the amygdala in Ho's findings correspond to the findings of hypo-activation of the orbitofrontal cortex and hyperactivation of the amygdala in many emotional task-based fMRI studies in ADHD. Taken together, the findings suggest that the impaired functional integration in task-free affective network, especially the amygdala and orbitofrontal cortical regions, may underlie or influence the abnormal task-based functional activation during emotion processing in ADHD.

2.4.4 Triple Core Network Model in ADHD

Studies discussed here examined intrinsic functional connectivity in ADHD. Although many of them focused on the same brain regions, they reported conflicting results, with some studies supporting the hyper- and hypoconnectivity while others supported the null findings. Moreover, previous studies have examined intrinsic connectivity of these networks in ADHD individually, whereas no studies have examined interactions among all three networks. A recent study (Cai, in press) investigated the triple core network model using novel computational techniques designed to overcome the weaknesses of previous studies and to provide an integrative framework for characterizing childhood ADHD. Based on the crucial role of SN in switching between CEN and DMN and allocating attentional resources, the investigators hypothesized that inter-network coupling between SN-FPCN and SN-DMN would be aberrant in ADHD compared to normal children and that such aberrations would be correlated with ADHD symptom severity. To test these hypotheses, an SN-centered resource allocation index (RAI) was computed to assess integrity of cross-network interactions among the three networks (large-scale brain network coupling), specifically the extent to which SN is temporally integrated with CEN while simultaneously dissociated from DMN. RAI has the advantage of capturing aberrant interactions simultaneously across all three networks. Specifically, RAI was computed as the difference in positive correlation between SN and CEN time series and negative correlation between SN and DMN. The rationale here is that SN and CEN are typically co-activated during cognitively demanding tasks while SN and DMN are typically anti-correlated. RAI thus captures the extent to which SN can temporally integrate itself with CEN and dissociate itself from DMN. Larger RAI values reflect more segregated cross-network interactions between the SN-CEN and SN-DMN systems in the context of the triple-network model.

To test the triple core network model, between-group differences in resource allocation index (RAI) (a measure of SN-centered triple network interactions) and the relation between RAI and ADHD symptoms in a group of 180 ADHD children compared with a normal group were investigated. RAI was significantly lower in children with ADHD than in control subjects, meaning that inter-network coupling of SN-FPCN and SN-DMN are less anticorrelated. The specificity of the above effects was also investigated by examining two alternate models involving parallel constructs with a FPCN-centered network and a DMN-centered network. Neither index was consistently different between groups. These results highlight the specificity of SN-centered deficits within the context of the triple-network model in childhood ADHD. Severity of inattention symptoms correlated with RAI. The relation between SN-centered RAI and hyperactivity/impulsivity scores was weaker and less consistent. Remarkably, these findings were replicated in three independent datasets. Further analyses revealed significantly higher cross-validation accuracies when using multi-network coupling than when using coupling of any two networks. The RAI has the advantage of capturing aberrant interactions simultaneously across all three networks, and it specifically quantifies the extent to which SN is temporally integrated with FPCN and dissociated from DMN. Our findings highlight the value of an integrative theoretically based model for understanding childhood ADHD and the unique role of SN within this model. Crucially, the AI node of this network is involved in signaling the frontoparietal attentional system to recruit cognitive resources essential for maintaining and manipulating information online. The findings suggest that neuroimaging-based brain network interaction patterns can serve as a sensitive quantitative biomarker for ADHD that can help inform clinical diagnosis. It will be critical to investigate these patterns in children with comorbid conditions with ADHD, including anxiety, autism and depression, to ensure that these findings are specific to ADHD. Classification accuracy for distinguishing the ADHD and TD groups using these measures ranged from 72% to 83%. Using theoretically informed neurocognitive models (triple core network model) has the potential to significantly advance our understanding of the neurobiology of childhood ADHD while also informing the development of reliable biomarkers.

2.4.5 Catecholaminergic Attentional Network Model (VAN-DAN-DMN-SN)

Sidlauskaite (2015) described a higher connectivity within DMN (posterior cingulate and anteromedial prefrontal cortex), within VAN (inferior frontal gyrus and inferior parietal gyrus), and within DAN (middle frontal gyrus, precentral gyrus and superior parietal gyrus) as well as an increased connectivity between SN (insula, ACC) and VAN and between VAN and DAN. On the other hand, connectivity between SN and DAN was lower. Overall, these findings differ from those that supported the triple core model by observing a decreased functional connectivity between DMN and SN. Sidlauskaite's findings imply an intact connectivity between DMN and SN in ADHD and indicate another locus of functional disorganization that may relate to attention deficits, namely the imbalance between SN and attention networks. Although different studies utilized different methods, an explanation might be of course that ADHD has several subtypes. In this study, the results as a whole suggest that individuals with ADHD may suffer from imbalanced ventral and dorsal attention systems, with the former playing a principal role in task engagement, introducing increased susceptibility to salient but task-irrelevant stimuli. Therefore, in the context of ADHD, this imbalanced ventral and dorsal attention systems might relate to symptoms of distractibility and inability to ignore irrelevant stimuli. The findings of this study suggest that the DAN and VAN are less segregated functionally in ADHD. This may create altered interactions between the attention networks in ADHD, where task-relevant inputs from the DAN filter stimulus-driven signals originating in the VAN and where task-relevant stimuli trigger the VAN to interrupt and reorient the DAN to relevant stimuli. More specifically, decreased intrinsic segregation of the attention networks may alter the information exchange threshold between the two systems, with VAN signals interrupting goal-directed task-relevant DAN activity. This is consistent with recent findings, which increasingly point to VAN as the locus of attentional dyscontrol and enhanced distractibility in ADHD. For instance, López (2006) observed that in the ADHD group, but not in controls, unattended task-irrelevant distractors elicited increased VAN-related P300 activity. The finding of increased within-VAN connectivity, and the same trend in DAN, may further suggest the potentially reduced flexibility and capacity to alternate between goal-driven and relevant stimulus-driven attentional processing in ADHD.

It is, however, difficult to compare these results with previous studies directly, as a differentiation between the VAN and SN is often not made. For instance, Sripada (2014) did not differentiate between the VAN and SN and included insula as part of the VAN. He found a lower connectivity between DMN (PCC/DMPFC) and right DLPFC/R superior frontal gyrus, and between posterior cingulate and DMPFC.

Hyperconnectivity within resting DMN, DAN, and VAN networks appears to be consistent with the concept of resting-state affinity proposed as a potential mechanism behind problems in state-to-state switching, with hyperconnectivity within resting networks increasing affinity for that state and reducing the potential for switching to active goal-directed states. The above evidence of similar patterns of hyperconnectivity within attention networks may also be consistent with this increasing affinity for that state and with reducing the potential for switching to active goal-directed states.

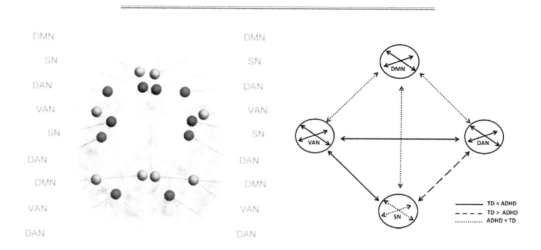

Figure 6. Imbalance between SN and VAN, DAN and a normal balance between DMN and SN, DAN, VAN. Within DAN, VAN, and DMN, there is increased connectivity (Sidlauskaite, 2015).

Impairment of large-scale antagonistic brain networks that normally contribute to attentional engagement and disengagement, such as the task-positive networks and the default mode network (DMN), seems to be important in ADHD. Related networks are the ventral attentional network (VAN) involved in attentional shifting and the salience network (SN) related to task expectancy. Aboitiz (2014) discussed the tonic-phasic dynamics of catecholaminergic signaling in the brain and attempted to provide a link between these dynamics and the activities of the large-scale cortical networks that regulate behavior. More specifically, he proposed that an imbalance of tonic catecholamine levels during task performance enhances phasic signaling and increased excitability of the VAN, yielding distractibility symptoms. Sidlauskaite (2015) demonstrated similar results on the VAN. Likewise, immaturity of the SN may relate to abnormal tonic signaling and an incapacity to build a proper executive system during task performance. While Aboitiz emphasized that the VAN is overactive in ADHD, his model does not contradict the triple core network model but supplements it.

Dopaminergic signaling is highly complex, involving different modes of transmission, which are antagonistic and relate to different behavioral states. On the one hand, there is the transient release of dopamine produced by intense bursts of dopaminergic neural activity (phasic signaling). This modality is associated with salient sensory stimuli and with attentional shifts, a highly focused but short-lasting behavior. It has been proposed that an abnormal emphasis on phasic signaling is associated with impulsivity (Grace, 2007). Conversely, the basal or tonic signaling, which emerges due to background levels of extra-cellular dopamine, changes slowly over time. In the cerebral cortex, tonic or basal activity produces an overall decrease in the inhibitory tone of neural networks, and it shows behavioral manifestations that are more complex. Abnormal variations in tonic signaling may have different long-term effects, including lack of motivation, distractibility, or anxiety, depending on the level of basal activity. Thus, ADHD symptomatology may not be explained simply by an overall dopaminergic deficit; instead, it may reflect an altered signaling dynamics of this and other neurotransmitters.

Aboitiz (2014) proposed a relation between the phasic-tonic balance of catecholaminergic signaling (dopaminergic and noradrenergic) and the dynamics between default and task-positive networks in the brain. Thus, the stability of the task-positive networks DAN and SN may be associated with the maintenance of an appropriate arousal tone during the focused state, which is determined by moderately high tonic signaling (mediated by D2-like receptors). DAN participates in working memory and sustained attention. This tonic activity may permit the maintenance of the focus over time as well as information update in a changing context. On the other hand, low tonic signaling may correlate with activation of the DMN. Phasic signaling (mediated mainly by D1-like dopaminergic receptors), which is mediated by salient or motivating stimuli, may importantly serve to shift the attentional focus, and it may be related to the VAN and initial activation of the SN in preparation for task performance. In ADHD, an imbalance of tonic signaling may result in abnormal activation of the DMN, which interferes with consolidation of task-positive networks and produces overactivation of the VAN and attenuation of the SN.

Tonic activity gradually increases with the expectancy of an uncertain event, which is associated with alertness and preparation for an outcome (Quartz, 2009). There is an interesting interaction between phasic and tonic signaling during tasks where the reinforcer is presented with some uncertainty (for example, the predicting stimulus is associated to the expected outcome – reward – in only 50% of the cases instead of 100%). In this case, phasic dopamine liberation that is normally associated with the predicting stimulus triggers a steady increase in tonic dopaminergic levels in the interval between stimulus and outcome, which acquires a maximal slope with maximal uncertainty (Schultz, 2007; Quartz, 2009). In other words, phasic liberation increases linearly with the probability of reinforcement while tonic liberation displays a bell-shaped curve with a maximum probability of 0.5 of reinforcement appearance. Tonic liberation in the interval between stimulus and reward has been associated with uncertainty-related expectancy (Schultz, 2007; Fallon, 2013). In other words, stimulus-related phasic activity sets the behavioral and executive systems on while the maintenance of alertness and behavioral preparation depends on the gradual increase of tonic activity that suppresses further bursts of phasic liberation. Nonetheless, while a moderate increase of tonic activity may keep the representation of the objective and increase performance active, levels that are too high result in anxiety and restlessness.

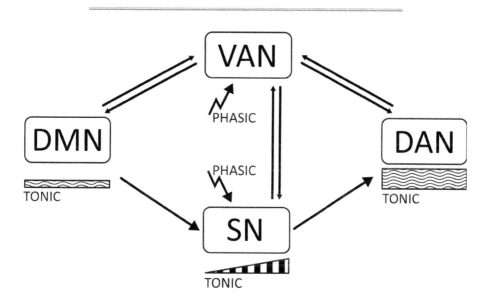

Figure 7. The DMN is associated with low tonic catecholaminergic activity while the DAN is related to moderately high levels of tonic activity. Stimulus–related phasic catecholaminergic signaling activates the VAN, inducing attentional shifts in focused states and transitions between the DAN and the DMN. In addition, phasic signaling activates the SN, which is associated with a buildup of dopaminergic activity related to task preparation and expectancy of future events. In ADHD, insufficiently regulated tonic activity results in a disbalanced DMN and distractibility due to a low threshold for phasic signaling, which yields overactivation of the VAN during task performance and short-term impulsivity. Dysregulation of tonic activity may also result in an attenuated SN due to an incapacity to build mid-term tonic signaling for task preparation (Aboitiz, 2014).

Aboitiz proposed that in ADHD, there is a disbalance between both signaling mechanisms, sometimes generating states of high impulsivity and distractedness to irrelevant stimuli due to emphasis on phasic liberation (Grace, 2007). On the other hand, a dysregulation of tonic dopamine levels might generate distractedness or anxiety when too low or too high, respectively. A key point here is that an incapacity to maintain appropriate tonic activity in a determined setting may result in a low threshold of phasic activity and an instability of large-scale brain networks that control behavior.

The above-described networks are partly consistent with a model of attentional regulation, described by Posner and collaborators (Posner and Petersen, 1990; Petersen and Posner, 2012). Based on performance on the attentional network test (ANT), these authors described three different networks involved in attentional processing: (i) the alerting network related to brainstem arousal modulators (particularly norepinephrine) that act diffusely in the brain; (ii) the orienting network that generates attentional displacements and includes the frontal eye-fields and the intraparietal sulcus, which is modulated by acetylcholine (this network overlaps with both the DAN and the VAN); and (iii) the executive network, that involves midline components (regulated by dopamine). Subsequently, the executive network became subdivided into a frontoparietal control system (allegedly distinct from the orienting network but nonetheless strongly overlapping with it), which participates in moment-to moment-control during a task, and a cingulo-opercular network (that overlaps with the SN) related to task set maintenance (Petersen and Posner, 2012). The orienting network is overactivated at early ages but as the child matures, it becomes progressively modulated by the executive network, gradually developing the capacities for effortful control and social development (Petersen and Posner, 2012). In Aboitiz' view, ADHD symptomatology fits this scheme, with an overactive orienting network and a poorly developed executive network compared to the general population of the same age.

Event-related potential (ERP) studies support Aboitiz' concept of an alteration in the balance between the DMN and the task positive networks and suggest an overactivation of the VAN in ADHD. In normal subjects, the P300 ERP, which is associated with the activation of working memory networks during the execution of a task, has a smaller amplitude in trials preceding erroneous responses and in those where subjects both children and adults reported to have been mind-wandering (Smallwood, 2008). In addition, ADHD (as well as other conditions) is characterized by a significant reduction of the P300 evoked potential amplitude, which restores to nearly normal levels after medication and after neurofeedback (Mayer, 2011).

López (2006) observed that in the ADHD group, but not in controls, unattended task-irrelevant distractors elicited increased VAN-related P300 activity. Sidlauskaite's finding of increased within-VAN connectivity and the same trend in DAN may further suggest the potentially reduced flexibility and capacity to alternate between goal-driven and relevant stimulus-driven attentional processing in ADHD.

In other words, ADHD implies a late differential distribution of attentional resources but not incapacity to initially focus on an area of the visual space. ADHD subjects are more likely to show a different pattern of attentional resource distribution. This attentional 'flexibility' might allow ADHD individuals to occasionally have a more rapid response style, somewhat in line with the popular view of ADHD subjects as 'Hunters in a Farmers World' (Hartmann, 1993). Within this context, it has been found that the

ADHD-associated 7R-DRD4 genetic polymorphism appeared some 40,000 years ago, and it was subject to intense positive selection, perhaps in an environment that favored risk-taking behavior and peripheral attention (Ding, 2002). An ADHD-like wide spatial attentional framework may thus correspond to a more primitive attentional system while in the course of more recent human evolution, the mechanisms involved in sustained attention have undergone significant development in relation to elaborate tool-making, reading, writing, and other human activities.

Finally, in a delayed visual search paradigm, where a preparatory signal precedes the task by 700 ms, normal children develop a steady increase in negativity in the EEG (the contingent negative variation, CNV) between the signal and task onset. This has been interpreted as a preparation potential. Interestingly, according to Aboitiz, this potential behaves similarly to the tonic dopaminergic 'ramp' observed in conditioning experiments in animals. In ADHD children; however, the CNV is clearly deficient. This evidence points to a deficit in the preparatory potential mechanisms for a given task in ADHD, which is consistent with the concept of a dysfunction of tonic dopaminergic activity and notably with a deficit in the SN, as described above. In addition, the incapacity to build an adequate preparedness for the task complies with the proposition that the executive networks are not well stabilized possibly due to interference from the DMN.

Summarizing all these data, we can conclude that in ADHD, the DMN is not functioning well. In addition, ERP studies have revealed an incapacity to protect the attentional focus from interfering stimuli possibly associated with abnormal VAN excitability and a difficulty to build an executive network in preparation for a task, which complies with the notion of an immature SN. This model can be seen as an expansion of Menon's triple core network model by adding an abnormal VAN excitability.

Interestingly, Aboitiz concluded that even if neurotransmitter dysfunctions may be at the basis of ADHD and other neuropsychiatric conditions, alternative therapeutic approaches using cognitive rehabilitation or neurofeedback in which the dynamics of the DMN, task-positive network, and VAN can be modulated top-down in order to control dopaminergic abnormal functioning are highly valuable. A similar reasoning has been proposed for alterations in the resting-state relationship between the FPCN/SN and DMN (Chen, 2013). Given that poorly regulated information processing is a hallmark of most neuropsychiatric disorders, rTMS methods provide a foundation for different ways to study network dysregulation and develop brain stimulation treatments for these disorders.

2.4.6 Ritalin and Network Connectivity

Previous task-based fMRI studies (Liddle, 2011; Peterson, 2009) have proposed that dopamine enhances the competitive relationship between connectivity networks. After a single dose intake of Ritalin in healthy adults, multiple regions of default network reduced their coupling with task positive intrinsic connectivity networks, including ventral attention network, dorsal attention network, and somatomotor network (Sripada, 2013). Default network regions also decoupled with medial and lateral orbitofrontal regions, which in previous studies have been associated with attention control and emotion regulation. One interpretation of this finding concerns increased segregation between default network and task positive intrinsic connectivity networks, which may also be related to the mechanism by which Ritalin produces enhanced attention functioning (Sonuga-Barke and Castellanos, 2007).

Within DMN, connectivity (between medial prefrontal cortex and posterior cingulate) improved in ADHD adults after Ritalin (Franzen, 2013). In adults with cocaine use disorder, a single dose of Ritalin increases the connectivity of the rostral with dorsal cingulate, an executive control, and attention network region while it reduces the connectivity of the rostral cingulate with the inferior parietal cortex/supramarginal gyrus, a 'default mode' region, which may play a role in Ritalin's attention-enhancing properties (Konova, 2013).

2.5. Graph-Theoretical Analysis (Topology) of Large-Scale Brain Networks

The first approach to study functional correlates of psychiatric disorders is to have a look at regional dysfunction. The second approach is to examine connectivity between pairs of areas. The third approach is to study the entire network organization. In addition to characterizing inter-areal synchronization according to its anatomical localization and hypothesized functional roles, anatomical and functional neuronal networks can be characterized with graph theoretical tools, as they share properties with network representations of many other complex systems (Bullmore and Sporns, 2009). In a graph representation of brain networks, brain areas are the graph's vertices (nodes) and the inter-areal interactions are the edges. Graph-theoretical metrics, such as clustering coefficient (index for local connectivity), path length, degree, and centrality, provide quantitative measures to characterize large-scale networks represented in a graph. Perhaps most importantly, anatomical networks share properties of small-world networks that can be seen as lattice structures (networks with only local connections) with rare long-range connections and can be described by the local clustering and average path length of the network. Anatomical networks have high local clustering and short average path lengths (Iturria-Medina, 2008; Gong, 2009; He, 2009) that are indicative of small-world structure in which dense local connectivity leads to greater local clustering than in random networks. Yet, because of the long-range 'short-cut' connections, their characteristic path length, i.e., the mean of shortest paths from each node to another node, are close to those in random networks (Watts and Strogatz, 1998). Small-world networks are associated with high local and global efficiency in information transmission as well as facilitate parallel processing within hierarchically organized modules (Bassett and Bullmore, 2006; Bullmore and Sporns, 2009). Small-world networks are economical, tending to minimize wiring costs while supporting efficient processing of complex information. The combination of these attributes promotes simultaneously high specialization and high integration within a modular architecture. Network analysis not only provides information about disruption of global organization, but also helps identify both subnetworks that are compromised and subnetworks that potentially compensate for dysfunction.

Several studies have addressed the graph properties of the synchronized networks at the EEG-sensor-level. Although the topological properties change during development in the alpha-band, they have been shown to remain constant across measurement sessions (Deuker, 2009).

Wang (2009) compared fMRI brain network topology in a group of 20 ADHD children and a group of 19 normal children. Although both groups exhibited economical small-world topology, altered functional networks were demonstrated in the brain of ADHD children when compared with the normal controls. In particular, increased local efficiencies combined with decreased global efficiencies often found in ADHD suggested a disorder-related shift of the topology toward regular networks. It has been suggested that the loss of long-range connections affect the global efficiency, as has been described for the connections between anteromedial prefrontal cortex and posterior cingulate and between dorsal anterior cingulate and precuneus, posterior cingulate, and anteromedial prefrontal cortex in ADHD individuals (Castellanos, 2007, 2008).

Higher local efficiency of a network has been associated with larger fault tolerance of the network at the face of external attack. The higher value of local efficiency in ADHD observed here might thus suggest a kind of defense mechanism responsible for suppressing the disorder affection.

It has been suggested that the small-world structure reflects an optimal balance between local specialization and global integration (Sporns and Tononi, 2002). Therefore, any abnormal shift caused by brain diseases toward either random or regular networks may reflect a less optimal network organization. The regular configurations in complex networks have been found to demonstrate low global coordination and slow information flow compared to small-world arrangements.

Additionally, significantly decreased nodal efficiency involving medial prefrontal (medial OFC), temporal, and occipital cortex regions was also found in ADHD. The nodal efficiency measures the extent to which the node connects all other nodes of a network, which may indicate the importance of the nodal area in the whole brain network. In contrast, the inferior frontal gyrus (IFG) was found to exhibit significantly increased nodal efficiency. The IFG was critical for response inhibition, which has been considered as the core deficit in ADHD (Barkley, 1997; Vaidya, 1998). The greater nodal efficiency may thus reflect greater inhibitory effort in the ADHD children.

Similar findings have been described for structural (white matter) connectivity topology in ADHD (Cao, 2013). The ADHD boys showed decreased global efficiency and increased path length. Given that the small-world topology reflects an optimal balance between global integration and local specialization (Sporns, 2000), these findings suggest that ADHD children exhibit a less optimized topological organization in their white matter networks. Notably, several studies have suggested that the maturation of the healthy human brain follows a 'local to distributed' principle (Fair, 2009; Dosenbach, 2010). Given that the global-efficiency and path-length metrics of the networks are usually associated with integrated information processing, Wang and Cao's findings of decreased global efficiency and increased path length in ADHD patients may reflect a delayed structural maturation.

Additionally, decreased nodal efficiency in ADHD patients was observed primarily in several frontal (left orbital part of the middle frontal gyrus), parietal (left supramarginal gyrus, left inferior parietal lobe, left postcentral gyrus and left angular gyrus), and occipital regions (left lingual gyrus). These regions are the key nodes of the attention networks and exhibit structural and functional abnormalities in ADHD.

2.6. Evolving Integrative Models of ADHD and Implications for Neurofeedback

Arousal Model

In the neurofeedback field, it is still common to use the outdated arousal model of ADHD, assuming a hypoarousal, which should be targeted by uptraining SMR and downtraining theta. Several studies, and especially Leech and Sharp's (2014) ABBA (Arousal, Balance, and Breadth of Attention) Model, have shown that arousal is only one dimension of neurophysiological problems in ADHD.

Motivation Deficit Model

In his earlier work, Barkley (1990) proposed a motivation deficit model for ADHD. More recently, this hypothesis has been revived in Sonuga-Barka's (2003) dual-pathway model in which the executive network (CEN) or the motivation network are dysregulated. Later on, it has been demonstrated that both networks are interacting and that the interactions in ADHD are dysfunctional.

CEN Model

In 1994, Barkley developed his model of a deficit of response inhibition or self-control, highlighting the essential role of problems with the executive functions. Later studies have shown that problems of executive functions are not present in all cases of ADHD, and more importantly, they have shown frequent presence of problems in several large-scale brain networks.

DMN Interfering Model

Sonuga-Barke proposed a model of dysfunctional anticorrelation between the default mode network and the task positive networks (DAN, CEN). During tasks, there is interference of the DMN in ADHD, which explains recurrent off task (daydreaming) behaviors. In more recent work (Leech and Sharp, 2014), it has been shown that the dorsal posterior cingulate of the DMN acts a superior hub, which is constantly scanning the internal and external world in a metastable way. An interaction model of collaboration has replaced the earlier idea of strict anticorrelation between DMN and DAN/CEN.

Triple Core Network Model

Menon (2010) demonstrated how the anterior insula and dorsal anterior cingulate, the core elements of the salience network (SN), act as a switch between the DMN and CEN. It has been demonstrated that in ADHD, the DMN is not well segregated from the task positive CEN because of a dysfunctional SN.

VAN-DAN-DMN-SN Model

Recent work has emphasized the role of an overactive ventral attention network (VAN) in ADHD, which plays a role in bottom-up attention reorientation. It is believed that this overactivity is the consequence of a dysfunctional modulating CEN.

Hierarchical Reinforcement Learning Model

Holroyd and Yeung (2012, 2013) proposed a hierarchical reinforcement learning model to explain decision-making, where the dorsal anterior cingulate acts as a behavior policy set, the DLPFC together with the dorsal striatum act as the behavior executer ('actor'), and the orbitofrontal cortex together with the ventral striatum act as the value attributor ('critic'). Hauser (2014) demonstrated dysfunctionality of this system in ADHD by measuring a poor feedback-related negativity in the dorsal anterior cingulate, which, together with a hypo-functioning orbitofrontal cortex, is an index of error negativity prediction.

Not all these models are mutually exclusive, and they can be integrated in one large model, where a central role is attributed to the dorsal anterior cingulate for salience detection, conflict and action monitoring, and hierarchical reinforcement learning. All these functions are interrelated and modulated by the dopaminergic system. In the Cz theta/SMR neurofeedback training protocol, it is assumed that the dorsal anterior cingulate, which is dysfunctional in ADHD, is activated. In addition to explaining increased balance of triple core networks, it also clarifies that the hyperactive VAN is modulated by CEN; that the dorsal posterior cingulate reassumes its metastable superior hub function for an optimal vigilance; and that hierarchical reinforcement learning normalizes, which is important for developing optimal decision-making, where long-term rewards reassume their behavior regulation role.

CHAPTER 3
EEG: Mechanisms of Attention, Vigilance, and Self-Regulation

3.1 EEG and Underlying Brain Activity

EEG (ELECTROENCEPHALOGRAM) REFERS to the electrical brain activity that is measurable at the scalp. It was first described in 1929 by the German psychiatrist Hans Berger who investigated EEG correlations with mental states and with substances, such as caffeine. After some years, psychiatry found no useful application for EEG, and from the 1960s onward, only neurologists utilized this technology as an applied research method within a clinical neurological context, although with little guiding theoretical framework. Gross abnormalities were described in patients with neurological injuries or in the brains of people with metabolic disorders. Accordingly, some exceptionally useful research was undertaken, especially with reference to epilepsy. The emergence of other brain imaging methods significantly reduced the practical importance of EEG to neurology, although EEG remained a useful research method that continued to shed light on the nature of epilepsy. Meanwhile, a stream of psychophysiological studies that emerged in 1964 adopted different ways to interpret the EEG more accurately. These studies focused on re-evaluating deviant brainwave patterns, as manifestations of varying degrees of vigilance, which according to neurological norms lay within normal variance.

The Berlin psychiatrist Bente (1964) offered a compact definition of the concept of vigilance (i.e., wakefulness), as the quality and degree of organization in an individual's adaptive interaction with the environment, which built on the clinical understanding advanced by the London neurologist Head in 1923. It is noteworthy that this description contains elements of the later formulation of the executive functions of the frontal lobe regions. In Bente's definition, vigilance is conceptualized as a function of a dynamic brain state that is mirrored by the global, organized EEG pattern. Vigilance, as conceptualized by Head and Bente, differs from the more recent concept of vigilance as alertness and sustained attention.

During the 1970s, EEG enjoyed a revival in research laboratories in the form of pharmaco-EEGs that allow one to characterize psycho-pharmaceuticals based on changes in the EEG spectrum. Since 1985, the wide scale availability of computers made it possible to use QEEG (quantitative EEG) in clinical practice. Not only the power of the frequency bands was considered important, but also the phase relationships for each frequency band between each pair of EEG electrodes and their stability (coherence). As QEEG technology developed, the establishment of age-normed databases significantly increased its usefulness, and researchers and clinicians can now verify statistically significant differences between the data obtained from various patient groups or between individual patient data and the distribution of normal age appropriate values (i.e., lifetime normative databases). Nevertheless, a major drawback of these exciting developments of the EEG as a practical, empirical examination method was the loss of impetus for the further development of theoretical models to better understand the internal dynamics of EEG. One such model that continues to retain its value, although mostly forgotten, is Bente's vigilance model based on sleep deprivation studies and the influence of pharmaceuticals on the EEG. The inherent ideas of this model were revitalized in more recent models of metastability and self-organizing criticality.

Further, EEG was not a priority for physiological research in the 1970's, and the research impetus shifted toward the study of neuron electrophysiology. Nevertheless, since the nineties, there has been a strong revival of scientific interest in EEG research accompanied by the emergence of a whole series of new signal analysis methods, such as joint time frequency analysis (JTFA), independent component analysis (ICA), entropy analysis, non-linear analysis methods, and more. In addition, the field of event-related potentials became important in psychiatry. A major new impetus for QEEG and ERP in psychiatry was the development of 3-D source reconstruction.

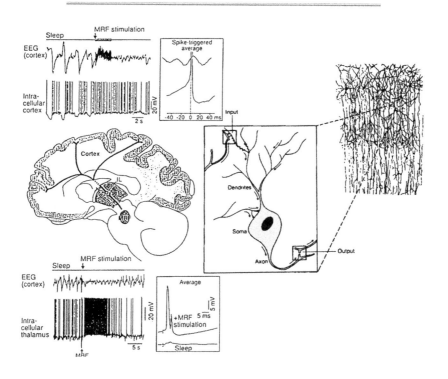

Figure 8. Slow waves are seen at the start of the uppermost EEG segment observed during sleep. The curve directly underneath displays the action potential measured with microelectrodes at the cell membrane of the cortical neurons. During sleep, action potentials occur in 'bursts,' and their duration determines the period of the EEG wave. If the center for consciousness in the reticular formation of the mesencephalon (MRF) in the brain stem is stimulated, fast low voltage EEG activity is generated paired with tonic action potentials. The lowermost EEG segment is identical but with the action potential of thalamic neurons displayed underneath. The middle figure illustrates axons rising from the brain stem to the thalamus at the base of the cerebrum via the mesencephalon, forming synapses with the cell bodies of thalamocortical neurons, axons of which connect to various areas of the cerebral cortex (shaded). In these brain areas, axonal fibers make synaptic contact with apical (that is, running perpendicular to the scalps) dendrites. The electrical fields near these cortical neurons are measurable in the EEG at the scalp. On the right, we can see a schematic cross section of a portion of cerebral cortex and a network of neurons. In the box above, we see an enlarged drawing showing an axon forming a synapse at a dendrite of the depicted neuron, allowing information transmission (in the direction indicated by the arrows) through the soma (the cell body) along the axon, which in turn synapses with the dendrites of a neighboring neuron.

The EEG is measurable at the surface of the scalp taken normally at 19 points and reflects the continuous electrical activity of the brain. The electrical rhythmic brain waves measured at the scalp reflect the massed activity of postsynaptic potentials of the neuronal *dendrites* in the underlying cerebral cortex. The EEG is therefore not the sum of the action potentials of the *neurons*, as was once thought. Nevertheless, the phase of an oscillation is always at least approximately related to spike timing. The presence of field-signal phase synchrony thus indicates the presence of neuronal-level spike synchrony, which is important in the light of the crucial role of spike timing in neuronal communication.

Around one hundred million neurons form the cerebral cortex, and these neurons possess essentially a tree-like structure with many extensions growing out of the cell body. Numerous dendrites further split into smaller branches and carry electrical signals from the postsynaptic sites to the cell bodies. From each cell body, electrical signals travel down along axon in a process comparable to transmission along a telephone wire before reaching yet even more divergent structures - the root-like axon terminals that connect to the next neuron within the circuit. The synapse is the 'contact zone' between one neuron and the next. It forms between the axon terminal of one neuron and the cell body, or the dendrites, of the recipient neuron in the circuit. Electrical information that arrives at the axon terminal triggers the release of a chemical substance, a neurotransmitter (e.g., dopamine). Neurotransmitters carry information to the postsynaptic neuron by binding to the receptors at the cell body or on the dendrites. The binding process triggers ion channels to open in the cell membrane of the postsynaptic neuron, altering that neuron's electrical membrane potential. Every neuron has a resting membrane potential based on differences in ion concentration inside and outside of the cell membrane. The membrane potentials vary continuously with the electrical activity of the synaptic receptors, which is determined by the ways in which neurotransmitters, such as dopamine, occupy receptors, carrying information from the previous cell in the neuronal circuits. The electrical potential difference changes along both sides of the cell membrane and is carried from the dendrites to the cell body and finally along the axon. When electrical excitation is sufficiently great, an action potential is generated at the base of the axon that produces a reversal of the membrane potential that lasts a few milliseconds. Sufficient excitation occurs from the summation of excitations from thousands of neighboring neurons that synapse with the target neuron. The average discharge frequency of an action potential is 50 Hz. Strong excitation can raise the frequency to 90 Hz or more while inhibition reverses the electric potential and reduces the discharge frequency to 30 Hz or less. The discharge frequency is the most important parameter from an information-processing standpoint. Ionic fluxes around the neurons form a field potential outside of them. An EEG electrode registers a negative field potential when excitation of an apical dendrite or inhibition of the cell body occurs. Apical dendrites branch back from the next neuron in the circuit to synapse with the axon. They lay closest to the surface of the cerebral cortex and run perpendicular down to deeper layers of the cerebral cortex.

The measured EEG activity is thus induced by a functional dipole, that is, long vertical parallel target dendrites with numerous predominantly excitatory synapses that lie at the surface of the cerebral cortex and the cell bodies that lie deeper in the cerebral cortex form inhibitory synapses, albeit they are much fewer in number compared to the excitatory ones. The EEG displays the typical wave pattern from repetitive discharge of surface postsynaptic potentials.

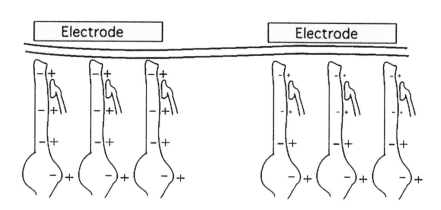

Figure 9. The drawing on the left depicts how neuronal axons synapse with apical neuronal dendrites at the surface of the cerebral cortex. There is no excitation at this moment, and the extracellular electropositive charge is maximal. Axonal excitation (depolarization) is depicted on the right. The two EEG electrodes at the surface measure a potential difference; on the right, the extracellular field potential around the active neuronal region is less electropositive compared to the inactive area depicted on the left. A short time later, the situation reverses.

Each of the 19 electrodes measures the summed activity from about a million neurons. The resultant waves have been classified in a purely descriptive fashion according to their frequency band: delta for the slowest (1-4 Hz), followed by theta (4-8 Hz), alpha (8-13 Hz), beta-1 (13-21 Hz), beta-2 (21-30 Hz), and gamma (35-45 Hz). Initially, little was known about the functional significance of these waves, and they were often regarded as noise generated by the underlying brain activity. This frequency band classification arose based on specific properties and consciousness states and, in recent years, its validity has been supported through statistical calculations that estimate the degree of variation of the underlying information (e.g., ICA, 'independent component analysis').

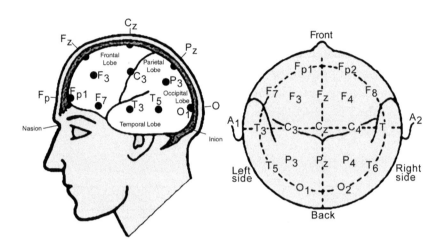

Figure 10. The 19 measuring points employed by the classical "10-20" EEG measuring system (Frontal, Central, Temporal, Parietal, and Occipital locations). Image created by WinEEG, Mitsar Co. Ltd.

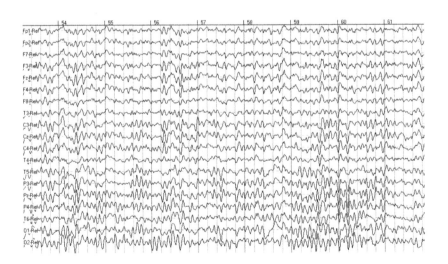

Figure 11. EEG readings from 19 measuring points on the scalp (each labeled on the left with a letter and number). Normally, as here, alpha rhythm is expressed maximally in the posterior brain areas (lowest two curves) mixed with faster (beta) and slower (theta) waves. This fragment lasts 9 seconds, as indicated by the time scale along the top line. Image created by WinEEG, Mitsar Co. Ltd.

Quantitative electroencephalography, or QEEG (and the graphical representation of the QEEG as a 'brain mapping,' which looks somewhat like a colored weather map), has remained in use since its introduction around 1985. The most frequent use of QEEG, even in the present day, remains restricted to the calculation of frequency spectra, which are then compared with average values from a database to calculate the coherency. A particular asset of QEEG is the capacity to calculate the strength of each frequency band between two measurement points, thus elucidating the degree to which each EEG wave type demonstrates more or less fixed phase relationships relative to each other. The phase relationship indicates differences in timing between wave patterns at two measurement points. Naked eye inspection of the EEG cannot reveal this information. Moreover, the processed values are interpretable only in comparison to values from a normative data bank.

3.2 EEG After Sleep Deprivation as a Model for Labile Vigilance

The first chapter of this book, 'Vigilance and Self-Regulation in ADHD', discussed how sleep deprivation in a normal person could produce characteristics akin to ADHD, including insufficient attention, poor organization and planning, more reflexive reactions to random environmental stimuli, and irritability. In 1952, the French psychiatrist Ey, who developed an 'organodynamic psychiatry' rooted in the consciousness dissolutions of Hughlings Jackson, took the dissolution of consciousness, which is seen in the gradual transition from waking state to sleep state, as a model for psychopathology. In 1967, Ey postulated furthermore a common time structure of 'destruction of the field of consciousness' on the one hand and the subvigilant intermediary stages that can be delimitated in the EEG on the other hand. In the main field of psychiatry, the path pointed out by Ey has been ignored. An exception was the Berlin psychiatrist Bente. In Bente's understanding of psychiatry, which was greatly influenced by Ey's neo-Jacksonianism, the EEG was far more than an auxiliary diagnostic tool. He considered it a heuristically fecund vehicle for his psychiatric thinking. The conceptual closeness to Ey is particularly evident in a study on sleep deprivation conducted with healthy volunteers to determine psychopathological dissolution levels, confirming Ey's theory (Bente, 1969). Concerning EEG-correlates of sleep deprivation, Bente's study revealed an initial dynamic labilization in the form of a discontinuous breakdown of the background alpha activity with an increase of low-voltage fast beta activity. With increasing duration of sleep deprivation, an increasing number of sequences of high-voltage slow waves were observed.

Later studies confirmed these findings, reporting global theta and beta-2 waves increase and alpha and beta-1 waves decrease in a healthy sleep-deprived person (Brunner, Dijk, & Borbély, 1993). These changes, visible to the naked eye, are most clearly measured along the middle of the head, the same location used to monitor different sleep stages in EEG research.

Interestingly, after sleep deprivation, theta has the highest amplitude at the vertex (Gorgoni, 2014), which is in line with the well-known theta/beta Cz ratio for inattention in ADHD during wakefulness. As early as the 1960s, Bente (1969) described three types of labile EEG dynamics after sleep deprivation: 1) decreased beta-2 (20-30 Hz) activity; 2) excess theta activity with a reduction in alpha and beta-1 (13-21 Hz) activity; and 3) discontinuous alpha activity interspersed with heightened theta and beta-2 activity. These 3 patterns compare remarkably well with different EEG-types observed in people with ADHD without prior sleep deprivation.

Quantitative analysis of the EEG (QEEG) in which the frequency spectrum of the EEG is calculated allows for precise measurement and comparison of these changes, with the spread of normal values across the life span. In addition, it has been found that in an EEG taken the night following sleep deprivation, an increased number of slow waves occur along with a reduced quantity of the 12-15 Hz waves that typically occur in series during sleep (sleep spindles) and are maximally measurable at the central point of the scalp (Cz) (Brunner, Dijk, & Borbély, 1993). Sleep spindles are normally weak during sleep stage *transitions* (I, II, III, IV, and REM sleep) and are consequently thought to play a role in sleep state *stabilization*, somewhat akin to shock absorbers (Evans, 1993). Such a function corresponds with Pavlov's concept of 'internal inhibition' (a process in which a conditioned reflex is extinguished through negative reinforcement). Sleep spindles are less numerous during the sleep of people with epilepsy and people with ADHD (Kahn, 1978).

Sterman, a founder of neurofeedback, in his early research with cats in the late 1960s demonstrated that a 12-15 Hz (or more broadly 12-20 Hz) daytime rhythm plays a similar role in the stabilization of daytime vigilance levels. He called this the 'sensorimotor rhythm' because it reached maximal levels over the sensorimotor cortex. Its anatomical origin was found primarily in the somatosensory cortex (where the sense of touch is processed) and in the VPL nucleus (ventral posterolateral nucleus) of the thalamus. Sterman argued that the somatosensory cortex is involved in the inhibition of movements alongside the motor cortex so that from a functional point of view, the sensorimotor rhythm is aptly named. However, the broader EEG community did not employ this term; instead, it labeled these rhythms as 'central cortical beta rhythms.' Inhibition of movement is a necessary but not the only condition for the creation of this rhythm. If inhibition of movement were the only condition, it would be very simple to alleviate hyperactivity and its attendant low quantity of SMR rhythm through traditional behavioral training. A number of researchers, including Sterman and Lubar, demonstrated a link with attention, such that focused attention increases the SMR rhythm. Canu and Rougeul (1982, 1992) showed that the beta rhythm in the somatosensory cortex and the thalamic VPL nucleus plays a role in focused attention in cats. On the other hand, they found that sleep spindles, measured over the entire surface of the scalp during sleep, originate essentially in the motor cortex and the thalamic reticular nucleus.

Anderer (2001; 2013), using LORETA source reconstruction, described a differentiation of sleep spindles based on localization and rhythm, with a slow precuneus rhythm peaking at about 14 Hz and a slower rhythm (peeking around 12 Hz) measurable in medial prefrontal areas. The frontal rhythm usually disappears in adulthood. Interestingly, the cortical generators localized for delta waves in slow wave sleep showed considerable overlap with the sleep spindle generators. With increasing depolarization of thalamocortical cells, spindles are gradually replaced by intrinsically generated delta waves. PET revealed the reported sources of delta waves in the medial prefrontal cortex spreading to the anterior cingulate and the orbitofrontal cortex, which are the crucial areas of the anterior default mode network that are perfectly in line with decreases in cortical regional blood flow during slow wave sleep. Both the medial prefrontal cortex and the precuneus, which are essential areas of the default mode network, are particularly active during wakefulness and thus might have a greater need for recuperation. It has been suggested that the spatially widespread and temporally coherent neuronal activity occurring during slow wave sleep could be used to reorganize cortical networks throughout the cerebrum (Steriade, 1993b). These processes are more marked in orbitofrontal cortex and anterior cingulate gyrus than in the rest of the cortex (Maquet, 1997). This indicates that sleep deprivation disrupts the functions subtended by these areas during waking. Patients with orbitofrontal or anterior cingulate lesions usually present with various clinical signs, such as impulsivity, loss of social constraints, emotional lability, and distractibility. It is noteworthy that similar signs, such as childish humor, disinhibited behavior and irritability, distractibility, and perseverations, are likewise observed after short-term total sleep deprivation, and their effects can be attributed primarily to slow wave sleep deprivation (Horne, 1993). After just one single night of sleep deprivation, a deficit in appropriate decision-making during a 'real economic world' simulation was present (Harrison and Horne, 1996). Adequate decision-making is needed for optimal behavioral adaptation in the best interest of the individual. After sleep deprivation, executive function difficulties, including poor attention and working memory, and poor divergent thinking (updating strategies based on new information, multitasking and flexible thinking, risk assessment, mood-appropriate behavior, maintaining interest in outcomes, ineffective communication, and poor insight) have been described (Harrison, 2000).

Thomas (2000) described similar deactivation of prefrontal and parietal areas, i.e., prefrontal cortex (including ventral and dorsal anterior cingulate gyri), the lateral posterior parietal (both inferior and superior lobules), and the medial parietal cortices (including posterior cingulate gyrus and precuneus) after sleep deprivation. Sleep deprivation elevates expectations (anticipation) of reward (monetary gains) and attenuates responses to losses following risky decisions (Venkatraman, 2007, 2011). The increased expectations of reward correlate with increased nucleus accumbens and VMPFC activity following risky choices and with attenuated responses to gambling monetary losses in left anterior insula and left lateral orbitofrontal cortex (reduced sense of loss). The reduced sensitivity to loss possibly related to the decreased error-related negativity (ERN) (Renn, 2012; Tsai, 2005) and a lower no-go N2 (Renn, 2012), which have been described after sleep deprivation as well as in ADHD.

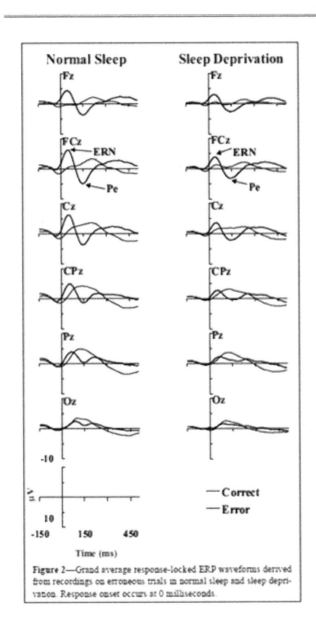

Normal Sleep
Sleep Deprivation
Fz
FCz
ERN
Pe
Cz
CPz
Pz
Oz
-10
μV
10
-150
150
450
Time (ms)
Correct
Error
Figure 2—Grand average response-locked ERP waveforms derived from recordings on erroneous trials in normal sleep and sleep deprivation. Response onset occurs at 0 milliseconds.

Figure 12. Lower ERN after sleep deprivation (Tsai, 2005 Sleep)

Regional cerebral blood flow during slow wave sleep is also lower in the precuneus, a crucial area of the posterior default mode network (Maquet, 1997; Thomas, 2000). Doucette (2015) found a significant correlation between processing speed - a construct reflecting the speed of executing cognitive operations - and parietal slow sleep spindle power in preschool children. The relationship of thalamocortical network activity with cognition, memory, and attention has been well established, and slow sleep spindles in particular have been linked to thalamocortical efficiency and higher cognitive abilities.

Rest state fMRI functional connectivity after sleep deprivation decreases between ventromedial prefrontal cortex and the posterior cingulate, showing less anticorrelation with the executive network (De Havas, 2012; Killgore, 2012). Similar findings have been described in ADHD (Castellanos, 2008). Volkow (2012) described downregulated D2/D3 receptors in the nucleus accumbens (less raclopride binding) after sleep deprivation, which could explain motivation deficits and attention deficits when motivation is low. Lower D2/D3 and DAT receptor availability have been described in never medicated ADHD adults (Volkow, 2009, 2011) in the dopamine reward pathway (ventral tegmental area, nucleus accumbens) as well as in the caudate nucleus, which can also explain why ADHD people are more prone to drug abuse. It is assumed that impairment in the dopamine reward pathway could underlie the clinical evidence of abnormal responses to reward in ADHD. The reward deficits in ADHD are characterized by a failure to delay gratification, impaired response to partial schedules of reinforcement, and preference for small immediate rewards over larger delayed rewards. Consistent with this important clinical feature of the ADHD syndrome, an fMRI study reported decreased activation of the ventral striatum (wherein nucleus accumbens is located) for both immediate and delayed rewards in adult participants with ADHD compared to controls (Plichta, 2009). The net result of downregulated D2/D3 receptors after sleep deprivation and the lower availability of these receptors in ADHD were the same.

3.3 EEG in ADHD

The EEG pattern in people with sleep deprivation is similar to that in people with ADHD, with measurements in the middle of the head (Cz) frequently showing an increase in theta waves and a decrease in beta-1 waves as well as a variant form that expresses low voltage EEG with predominately beta-2 activity. Monastra (1999, 2001) used the central theta/beta-1 ratio as a measure of distraction. This ratio is increased in 94% of people with ADHD compared to barely 2% of control subjects. Jasper already in 1938 reported increased slow-wave activity in fronto-central regions, a putative indicator of abnormal brain function in a group of 'behavior problem children' described as hyperactive, impulsive, and highly variable.

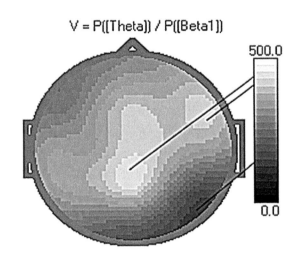

Figure 13. This example illustrates an increased theta/beta-1 ratio in central scalp regions: 21.9/5.2 (normal ratio <3.31 for a comparable age range).

In recent years, consecutive studies from Clarke's Australian research group (2001) confirmed Monastra's results, supporting an increased theta/beta-1 ratio in central and frequently also in frontal areas in ADHD children with and without hyperactivity. This anomaly is more marked in the group with hyperactivity than in the group without hyperactivity, and it is frequently accompanied by increased frontal coherence of alpha and/or theta waves. Clarke also showed that, on average, the hyperactive subgroup evidenced this increased activity maximally at the frontal midline while the subgroup without hyperactivity expressed maximal activity in the centroparietal area along the midline. As the children matured, both subgroups had a similar ratio. Both Lubar and Kropotov found that in 6-year-old children or younger, the maximal deviation is found along the parietal or centroparietal midline while in 7-8 years old children, this occurs maximally along the central midline. By 15 years of age, this pattern maximizes along the frontocentral midline. After 2010, however, several independent research groups published the results that failed to support the early results on the TBR and ADHD diagnosis (Loo and Arns, 2015).

Clarke observed that in a group of 298 ADHD children aged 8 to 12 years, 15% showed increased beta activity (12.5-25 Hz) over the entire scalp that was maximal in frontal areas and a diminished (rather than increased) theta/beta-1 ratio. Principally, this was measured predominately in boys with the hyperactive form of ADHD. Typically, more tantrums and moodiness were described in this group. Initially, Clarke considered that the excess beta activity was a marker of hyperarousal. However, he later showed that Ritalin has an equally good therapeutic effect in the heightened beta subgroup as in the theta group (Clarke, 2003). Consequently, he no longer thought that this increased beta activity could be considered a sign of hyperarousal. Clarke went on to propose that this likely represents a problem with frontal behavioral regulation, independent of arousal strength, because children with this subtype display mostly hyperactive and impulsive behavior. This subtype frequently shows greater frontal alpha coherence.

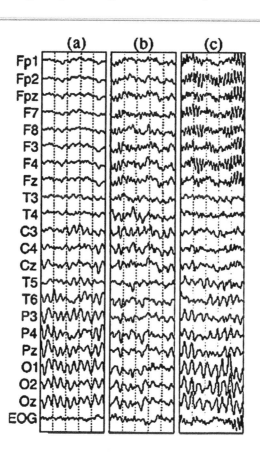

Figure 14. QEEG subtypes of ADHD, as expressed by increased frontal beta activity (12.5-25 Hz): a) normal; b) increased frontal beta activity; c) frontal beta spindles. Reprinted from Psychiatry Research, 103(2-3), Clarke, Barry, McCarthy, & Selikowitz Excess beta activity in children with attention-deficit/hyperactivity disorder: An atypical electrophysiological group, Copyright (2001), with permission from Elsevier.

Increased beta-2 activity is also seen in people without ADHD after sleep deprivation. In adults with ADHD, 10% show increased beta activity, reaching a maximum frontally at the center (i.e., Fz) of the scalp (Gurnee, 2000). EEG source localization frequently indicates that this beta activity originates in the dorsal anterior cingulate. The increased beta-2 activity subgroup often shows additional difficulties, including sleep disorders, anxiety disorders, alcoholism, bipolar disorder (manic-depressive disorder), irritability, impatience, compulsion disorders, and a hyperactive stream of thought. Bente suggested that beta-2 plays a compensating role in vigilance B to prevent a shift to vigilance C (sleep stage I).

In agreement with Monastra and Clarke's research, Thompson and Thompson (2005) described a group of 154 adults with ADHD of whom 80% showed increased theta/beta-1 ratio measurable at the Cz position. In 40% out of the 80% (thus 32% of the complete group), he also observed an increased 26-34 Hz/13-15 Hz ratio at Cz, and this often appeared to correlate with an overactive thought stream.

In another subgroup of ADHD adults, and sometimes in children with ADHD, an excess of slow alpha activity has been found, especially in the frontal areas (often on the right more than on the left). The most likely explanation for this phenomenon is that theta waves evolve into slow alpha waves by a small frequency increase (Gurnee, 2000) often accompanied by reduced frontal delta activity (Chabot, 1996). This is a striking discovery because in neurology, delta activity is normally associated with pathology. Repeated QEEG studies of normal adults have shown that delta activity uses 20-30% of total energy in frontal and central areas. In typical adults, this delta activity is associated with higher mental functions and covaries with P300 amplitude (Basar, 1984; Intriligator, 1994). Delta activity in typical adults increases during calculation, reaction time tasks, and abstract thinking. A functional role of delta waves reflects an 'internal concentration' in which external cortical inputs are inhibited to maintain maximum available attention during tasks that involve internal representations (Fernandez, 1995). A lowered frontal delta quantity can correlate with decreased frontal regulation or blockage of inadequate behavioral impulses or external stimuli. The existing research suggests a significant functional relationship between the delta rhythm and the *mesotelencephalic dopamine* projection system that also plays a role in ADHD. Studies with dipole models (Michel, 1992, 1993) and correlations of PET with EEG (Alper, 1994, 1998) have estimated the location of the main delta generator site on the midline of the anterior part of the frontal cortex, which corresponds to the location of the most important terminal field of the mesotelencephalic dopamine projection system. Delta electrical activity of individual neurons has been measured directly in the nucleus accumbens (Leung, 1993), frontal cortex (Steriade, 1993), and the ventral tegmental area in the brain stem (Grace, 1995). Negative shifts of the slow frontal (DC, direct current) potentials occur in humans in situations of expectation; the analogous states in animals are associated with heightened VTA activity (Caspers, 1993; Haschke, 1993; Kivatkin, 1995).

This is consistent with the well-known finding of a diminished contingent negative variation (CNV) in ADHD, which an appropriate treatment can normalize. Moreover, behaviors related to dopamine increase selectively through stimulation of dopamine cell axons at 2-3 Hz (Grace, 1995), which is consistent with the resonance of delta frequency bands in the mesotelencephalic dopamine projection system. Interestingly, Broyds and Helps (2011) described a lower amount of infraslow EEG oscillations in ADHD, which have their source in the anterior medial prefrontal cortex (part of the default mode network), that is, the same source as for delta activity. This suggests that delta might be the upper end of infraslow oscillations.

Gurnee (2000) noted that in the subgroup of ADHD adults with excess frontal alpha activity as well as in the subgroup of ADHD adults without EEG abnormalities, at least half of cases showed an abnormal rise in theta and alpha activity during an attention task. Lubar (1999) described the same phenomenon. Further, this is in agreement with Amen (1998) who have conducted research using functional neuroimaging, expressly SPECT (single proton emission computerized tomography), and found that many people with ADHD have less frontal activity during mental effort that requires attention. In the hyperactive form of ADHD, frontal activity decreased on both the outside (dorsolateral) and the underside (orbitofrontal) of the prefrontal cortex while in the variant without hyperactivity, decrease was noted only in dorsolateral prefrontal activity. When the participants from these subgroups are instructed to intensify mental effort in a task that did not interest them, paradoxically, the quality of their attention decreased further. This means that performance of children with ADHD might be even poorer when they are asked to pay more attention.

Chabot (1996) distinguished two types of EEG profiles in children with ADHD. First, 46% showed an increase in theta and/or alpha activity in maximal frontal and/or central cortex associated with a normal peak alpha frequency and a decreased quantity of frontal delta waves. This pattern has also been observed in cocaine users and subjects with depression. Increased alpha activity in ADHD, in Chabot's view, is predictive of a favorable response to treatment with Zyban™ (bupropion) and to antidepressants, according to Suffin (1995). Increased theta activity seems to respond better to Ritalin™. Second, 30% demonstrated an increase in alpha and/or theta together with a slower alpha peak frequency.

An increased coherence of alpha and theta waves has been observed in both EEG profiles, especially between left and right frontal areas. According to Suffin, increased alpha or theta activity that is paired with increased coherence responds best to treatment with anti-epileptics. In 2000, the official guidelines of the American Academy of Pediatrics argued that the diagnosis of ADHD can be made only on the basis of behavioral observations and behavioral rating scales (i.e., symptom check lists) for ADHD. In 2004, the American Academy of Pediatrics proposed a different perspective in the monograph, 'ADHD: A Complete and Authoritative Guide'. It argued that brain scans, such as quantitative electroencephalography (QEEG), will provide more distinctive classification of the neurological and behavioral features of ADHD, which may help expand the knowledge base and treatment of ADHD. This re-evaluation was reached based on 13 studies published after 1997 covering 2,642 children with ADHD and conducted by five independent research groups. In 2013, the U.S. Food and Drug Administration allowed marketing of the NEBA (Neuropsychiatric EEG-based Assessment Aid) System to help assess ADHD in children and adolescents between 6-17 years old. It is remarkable that this objective diagnostic assessment (QEEG) is used so little in daily clinical practice. The NEBA method is based on the measurement of the theta/beta ratio, and NEBA Health has reported an accuracy of 88% in diagnosing ADHD when the EEG measurement is combined with standard diagnosis performed by a clinician, compared to a 61% accuracy when only standard clinical diagnosis is performed.

In earlier sections, we briefly discussed how sleep deprivation leads to behavioral changes similar to those that occur in ADHD and that this can be described in terms of decreased activity in the anterior cingulate, the orbitofrontal cortex, and the dorsolateral prefrontal cortex (DLPFC). Functional imaging studies (PET) of the brain during an attentional task following a night of sleep deprivation further confirmed decreased activity in these areas as well as the thalamus, caudate nucleus, and the posterior association cortex (Thomas, 2000; Maquet, 2007). Evidently, these areas are most sensitive to sleep deprivation and have a greater need of restoration processes during sleep. We shall examine how lowered activity in the DLPFC, the nucleus caudate, and the orbitofrontal cortex leads to fewer sleep spindles in the sleep EEG and lesser quantity of beta-1 waves in the waking state.

The majority of EEG waves measurable at the scalp are generated in the neuronal circuits between the cerebral cortex and the thalamus. Deep in the brain, lying at the top of the brain stem, the thalamus is the central 'relay station' through which most sensory information passes before it is diverted toward posterior areas of the cerebral cortex (where sensory perception is processed). The continuous cyclic flow of information between the thalamus and the cerebral cortex establishes the awareness of sensory information. We know that the wave properties of the thalamocortical circuits are important for normal functioning of the cerebral cortex. Theta waves in the EEG indicate slower rhythms. Abnormal amounts of theta are seen in multiple psychological and neurological disease states. States with excess theta waves are often coupled with 'burst' discharges in the thalamus, resulting in excessive inhibition. Burst discharges are action potential firings that constitute a complex periodic eruption of activity in thalamocortical neurons (these neurons originate in the thalamus with dendrites connecting to the cerebral cortex). Normally, they occur only during sleep, as neurons in waking states normally fire in tonic bursts (continuous discharges of action potentials with a sustained voltage). Source localization methods can uncover the brain areas responsible for the dysfunction in theta activity. These dysfunctional regions are responsible for the inhibition of thalamic areas whereby the thalamic neurons show a slower rhythm in thalamocortical circuits.

In 1999, Llinas and Jeanmonod defined a number of disorders as thalamocortical dysrhythmias that included movement disorders (Parkinson's disease, for example), depression, neurological pain, tinnitus (the perception of phantom sound), and epilepsy. In these cases, increased coherence among theta, alpha, and beta rhythms is frequently observed, specifically the simultaneous deployment of these various wave types suggests increased cooperation but at the same time, decreased differentiation between different neural operations. In ADHD, the increased theta activity is often maximally measurable in the middle of the head and source localization frequently identifies the source of this theta activity in the dorsal anterior cingulate (Lubar, 1997). This suggests a disturbance in the circuit linking the thalamus and cingulate. Moreover, increased coherence between theta activities in the two cerebral hemispheres is often observed in ADHD, which is probably an indication of poor differentiation between the functions of these brain areas.

Summary

The *electroencephalogram* (EEG) consists of different frequency brain waves (in order of increasing frequency: delta, theta, alpha, beta, and gamma). The quantitative EEG (QEEG) demonstrates distinctive patterns in 94% of people with ADHD, making it a useful objective diagnostic tool. Insufficient beta-1 waves (plays a role in guiding attention) and excessive slow theta waves (normally only present in elevated levels during sleep) characterize the most common pattern. During sleep, there are less stabilizing sleep spindles (rhythmic series of 12-15 Hz waves). Lastly, the excess of theta waves originates in the dorsal anterior cingulate.

3.4 The Stabilizing Role of Sleep Spindles and SMR

The motor cortex, the originator of some sleep spindles, is anterior to the somatosensory cortex, with a large groove separating the two areas. Sleep spindles have been found to originate in the thalamic reticular nucleus. The reticular nucleus of the thalamus also plays an important role in the mechanisms of selective attention, and it is modulated by the orbitofrontal cortex (Skinner and Yingling, 1977). Although the SMR rhythms originate in different regions of the cerebral cortex and the thalamus, there is some slight overlap with other regions, and there are many indications that these areas functionally relate to or mutually influence each other. Furthermore, it has been suggested that sleep spindles and selective attention employ the same neural networks.

Over long time scales, a certain minimum quantity of sleep spindles is required to maintain the stability of the sleep stage level. In wakefulness, the corresponding 12-20 Hz maintains the stability of wakefulness. The 12-20 Hz SMR rhythm in the waking state prevents vigilance from shifting to a labile vigilance B while over shorter time scales, the 12-20 Hz SMR rhythm plays a role in focused attention. If after sleep deprivation a person without ADHD takes an attention test in which he or she must push a key after every stimulus except one, then the fastest, most accurate responses occur at moments of minimal theta and maximum alpha and beta activity in the EEG (Townsend, 1979). The slowest reactions or omission errors occur moments after a change in the EEG pattern or after a short period in which the characteristic features of sleep deprivation in the global EEG pattern are exaggerated.

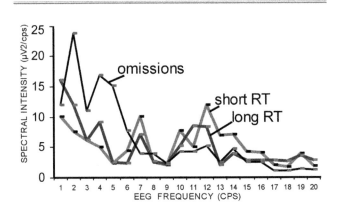

Figure 15. EEG frequency spectrum (C3 –right ear) over 1 second period corresponding to a reaction in a continuous performance test by a normal adult following sleep deprivation. Reprinted from Electroencephalography and Clinical Neurophysiology, 47(3), Townsend & Johnson, Relation of frequency-analyzed EEG to monitoring behavior, Copyright (1979), with permission from Elsevier.

In children with ADHD, their daytime EEG pattern often shows the same characteristics as in normal people after sleep deprivation: increased theta, less beta-1, decreased alpha, and more beta-2. In addition to this general pattern, in children with ADHD, at moments during which these characteristics are more pronounced, attention is weaker (Achim, 2004). Townsend (1979) described a similar phenomenon in normal adults after sleep deprivation.

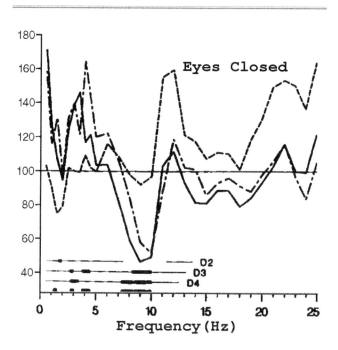

Figure 16. Percentage of EEG frequency spectrum values (C3-right ear) following partial sleep deprivation on day 2 (D2), 3 (D3), and 4 (D4) compared to day 1 in normal adults. A dotted line represents D2, alternating dots and dashes represent D3, and an unbroken line represents D4. The central horizontal midline marks 100 % (that is, day one values). The black bands in the left bottom corner emphasize the area of the EEG frequency that shows significant changes from day one. Reprinted from Sleep, 16, Brunner, Dijk, & Borbély, Repeated partial sleep deprivation progressively changes the EEG during sleep and wakefulness, Copyright (1993), with permission from American Academy of Sleep Medicine.

This phenomenon brings to mind an anecdote of the mathematician Mandelbrot (1982) about the development of fractal theory. One day, he received a call from a company that suffered interference on the lines connecting their computers and needed his help. Human error or technical fault did not seem to cause the interference. Mandelbrot noticed that certain storage 'densities' occurred in groups over a period of a day. That was nothing special, but as the duration shortened to half a day, this interference-grouping pattern stayed the same, regardless of whether the period was a few hours or less. The percentage of disturbance in different time periods was identical, showing a self-repeating pattern that was accumulating. Every time, the scale repeated the same figures (groups, fractals). In other words, the pattern of phone interference continuously repeated itself across different time scales.

The consistency of the sleep spindles and the SMR rhythm indicates the stability of both sleep and wakefulness phases, and these states determine the flexible stability of the individual's power to adapt to changing circumstances. In ADHD, people who have insufficient sleep spindles and decreased beta-1 rhythms, and their consequently disrupted system is manifested in broken sleep and a deficit in flexible attention and behavioral modulation. A phase transition in wakefulness level occurs whenever the density of the rhythm decreases periodically around the onset and completion of each sleep cycle (about 90 minutes). This also happens during sleep state transition periods within each sleep cycle. This sequence of cause and effect is circular. The diminishing cyclic action of the rhythm near a phase change is the result of the interaction of different system components within defined wake or sleep states while the cyclic action in turn influences the composition of component systems. Briefly, the cyclic variability of the sleep or wake cycles determines the variability of the cycle at any particular moment. The sleep-wake cycles, the sleep cycles, and the vigilance cycles, are necessary to provide adequate behavioral flexibility during wakefulness by enabling fluctuations at smaller time scale. The need for a sleep wake cycle arises because a living being must maintain integrity against the forces of its environment and never achieve a stable balance, as evidenced by the work of Belgian Nobel Prize winner Ilya Prigogine (1984). On the contrary, permanent imbalance is a necessary condition for a living system that must maintain itself while adapting to internal and external disturbances and environmental changes.

To understand the concept of circular causality, think of toy boats on a pond. Each boat generates own wave. Individual waves combine to form a big wave to which all the boats are subject. We can therefore argue that although weakening of the sleep spindles (or the beta-1 rhythm) arises from interaction between the subsystems, self-organization reconfigures the component systems.

A small-scale study (Khan, 1978) demonstrated a decreased quantity of sleep spindles in people with ADHD (12-15Hz) and their normalization after the administration of Ritalin. Additionally, a more recent larger-scale study (Miano, 2006) showed fewer alternating sleep stabilization cycles in ADHD. These discoveries provide an explanation for the ample evidence linking broken sleep to ADHD as well as an increased movement (hyperactivity) that it is probably linked to less stable sleep accompanied by more sleep phase transitions. Other research links broken sleep with fewer sleep spindles. Lastly, it has been demonstrated that a much greater variability in sleep duration and waking and falling asleep time occurs in people with ADHD over the course of a week (Gruber, 2000).

Developmental psychology emphasizes the role of stability and instability in the development of neurological behavioral systems (Thelen, 1993). Generally, a high level of variability points to an unstable system. Normally, a reliable stability develops in which the organization of a stable sleep wake cycle reflects the maturation of the nervous system and the development of systems of inhibition and feedback control (Halpern, 1995; Parmalee, 1972). A greater variability in this system can affect other systems. The prefrontal cerebral cortex, which acts as an interface among the sleep/wake system, emotion system, higher cognitive functions, and behavioral system, appears to modulate the relationship between higher cognitive functions and the regulation of sleep and emotions (Dahl, 1996). The influence of unstable sleep patterns on daily functioning can be compared to that of sleep deprivation.

Various research studies have shown that broken sleep is associated with the weakening of many mental functions, including selective and sustained attention (Sadeh, 2003; Van Dongen, 2003), memory consolidation (Macquet, 2003; Naylor, 2000), executive control (Fluck, 1998), consolidation of motor skills (Fischer, 2002), and P300 amplitude (Kingshott, 2000).

Conversely, studies have shown that fewer sleep spindles correlate with increased reaction time. It has been known for a long time, as noted previously, that sleep spindles play a role as stabilizers of ongoing sleep states during sleep. A gating mechanism allows this by diminishing or blocking sensorimotor information via the inactivation of thalamocortical circuits. As a result, the information interferes less with the processing of endogenous neural information during sleep. In the daytime, decreased capacity in this system can lead to failure of the thalamocortical circuit (required for the automatic sensorimotor processing requisite for sensory attention). This supports the hypothesis that selective attention and sleep spindles use the same neural network. In this regard, sleep spindles can reflect a sleep specific process that focuses on the maintenance or repair of some aspects of sensorimotor performance. A diminished quantity of sleep spindles can thus reflect a disturbance in the capacity of the thalamocortical circuit to contribute to the filtering of incoming sensory information.

Roth and Sterman (1967) showed that sleep spindles, as well as the beta-1 rhythm in waking states, can be seen as a mark of 'internal inhibition,' as Pavlov described. Pavlov argued that conditioned reflexes fade if no reward or punishment follows the expression of the conditioned reflex after stimulus onset. According to Pavlov, a generalized internal inhibition leads to the transition from sleep to wake state. Based on his experiments with dogs, Pavlov proposed individual differences in internal inhibition, which are linked to differences in individuals' temperaments. Roth and Sterman noted that after establishing a state of internal inhibition in cats using the conditioning methods described by Pavlov, a rhythm of 12-15 Hz (or more broadly 12-20 Hz) was measurable in the sensorimotor cortex, which he named the SMR rhythm (sensorimotor rhythm). He also observed that the rhythm arose in the cats' ventrobasal complex in the thalamus, which relays sensorimotor information to the cerebral cortex. Rougeul-Buser and Bouyer confirmed these findings in 1983.

Inhibition of cortically induced movement and an increase in attentive focused awareness accompany the appearance of the SMR rhythm. Activity in multiple brain areas contributes to this rhythm, obtaining sensory information about spatial movements of the limbs from the ventrobasal thalamus and information from the orbitofrontal cortex, the cerebellum, and from frontal, central and near-midline areas in the head of the caudate nucleus.

The generators of the SMR rhythm and the sleep spindles are located in the thalamus. Although their thalamocortical projections and the associated behavioral states differ slightly, it seems that the functional origin of both is a mechanism specifically involved in suppression of movement (phasic motor activity) and in perceptual excitability. The neural mechanisms responsible for the establishment of these rhythms in the somatosensory thalamocortical loops are essentially identical. This would explain why behavioral modification (by applying neurofeedback) that increases the SMR rhythm also increases the quantity of sleep spindles.

The reticular nucleus is a thin layer around the thalamus that has an inhibitory effect on sensory information passing from specific thalamic areas to the posterior cerebral cortex for perceptual processing. The reticular nucleus has a major modulatory influence on the generation of both sleep spindles and the sensorimotor rhythm, although regarding the sensorimotor rhythm of the cat, investigation with deep electrodes could not confirm this effect (Canu, 1992). The prefrontal cerebral cortex and the caudate nucleus modulate the reticular nucleus such that higher behavioral strategies (executive functions), including goal directed attention, modulate the passing of selective information to the cerebral cortex. Thus, the 'executive functions,' including behavioral strategies and goal focused attention, can select information that is likely to reach the stimulus bound posterior cerebral cortex. Scheibel (1984) later extended this model to include Sterman's suggestion that the sensorimotor information, which arrives in the cortex itself, can also inhibit the reticular nucleus through a feedback loop.

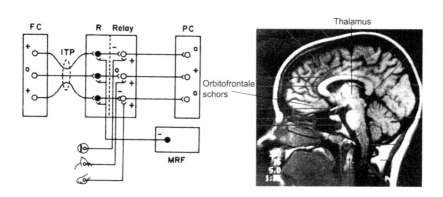

Figure 17. Skinner and Yingling's (1977) thalamic gating model of sensory cerebral cortex activity. Gates in the thalamic relay areas that allow the flow of sensory information to the posterior cerebral cortex (PC) are closed (inhibited) by the reticular nucleus (R). The orbitofrontal cortex (FC) stimulates the inhibiting neurons in the reticular nucleus (R) of the thalamus via the inferior thalamic peduncle (ITP). These inhibiting neurons are themselves inhibited by neurons arising from the brain stem (MRF: mesencephalic reticular formation). In addition to the orbitofrontal cerebral cortex, the cerebellum and the caudate nucleus can also stimulate this system.

Sterman (1979) also examined the wakefulness cycle (basic rest-activity cycle, BRAC) and sleep spindles during the first few weeks after birth. Based on this research, he came to some conclusions on the fundamental role of sleep and the alternation of dream sleep and non-dream sleep in the "biological economy."

Sterman showed that the BRAC cycle lasts 60 minutes in one-month-old infants (compared with 90 minutes later in life). The remaining phases are associated with increased EEG slow-wave activity (delta waves between 0-3 Hz) and decreased quantity of movements, heart, and breathing rhythms. Such periodicity can be discerned as early as at 24 weeks gestation in the movement of the fetus. These cycles originate in the pons in the brainstem.

From just 10 weeks after birth, the sleep-wake cycle gradually superimposes over the rest of the activity cycle, and the sleep-wake cycle's progressive development, together with that of the sleep spindles, becomes associated with a periodicity that coincides with the slow EEG waves. At 19 weeks old, the periodicity of the sleep spindles is still 60 minutes while the periodicity of the delta waves reaches 120 minutes. The development of these slower cycles appears to reflect a more mature sleep-wake cycle. The BRAC cycle length extends to 90 minutes by the age of 24 months.

During sleep, five to six 90-minute cycles occur, each consisting of a sequence of four stages of NREM sleep and an REM stage (rapid eye movement sleep). These NREM-REM 90-minute cycles coincide with a cyclic weakening in the density of sleep spindles and no longer primarily with cyclically changing quantity of slow waves in the EEG.

Sleep spindles originate in the thalamus (in the midbrain) and continue to develop until full maturity. This leads to ripened awareness accompanied by the alertness necessary for adapting to the environment beyond reflexive brainstem mechanisms, such as breathing, sucking, and swallowing. The orbitofrontal cortex, the cerebellum, and the caudate nucleus modulate sleep spindles later during the development, allowing for more differentiated behavior adaptations.

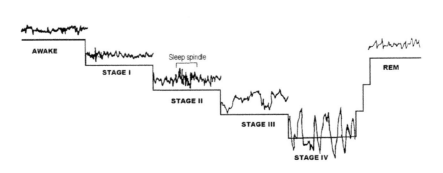

Figure 18. Course of a NREM-REM 90-minute sleep cycle preceded by a waking state: The 4 REM stages and the NREM stage. A representative sleep fragment from each stage is illustrated.

It is stimulating to note that the increase in the quantity of sleep spindles in the first 6 months of life is associated with a decrease in the quantity of movement and variability of the heart and breathing rhythm. Possibly, if the frontothalamic system that modulates sleep spindles is insufficiently developed, the flexible state regulation described in the first chapter will also be insufficiently developed; thereby, weakening the internal control mechanism's ability to adapt, leaving a deficient and somewhat more primitive, reactive external regulatory system.

These EEG findings can also be linked to the development of neuronal organization. The apical dendrites of the cortical pyramid cells are first to mature. They provide the medium for receptive interaction between the cortical cells and the synchronous activity of diffuse delta waves in the EEG. This early delta activity can be seen as the beginning of intracortical communication that precedes other connections in this early developmental state. In time, this leads to maturation of dendritic projections that receive efferent sensory information and are involved in the patterns of thalamocortical interactions that create the 12-15 Hz sleep spindles and, somewhat later, the alpha and theta rhythms.

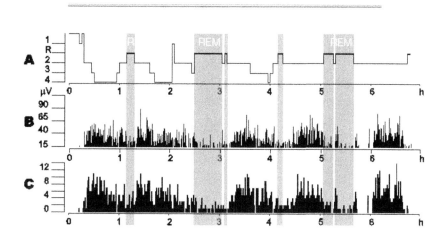

Figure 19. The uppermost diagram (A) is a hypnogram depicting the course of the NREM stages and the REM stage. An NREM-REM cycle lasts an average of 90 minutes. Deep sleep (III–IV) occurs early in the night and REM sleep dominates in the later part of the night. The middle diagram (B) illustrates the density of sleep spindles per minute. Bottom diagram (C) shows the amplitude of the sleep spindles. Note that during the REM stage, there are almost no sleep spindles; indeed, the sleep spindles mark the beginning and the end of the NREM stage. During the NREM stage, the sleep spindles are strongest in stage I–II and weakest in III-1V (deep sleep with slow waves). The vertical grey lines indicate the REM states, showing the least sleep spindles.

There are indications that the 90-minute cycle occurs not just in sleep but also during wakefulness throughout the day. The quality of performance of many tasks, measurable during task performance by physiological measures (such as the EEG), varies with a cycle of about 90 minutes. Kleitman (1963), who was the first to describe REM in sleep in 1953, advanced the basic rest-activity cycle (BRAC) hypothesis that the rhythmic action of REM sleep is just a fragment of broader biological rhythms that are continually expressed during sleep as well as in the waking state. REM sleep is associated with desynchronization of the EEG (as in the waking state). For that reason, REM is called paradoxical sleep, representing the active part of the cycle, while NREM sleep is associated with synchronization of the EEG and represents the restful section of the cycle. Indeed, multiple researchers have demonstrated that these 90-minute cycles occur in the daytime. Superimposed on these are even slower rhythms that may possibly arise from interaction with the 90-minute cycles. Sleep spindles increase in density around the time of transition from one sleep phase into another, lasting about 90 minutes. Slower 90-minute cycles are expressed within daytime wakefulness cycle. Most people reach peak alertness about six hours after waking. Afterwards, wakefulness clearly declines in the early afternoon in adults, which is considered a remnant of the child's need for an afternoon nap. The next period of wakefulness occurs at around 5 p.m. for most people. Body temperature also reaches its maximum.

Kripke (1978) discovered that daydreams follow a 90-minute cycle, accompanied by continuous alpha waves and fewer rapid eye movements. Although this has been measured in people in a natural social environment, it is more pronounced in sensorimotor isolation. Lavie (1982) suggested the hypothesis that alertness rhythms reflect the degree of difficulty experienced in falling asleep at different times in the course of the day. To test this hypothesis, nine adult participants were asked to close their eyes three times per hour and to try to sleep for five-minute periods of darkness over twelve daytime hours. Sleep and wakefulness were measured using EEG. Significant fluctuations within 90 minutes were measured in sleep stage 2. Theta waves increased and alpha waves decreased in the EEG during the sleep stage 2 episodes. This seems to correspond well with cyclical alpha waves and their correspondence to daydreaming observed in Kripke's study. In the latter case, alpha waves correlated negatively with wakefulness, that is, increased alpha waves related to decreased wakefulness while in Lavie's research, the darkness condition reinforced the increase in theta waves. Lavie showed that the ability to fall asleep showed a periodic increase over a ninety-minute cycle. Moreover, the slower cycles that we have already mentioned modulate these cycles as well. Increased wakefulness occurs around 1:30 p.m., 3 p.m., and in the late afternoon (5:30 to 6:00), with an increased susceptibility to sleep stage 2 around midday (12:30 to 1:30) and afternoon (around 3:30 to 5:00). After a night of sleep deprivation, the 90-minute cycles disappear. This may possibly suggest that no clear daily cycle exists in people with ADHD, which would explain the dysfunctional behavioral regulation.

Another study investigated fluctuations in EEG parietal activity in healthy volunteers through the course of a day. The study measured EEG activity for 2-3 minutes with eyes open (staring at a blank screen) at various times between 8:00 a.m. and 8:00 p.m. (Kaiser and Sterman, 1994). The absolute quantity of EEG activity from frequency bands lower than 15 Hz showed increasingly slower rhythms with a low between 10:00 a.m. and 12:00 p.m. and again between 4:00 p.m. and 6:00 p.m., with a peak around 2:00 p.m. A visual inspection of figures published by Kaiser (not shown) shows a weaker cycle modulating every 90 to 120 minutes (Kaiser and Sterman, 1994).

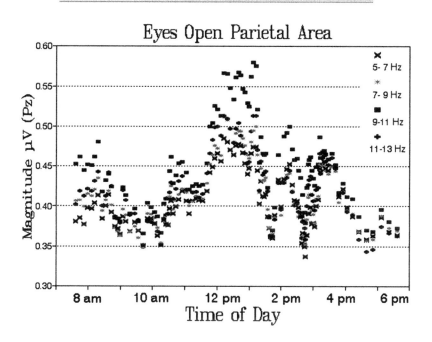

Figure 20. The valleys occur between 10:00 a.m. – 12:00 p.m. and 4:00 – 6:00 p.m., and the peak is just before 2:00 p.m. (lowest alertness). Less pronounced cycles of 90–120 minutes are visible (Kaiser & Sterman, 1994). Figure appears courtesy of David Kaiser.

Whenever the percentage of alpha and theta activity is examined over the course of a day for the same group of participants, a 90- to 120-minute alpha activity cycle (BRAC) is found. There is no clear daily cycle for slower waves.

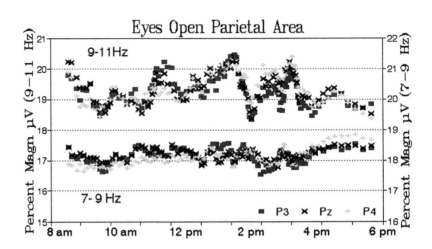

Figure 21. The percentage of alpha activity (9-11Hz) cycles every 90-120 minutes, but that is not the case for the percentage of theta activity (7-9Hz). Figure appears courtesy of David Kaiser (Kaiser & Sterman, 1994).

Sleep is now considered a prime example of the emergence of self-organization in neuronal circuits and systems without the intervention of a supervisor or instructions (i.e., does not require a specific localized supervising system). Disturbances in sleep structure in psychiatric disorders, such as in ADHD, are often seen as consequences of daytime difficulties. However, contemporary insights strongly suggest the contrary, showing that changes in normal sleep structure can cause altered brain functioning during wakefulness. Deciphering the dynamics of self-organization in neuronal circuits involved in sleep structure may be the key to understanding the brain's response to environmental processes. EEG rhythms in sleep offer a striking example of 'reciprocal causality,' i.e., emergent rhythms at the macrosystem level in the EEG may be considered as 'order parameters' that force certain limits on the timing of neuronal action potentials (Haken, 1986; Kelso, 1995).

Furthermore, evidence suggests that the relationship between sleep and wakefulness can be extended to the relationship between sensorimotor coordination and dynamic attention, giving greater insight into the functional relationships between sleep spindles and the SMR rhythm. Therefore, it seems no coincidence that the rhythms involved in the dynamics of attention also play a role in sensorimotor coordination. Sleep spindles and sensory motor rhythms both occur spontaneously without movements; thus, they are self-generating. That does not mean that an absence of movement is sufficient for their generation. Nevertheless, movements can certainly disturb the central generating mechanism by introducing external triggers via sensory feedback to the brain.

In general, we can think of sleep as the uncoupling of the brain from the environment and, largely, from the body. In infants, movement via sensory feedback triggers sensorimotor EEG rhythms. Over the course of the development, from childhood to adulthood, sensorimotor coordination matures and the thalamocortical circuits come under control of subcortical modulating systems that can hinder triggering of these sensorimotor rhythms. Early development can be viewed as the process of the brain's 'awakening' from an overwhelming drowsiness. Adults still display sporadic sensorimotor rhythms triggered by the sensory feedback that follows movement but for the most part, causation is reversed since the absence of movement triggers these rhythms. Crucially, these rhythms arise constantly out of self-organization processes and play a part in the creation of a 'default state' in the brain responsible for adapting to changing circumstances. This is in agreement with Head and Bente's concept of vigilance being not merely an activation state but a modulated activation state in which an inhibition mechanism operating from the frontal cortex plays a modulatory role.

Therefore, we can infer that sleep stabilizes the dynamics of sensory motor coordination and hence the 'situated' nature of the brain within the world and within environmental processes (Varela, 1991). Moreover, this leads to stabilization of waking states and to 'situated wakefulness' or vigilance. Adequate vigilance corresponds to adequate behavioral organization and implies interaction between exploratory motor output and the flow of sensory perception. Sleep shares many characteristics with autonomous early brain development in which EEG rhythms temporarily stabilize brain dynamics.

Summary

 The 12-20 Hz (or 12-15Hz) sensorimotor EEG rhythms and the sleep spindles (12-15 Hz series during sleep) play a stabilizing role in attention and in sleep levels. They originate in the thalamus (a central relay station deep in the brain) and are modulated by the frontal cortex and the caudate nucleus (a tail shaped structure near the center of the brain). They have a functional relation with the dynamics of sensorimotor coordination that ensures, during early development, that behavior and wakefulness are 'situated' as they develop in the real world environment. There are indications that EEG rhythms play a modulating role in the 'basic rest activity cycle' that lasts 90 minutes and expresses itself not only

in sleep, but also in wakefulness. Slower cycles are superimposed on them. Lastly, both the sleep spindles and the sensorimotor rhythms play a role in learning through the promotion of neural plasticity.

3.5 Gamma Rhythms (35-45 Hz) EEG Activity: Consciousness and 'Focused Arousal'

Measuring 40 Hz ('gamma rhythms' from 35 to 40 Hz) EEG activity at the scalp is technically very difficult due to the difficulty in separating the many small low voltage waves of around 5-10 µV arising from noise and from the electrical activity of the muscles that circle the scalp. Only in the last few years has it been possible to measure these rhythms without interference, following the development of technologically advanced techniques.

When electrodes are placed directly in the brain, the signal varies strongly from 20 µV in passive states up to 100 µV in focused attention (Rougeul, 1994). Signal strength at the scalp is only 5-10 µV because of volume conduction by the skull and surrounding tissues. Several decades of published studies point to a role of these rhythms in focused attention. More specifically, they could play a role in the conscious experience of perception. Llinas (1991) has demonstrated that the thalamocortical and the thalamic reticular nucleus can both generate 40 Hz rhythms, just like the cerebral cortex, making it likely that an intrinsic network resonance exists at about 40 Hz. This is observed during wakefulness and during dreaming. This resonance begins in the brainstem, receiving sensory input during wakefulness and input from intrinsic activity during dream sleep. The dream state can be considered a state of hyperattention in which sensory information is blocked from reaching the mechanism that generates conscious perception, that is, we cannot perceive the external world because the intrinsic activity of the nervous system does not locate the sensual information in the context of the functional state, which serves to generate awareness.

Both the specific and non-specific thalamus nuclei generate the 40 Hz rhythms. The 'specific' system provides the sensory information for cognition while the 'non-specific' system is responsible for the simultaneous 'binding' of these different 'specific' aspects, as is necessary for the unity of cognitive experience. Focusing attention on a specific perceived stimulus leads to an increase in 40 Hz activity. Desmedt and Tomberg (1994) performed an intriguing experiment that revealed the neurophysiological nature of consciousness. Recognizing that gamma activity is measurable in all the thalamocortical and cortical areas and that it increases with increased wakefulness, they wanted to know whether this rhythm plays a role in specific cognitive functions. A brief electrical stimulus was delivered to the fingers of both hands during the experiment. Whenever the stimulus was delivered to the right hand, subjects were asked to make a foot press on a button, insuring that they focused selectively on the right hand because that stimulus was allocated a special significance. Then, 130 ms after the stimulus appeared on the right side, increased gamma activity over a 125 ms period was observed in the left parietal and prefrontal areas. It was possible to reliably measure this induced rhythm by calculating the average value of the 35-45 Hz filtered EEG segments, which appeared after a complete series of these stimuli as phase-coupled cognitive induced 40 Hz activity. Calculating the average curve erased other 40 Hz rhythms unrelated to the task. The processed 40 Hz activity had amplitude of 0.5-2 μV. The researchers concluded that increased vigilance increased gamma activity over the entire cerebral cortex via the thalamocortical circuits, which form the basis for specific cortico-cortical connections that further increase gamma activity. This last increase starts 130 ms after the stimulus, when representations of objects and events stored in the prefrontal cortex are activated. A functional 'binding' of processes in the prefrontal and parietal cortices is necessary for their functional integration in the conscious perception of an object. The transient selective frontoparietal increase in 40 Hz rhythms is responsible for this integration. Selective attention is therefore associated with awareness, both of which play a critical role in integration of the relevant cortical processes in object identification, thus, enabling informed behavioral decisions.

As far back as 1956, Morrell and Jasper had already examined the effects of classical sensory-sensory conditioning of apes on EEG 'desynchronization', which is always low voltage and refers to flattening of classical alpha and beta waves interpreted as a manifestation of general cerebral activation consisting of 40 Hz activity. Pavlov's reflex is the archetypal example of classical conditioning, as dogs previously conditioned to the ringing of a bell immediately before feeding begin to salivate on the ringing of a bell. This differs from operant conditioning in which a reward reinforces desirable voluntary behavior. Morrel and Jasper's experiment was not EEG biofeedback but was similar to Sterman's early experiments with cats in which the cats' EEG activity was recorded after behavior had brought them to a state of internal inhibition. Morrel and Jaspers found that generalized desynchronization spread throughout the cerebral cortex only during the first stage of behavioral conditioning. Stable localized desynchronized activity was demonstrably limited to the relevant area of the cerebral cortex once conditioning was completed. The first stage of conditioning, diffuse cortical desynchronization, gives rise to the initial response to the new stimuli within the complex matrix of irrelevant environmental stimuli. Whenever neuronal connections form because of pattern formation in space and time, as is the case for classical conditioning, groups of neurons show synchronous 40 Hz activity limited to the relevant circuit. EEG desynchronization is not more diffuse but can often seem more desynchronized because the synchronized neurons are limited to certain selective brain areas hidden within the total EEG activity. Sheer (1975) labeled these localized 40 Hz activities, which reflect a definitive cortical activity optimized for conditioning, as 'focused arousal'. During a visual discrimination task,

Sheer (1970) demonstrated the existence of a consistent link between 40 Hz activity in the visual and motor cerebral cortex and the acquisition phase of learning in a cat. During a period of 10 seconds in which a 7 Hz flickering light acts as a warning signal, a discharge of 40 Hz activity in visual and motor cortex appears 0.5 second before a correct lever response as well as during this response and lasts 1.5 seconds after the correct response. In 1970, he demonstrated that significant coherence and phase synchrony of 40 Hz activity occurred in reticular areas in the mesencephalon (lower brain stem) and in cortical and visual areas whenever a cat began to satisfy the learning criteria in a consecutive visual discrimination task. The method of phase coupled with induced cognitive 40 Hz activity was also used in this experiment.

Galambos (1958) induced 40 Hz activity in both the nucleus caudate and globus pallidus of cats and learned that the last click in a series of 11 loud clicks led inevitably to an electric shock. Rowland (1958) induced 40 Hz activity in the lateral cerebral cortex and the medial geniculate body of cats by pairing an auditory conditioned stimulus with an electric shock as the unconditioned stimulus. Freeman (1963) showed that neutral stimuli could condition 40 Hz activity in the prepiriform cortex (concerned with the sense of smell) in cats. Smell is a vital sense in animals, allowing perception of remote stimuli, and thus triggering important orientation reactions. Killam (1967) demonstrated 40 Hz activity in the lateral geniculate body in the thalamus in cats once they were fully trained to distinguish the correct visual pattern from three different patterns offered. Pribram (1967) discovered 40 Hz activity in the striate area of the occipital lobe in apes just after making an erroneous response to a difficult visual discrimination task. Dumenko (1961) induced 40 Hz activity in the auditory, somatosensory, and motor cortex of dogs whenever they responded, with one limb, to a tone, as the conditioned stimulus, and an electric shock, as the unconditioned stimulus. Sakhuilina (1961) also demonstrated this 40 Hz activity in the sensorimotor cortex of dogs when various conditioned stimuli accompanied the bending of opposite hind paws. Subdural metal electrodes were used in all animal subjects. It is very well known that these extremely low voltage gamma frequencies are barely measurable at the scalp due to volume conduction phenomena in which transmission through scalp and tissue underlying the electrodes weaken the signal.

Normally, generalized desynchronization of brain activity occurs during phases of exploration and focused attention on the surroundings. However, Bouyer (1981, 1987) and Rougeul-Buser (1994) demonstrated that 40 Hz activity is measurable in cats and apes with subdural electrodes placed in motor (areas 4 and 6a) cortex and posterior associative parietal cortex (area 5), and that this activity increased whenever a cat focused motionless on its surroundings. Moreover, coherency of the 40 Hz activity increased in the thalamic areas linked to these cortical areas; however, no relationship was observed with the thalamic reticular nucleus. Rougeul-Buser suggested that the 40 Hz activity that he had measured in cats indexed a more general focusing of attention. Area 5 of the cerebral cortex thus plays a strategic role, allocating attention to the areas of sensory cerebral cortex and acting as a kind of supramodal structure (Rougeul, 1994). It is important to recognize that 40 Hz rhythms in frontoparietal cerebral cortex accompany every modality of focused attention (visual, aural, and smell). In a sense, Rougeul's hypothesis concurs with Crick's proposition (1984) that attention is required to bind different sensory domains.

Area 5 also functions as an interface in the transformation of a sensory response into a signal in a motor command chain. The 40 Hz activity in this area signals that a kind of inhibition process is developing in the named motor and parietal areas that interact with neurons responsible for the organization of movement orders during focused attention, thus provoking immobility. Bouyer (1981), however, considered that the 40 Hz fronto-parietal rhythm in cats and apes is homologous to a weaker 16-20 Hz rhythm in humans during freely willed movement, the rhythm of which in turn is functionally homologous to the central mu rhythm (9-13Hz) (Pfurtscheller, 1980). Sheer (1975) found only a low correlation of 40 Hz with 21-30 Hz activity; therefore, he proposed that the 40 Hz activity is a manifestation of focused arousal and the 21-30 Hz activity is an expression of diffuse arousal. Increased 40 Hz activity is experienced as concentrated attention associated with effort while 21-30 Hz is experienced as active, energetic, and restless (Sheer, 1977).

It was also shown that the ventral tegmental area (VTA) in the brainstem, which releases dopamine to modulate many brain areas, could modulate the sensorimotor 40 Hz rhythm. In 1994, Rougeul-Buser was able to demonstrate that dopamine strongly modulates certain thalamic areas (the posterior medial complex, the POm) and the corresponding cortical area 5. An increase in 40 Hz coherency in these two areas occurs during attentive stillness. In 1980, Simon showed that rats with injuries to the VTA showed hyperactivity and an inability to focus attention. Rougeul-Buser demonstrated the same result in cats and further noted that the 40 Hz rhythm disappears completely after such injuries. Administration of DOPA, a precursor of dopamine that has also been used to treat Parkinson patients, produced an increase in 35-40 Hz activity in healthy cats but had no effect after injury to the VTA. On the other hand, apomorphine, an agonist of postsynaptic dopamine receptors, produced an increase in 40 Hz activity and normalized the components of the thalamocortical system. Dopamine has probably no direct effect on thalamocortical circuits but an indirect effect via the amygdala and nucleus accumbens.

Giannitrapani (1969) measured 40 Hz activity along the middle of the scalp in children of normal or high intelligence just before responding to a multiplication task. This 40 Hz activity was not present in passive states. Sheer (1976) determined no difference between the 40 Hz activity in children with learning difficulties and normal children. However, in problem solving tasks, children with learning difficulties showed no significant increase in 40 Hz activity in contrast to normal children, which was consistent with Giannitrapani's (1969) conclusion. Sheer described his group of children with learning difficulties by noting that the primary deficits were observed in 'focused arousal,' followed by problems with higher order processing, sustained attention, weak modulation of activation, hyperactivity or hypoactivity, and to varying degrees of motor clumsiness and reading problems. Sheer suggested that the central problem for these children was that they cannot learn as they cannot assimilate new material and cannot solve problems at the level of their peers. Therefore, it seems likely that Sheer was primarily thinking about children with ADHD. ADHD as a diagnosis did not exist then, as it was officially introduced only in 1980. In his experimental group, Sheer did not observe an increase in 40 Hz activity during problem solving tasks in contrast to healthy children. This 40 Hz activity plays a role in the storage of sequential information in short term memory, which is necessary for problem solving and transferring information into long-term memory.

Sheer's study compared 20 typically developing children with two groups, each comprising of 30 children with learning difficulties. The second group with learning difficulties had poorer school results compared to the other group with learning problems. The average age was 10 years and the average IQ was 100, with the learning difficulty group showing a greater variation. The investigation covered three sets of problem solving tasks, each set comprising three tasks:

- Verbal-visual task involved calculation problems using pictures, visual classifications, and visual rhymes.

- Verbal-auditory task involved calculating problems with words, auditory classifications, and auditory rhymes.

- Tactile-kinesthetic task involved form board, comparison of section outlines, and comparison of different threads.

The two groups with learning difficulties made significantly more errors compared to the group with typical development. EEG activity was measured at the left and right parietal and occipital electrode, with the central Cz point providing the reference electrode. The detection criteria for a 40 Hz discharge were a minimum of three cycles of 40 Hz activity above 3.1 µV (corresponding to a duration of 75ms) and no measurable electrical muscular activity (65-75 Hz) within a 100ms (the same criteria that he used with adult participants). The research established that in the typically developing children, 40 Hz activity increased in both parietal areas during problem solving tasks, but this was not the case for children with learning problems. Sheer suggested that this group of children failed to activate the temporo-parieto-occipital junction (corresponding to the angular gyrus and supramarginal language areas) in the cerebral cortex and that their difficulties in solving the problem tasks supported this interpretation. Sheer argued that 40 Hz activity is optimal for consolidating the processed contents of short-term memory because repetitive synchronous excitation of these neurons maximizes the efficiency of synaptic transmission and transfer of information over this limited circuit. In all, 40 Hz activity does not simply correlate with diffuse cortical activation level; it also mirrors interaction between cortical facilitation and the processing of specific sensory input located in specific areas of the cerebral cortex. Inhibition of synaptic activity in surrounding areas accompanies this localized processing, leading to a sharpening of attention and curbing of gratuitous movement together with greater precision of relevant movements. Cholinergic input from the reticular formation of the mesencephalon (at the top of the brainstem) facilitates this 40 Hz activity. Others have demonstrated that direct electrical stimulation of the reticular formation facilitates learning if the stimulation immediately precedes the registration of information (Block, 1970). Amphetamine administration increases the activation level through its effect on the reticular formation. Sheer believed that the behavioral data indicates no deficit in general arousal in most children with learning difficulties/ADHD; however, a deficit in focused arousal in the cerebral cortex has been indicated. Acetylcholine also plays a central role in these processes. As early as 1982, Spydell and Sheer had demonstrated an increase in 40 Hz activity during verbal tasks in the left cerebral hemisphere and during spatial tasks in the right hemisphere.

Lutzenberger (1994) demonstrated that reading meaningful information rather than reading pseudo words was associated with greater 25-35 Hz activity over the left cortical language areas. Tallon (1995) additionally showed that visual perception of meaningful figures rather than pseudo figures was associated with more frequent 40 Hz activity over the visual cerebral cortex. Mattson and Sheer (1992) showed less frequent 40 Hz activity measurable over the left hemisphere during a verbal task in dyslexic children rather than in typically developing children while in children with mathematical learning problems, less 40 frequent Hz activity was measured in the right hemisphere during a visual face recognition task. In 1989, Sheer found that 40 Hz activity was lower in patients with Alzheimer's dementia compared to the healthy elderly, and more saliently, that 40 Hz activity did not increase during problem solving tasks. This was already established in the early stages of the disease, when only subtle behavioral symptoms are expressed. In 1989, Sheer used new methods, specifically averaged gamma oscillations phase-locked to a cognitive event, which delivered greater accuracy compared to previous methods that filter raw EEG to derive the 40 Hz activity. Ahveninen (2000) observed a suppression of the transient increase of 40 Hz activity in healthy participants focusing on a series of tones from headphones after ingesting 2 mg haloperidol, a dopamine-2 receptor antagonist. The findings of this method administered to ADHD individuals are discussed in section 4.5.2.

Summary

The 40 Hz gamma rhythm is very low voltage, and it occurs in the cerebral cortex whenever a specific functional area is active. Therefore, it is more active in specific perceptual conditions. Both the thalamus and certain parts of the brainstem play decisive roles in generating this rhythm. The simultaneous action of this rhythm in different areas of the cerebral cortex contributes to the 'binding process' necessary to produce a unitary conscious experience of action. Dopamine and acetylcholine promote this synchrony. The 40 Hz rhythm decreases in people with ADHD. A localized 40 Hz rhythm can be measured following behavioral conditioning. However, only advanced EEG technology is able to filter out interference from EEG 40 Hz rhythms reliably.

3.6 Event Related Desynchronization (ERD) and Synchronization (ERS)

In recent years, the recordings of different levels of task performance in the EEG have been studied. Immediately after presenting distinctive auditory or visual stimuli that require a specific reaction from the experimental participant, the EEG can show a weakening of certain rhythms (event related desynchronization, ERD). Desynchronization denotes that more neuron groups are active independently from each other, facilitating a more differentiated response. On the other hand, a temporary strengthening of certain rhythms can also be seen (event related synchronization, ERS). Synchronization describes the simultaneous action of varied neuronal groupings.

3.6.1 Alpha ERD and ERS

In an attention task (CPT, Continuous Performance Test) in which the participant presses a button on hearing a tone or viewing a certain letter (or geometric shape), a fast ERD normally appears in posterior brain areas, followed by a quick recovery. Conversely, paradoxical ERSs followed by late ERDs and a slow recovery can reflect inefficient cognitive processing. The alpha rhythm, normally dominant in rest states as a base rhythm, is weakened (desynchronized) in connection with task execution in well-functioning subjects. In passive situations with eyes closed, a clear alpha rhythm is seen in the EEG. This indicates that alpha synchronization of large-scale information processing takes place as large neuronal populations fluctuate at the same phase and frequency. In cognitive processing, mutually different alpha rhythms are uncoupled at different phases of these rhythms and different neuronal networks fluctuate with different frequencies and different phases. This gives an impression of global desynchronization, although in reality, it reflects the progression of a complex pattern of microsynchronizations.

Possibly, the complex nature of human cognitive function throughout alert waking behaviors produces continued alpha ERD-ERS sequences expressed by the instability of the EEG. In these sequences, restoration follows the expression of cognitive responses, allowing recovery of the system in preparation for the next challenge. In a well-functioning system, the ERD alternates with the ERS.

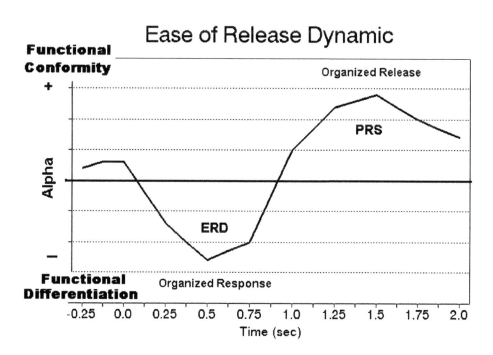

Figure 22. ERD (event related desynchronization) and PRS (post response synchronization) in a model of adaptive functioning of the brain, a theoretical framework for neurofeedback therapy (Kaiser, 2001). Figure appears courtesy of David Kaiser.

Kaiser (2001), a collaborator of Sterman, proposed a functional model based on alpha event-related desynchronization phenomena in order to introduce a more functional framework into neurofeedback training. He argued that a healthy system adaptively responds to a stimulus. Global neural networks can proceed with information processing either with functional conformity or with functional differentiation. How quickly and fluently these two extremes can be achieved is an objective measure of adaptive functionality. Differentiation refers to the dissimilarity of reactions in different neuronal groups (desynchronization) while conformity reflects similarity of responses from various different neuronal groupings (synchronization). Ideally, the system is able to move freely from one extreme to another. This can be assessed by the form of ease of release dynamic, which shows how fluidly the brain adapts itself to processing requirements (ERD: event related desynchronization), followed by how quickly it releases from activation and returns to base state (PRS: post response synchronization).The combination of both a less pronounced alpha ERD and ERS would suggest that in ADHD, actions are more poorly adapted to processing requirements and that the functional activity of the underlying neuronal circuits after action execution is less likely to return to the resting state, which is necessary in preparation for the next action. Increased motor reactivity in the cerebral cortex and the motor activity associated with it can obstruct attentional processes. Moreover, weakened attentional mechanisms can weaken these processes.

3.6.2 Theta ERS

During mental tasks, usually serial addition tasks, 6-7 Hz theta rhythms are often evoked at the frontal midline (fm-theta) area in EEG (Ishihara and Yoshii, 1972). Previous studies have suggested that fm-theta appearance corresponds to the concentration of attention (Mizuki, 1980; Nakashima, 1992, 1993). Relatively long periods of increased (composed of theta bursts) can be observed during such cognitively demanding tasks as retention of objects in working memory (Sauseng, 2004) or arithmetic operations (Iramina, 1996). Part of fm-theta power can be related not as much to the theta oscillatory process per se as to the event-related potential components, such as N2, ERN or FRN, thus, theta-activity can be considered to reflect an internal process, which is modulated by external events. It usually has an amplitude of 20-60 µV during cognitive tasks. In normal people, the subgroup with the highest amplitude of the generated fm-theta showed the lowest anxiety score, the highest score in the extraversion scale, and the lowest score in the neurotic scale during an arithmetic task (Inanaga, 1998). The fm-theta in the resting state can be found in the raw EEG only in a small group of normal population and seems to be related to a genetically determined behavioral trait, which is also low in anxiety scale, low in neurotic scale, and high in extraversion scale. The source has been located in the dorsal anterior cingulate, and for memory tasks, it has been associated with hippocampal theta activity. Buzsáki suggested using the term 'limbic theta oscillations' instead of hippocampal rhythm to reflect the complexity and distributed nature of theta oscillations. The anterior cingulate and the parahippocampal gyrus also generate theta oscillations with different functions.

Mazaheri (2010, 2014) has studied frontal theta ERS (at 0.05-0.3 s after the cue), followed by parietal alpha ERD (at 0.3-1 s after the cue), in a go/no-go task in ADHD children. In normal children, he was able to demonstrate frontal-parietal anticorrelation, which he interpreted as an expression of a well-developed top-down frontal attentional control the role of which is to prepare the parietal cortex to attend a visual imperative stimulus to which participants had to respond by pressing a button. In ADHD children, this anticorrelation is typically absent. Moreover, an adequate alpha desynchronization is able to predict an adequate motor response by the subject. An adequate frontal theta synchronization correlates with a well-developed ERN (Mazaheri, 2009), both of which are less developed in ADHD. Kropotov (2007) published similar results for frontal theta synchronization and parietal alpha desynchronization after the cue in a go/no-go task.

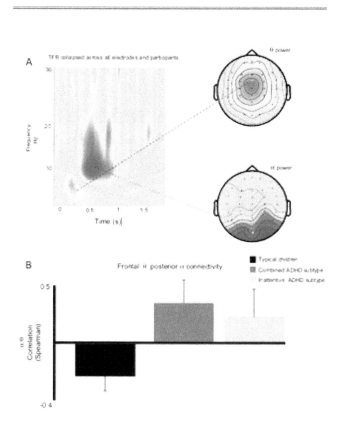

Figure 23. Frontal theta synchronization, followed by parietal alpha desynchronization after pressing a button after a cue stimulus (Mazaheri, 2014)

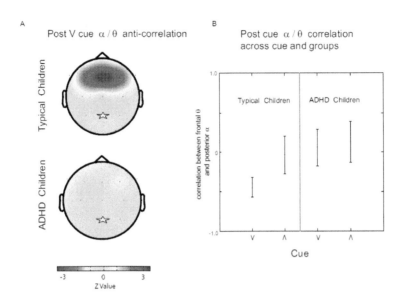

Figure 24. Post cue parietal alpha/frontal theta anticorrelation: Lower in normal children compared with ADHD children (Mazaheri, 2010)

Source localization shows that this frontal midline theta activity originates in the dorsal anterior cingulate and has strong connections with the hippocampus.

Recent neuroimaging studies have indicated that activity in the superior parietal lobule (SPL) is associated with shifting attention in visual or auditory tasks. The SPL seems to supply the initial signal to switch attention, whereas inferior parietal lobule (IPL) reorients attention to the to-be-attended location. Suppression of posterior alpha was preceded by increased activity in the regions of the dorsal attention (spatial) network and decreased activity in the regions of the cingulo-opercular network (Mathewson, 2014).

It is postulated that a key function of attention in goal-oriented behavior is to reduce performance variability by generating anticipatory neural activity that can be synchronized with expected sensory information. The cerebellum could hypothetically reduce performance variability through feed-forward activation of the IPL by timely coordinating the interactions between the IPL and prefrontal cortex. A network encompassing the prefrontal cortex, parietal lobe, and cerebellum may be critical in the maintenance and timing of such predictive neural activity. Dysfunction of this temporal process may constitute a fundamental defect in attention, causing working memory problems, distractibility, and decreased awareness. The same network identified for spatial attention is also activated in working memory tasks. Maturation of the white matter tracts running between the prefrontal cortex and IPL, identified with MRI-based DTI, has been found to correlate with performance in working memory tasks.

Voluntarily shifting attention to a location of the visual field improves the perception of events that occur there. Regions of frontal cortex are traditionally believed to provide the top-down control signal that initiates a shift of attention because regions in frontal cortex are involved in the executive control of other cognitive and motor operations. However, there is still much debate about the precise sequence of activity in the fronto-parietal network. Some evidence has suggested that frontal cortex becomes active before parietal cortex while other evidence has suggested the opposite sequence. Because of the temporal limitations of fMRI, the timing and sequence of attentional-control operations remain unknown. Green and McDonald (2008) specifically examined attentional control activity, which precedes attention and perception; hence, they opted to focus the nonlinear beamformer analysis on the low-frequency theta band (4-7 Hz) oscillations to reconstruct the anatomical sources of theta EEG brain waves in humans associated with attentional control over time.

Following a signal to shift attention, control activity was seen in parietal cortex 100-200 ms before it was seen in frontal cortex. Parietal cortex was then reactivated prior to anticipatory biasing of activity in occipital cortex. The magnitudes of early parietal activations were strongly predictive of the degree of attentional improvement in perceptual performance. These results show that parietal cortex, not frontal cortex, provides the initial signals to shift attention and indicate that top-down attentional control is not purely top down. Given that IPL was active twice and SPL was active only early on, the two regions appear to mediate different attentional-control operations. The combined early activity in parietal cortex likely reflects a signal to switch attention to a specific location that is sent to executive control structures in frontal cortex. Recent neuroimaging studies have indicated that activity in SPL is associated with shifting attention in spatial and nonspatial visual tasks as well as in auditory and audiovisual tasks. On this basis, it seems that SPL supplies the initial signal to switch attention, whereas IPL supplies spatial information about the to-be-attended location. An alternative interpretation is that IPL, as a part of the ventral attention network, is reorienting attention before prefrontal intervention.

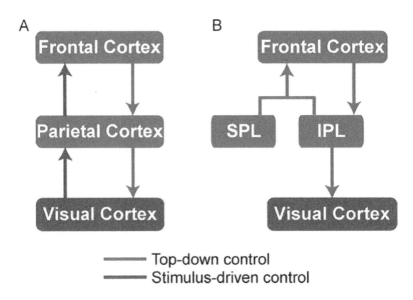

Figure 25. Models of Voluntary Attentional Control: (A) Traditional model of top–down attentional control initiated in frontal cortex; (B) Model proposed by Green and McDonald (2008) wherein attentional control is initiated by parietal structures.

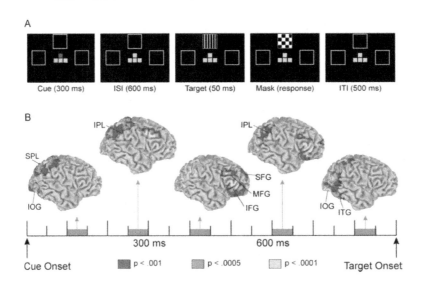

Figure 26. Attentional control across time (theta in beamformer): Alerting at 100 ms, orienting at 300 ms, and working memory (expectancy) at 400–500 ms (Green and McDonald, 2008)

Parietal activation is in some cases antecedent to prefrontal cortex in attention tasks (Corbetta, 2000), as indicated by a desynchronization in the alpha range of the EEG signal and subsequent increase in gamma frequency over prefrontal cortex (Fan, 2007). Parietal activation is seen before prefrontal cortex in bottom-up processing compared to top-down processing where the reverse is reported (Buschman and Miller, 2007).

Accurate anticipation, resulting in synchronization of external and/or self-generated events, produces lower performance variability, a heightened focus of attention, and enhanced self-agency. Under such conditions, performance will be less prone to interference or distraction. The better one attends to the object of attention, the more one is aware of one's interaction with this object. Children who have higher performance variability compared to adults are more distractible and show weaker activity in DLPFC and IPL on working memory tasks that have distractors (Olesen, 2007).

3.6.3 Gamma ERS

Research has shown that gamma waves are necessary for consciousness. Already in 1989, Sheer employed gamma synchronization methods to study specific cognitive functions. Many others followed, including Desmedt and Tomberg (1994). Sheer assumed that the spontaneous gamma activity measurable in EEG is actually a summation of multiple gamma rhythms, each of which is itself the expression of different functional mechanisms. In a typical EEG, these different gamma rhythms are not separable from each other. However, whenever a specific task is linked to the start of an EEG segment lasting one second, phase-locked induced gamma activity is obtained. This can be demonstrated, for example, by using the go/no-go task in which the participant must press a button only on perception of a definitive stimulus and not the other stimulus. The filtered gamma activity is calculated as it occurs, immediately upon pressing the button. From 50 one-second segments, the averaged curve is calculated from which all the gamma activity that is not directly connected to the button pressing is smoothed, resulting in greater visibility of the phase-locked gamma activity. Gamma synchrony that occurs after the perception of a stimulus, as in the go/no-go task, is a measure of the cortical binding process necessary for conscious perception. Dopamine and acetylcholine are important modulators in this process. In the go/no-go task, an early (90 to 150 ms) and a late (200 to 550 ms) gamma synchrony occur after a stimulus in which the pressing of a button is required. Early gamma synchrony reflects the integrative aspects of preparatory attention. In ADHD, this early gamma synchrony is weaker in global, frontal, centrotemporal, and centroparietal areas in both hemispheres (unpublished data from the Brain Resource Company, Australia). This could indicate a functional disconnect brought about by an inadequate alignment and integration of the network. Late gamma synchrony indicates the preparation of a motor response.

Additionally, Kropotov found a weaker gamma ERS after a forewarning cue in ADHD, which were nested in theta cycles.

Lishman (1995) demonstrated that during a memory task, the gamma waves nest in packets within theta waves (the theta waves of the hippocampal circuit that are responsible for storing information in memory), which would mean that some six to seven packets are processed per second. This principle plays a role in attention and perceptual as well as memory processes, and it can explain why people can hold, on an average, a series of about seven figures in short term memory (the average is somewhat lower in ADHD). Theta waves act as an internal clock, determining the gamma activity that is responsible for any particular perception or memory characteristic. This could explain why a short time is needed to complete the Sternberg test in which the participant must decide, for example, if the letter B is present in a series of three letters. If, however, the series consists of four letters, then participants need another 30 ms, corresponding to the duration of a gamma wave. Apparently, various letters pass through memory with a speed that corresponds to that of gamma waves.

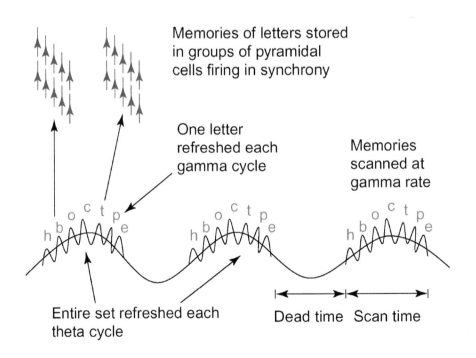

Figure 27. During a memory task, gamma waves are nested in theta waves (Lishman, 1995).

Lenz (2010) however found increased early gamma synchrony in parieto-occipital areas in ADHD children during visual stimulus encoding. These stronger evoked gamma oscillations could indicate the activation of additional neural resources in ADHD patients to compensate for inefficient processing during extraction and integration of stimulus features. Lenz concluded that the unspecific and uncorrelated enhancement of brain excitation probably yields a downgraded signal-to-noise ratio, and it could be involved in different aspects of ADHD pathology, including difficulties maintaining the attentional focus or motor inhibition. Neuronal fine-tuning of the enhanced excitation in ADHD patients is achieved by treatment with Ritalin that blocks dopamine transporters. This raises the signal-to-noise ratio during task-related processing by increasing the concentration of extracellular dopamine (Volkow and Swanson, 2003), which changes the relation between excitatory and inhibitory actions in tonic and phasic dopaminergic neural activity. ADHD patients demonstrate lowered tonic dopaminergic activity and enhanced phasic activity that cause dysregulated motor and impulse control (Grace, 2001). Ritalin targets these activities by increasing dopamine tone and diminishing phasic dopamine release. Therefore, a facilitation of inhibition is achieved and the signal-to-noise ratio is enhanced.

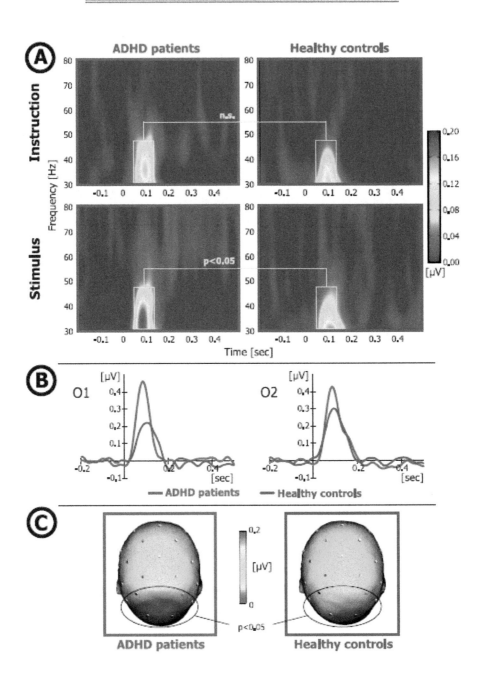

Figure 28. A: time-frequency plots of parieto-occipital gamma ERS in ADHD and healthy subjects; B: averaging the time courses for the gamma peak frequency in ADHD and healthy subjects; C: topographic maps of the gamma ERS in both groups (Lenz, 2010).

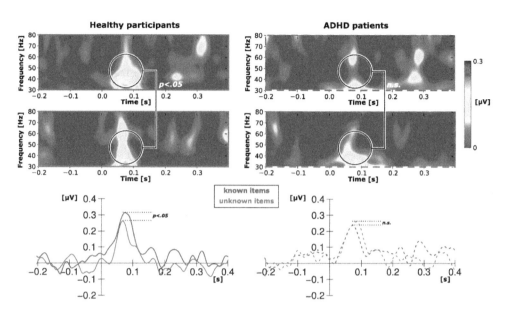

Figure 29. Time-frequency plots (top) and individual time-courses of the gamma peak frequency (bottom) depict strong differences in the memory based activation pattern of healthy participants and ADHD patients: The healthy group showed augmented gamma ERS following stimuli that matched a representation already stored in memory (red line) compared to new items without such memory presentation (blue line) as early as 90 ms after stimulus onset, whereas gamma ERS in ADHD did not differentiate between these two conditions (Lenz, 2010).

In contrast to healthy children, in ADHD children, no association could be found with memory retrieval (subsequent recognition) performance, which indicates that the observed increased early gamma synchrony in ADHD children is rather unspecific and does not foster a better behavioral performance. In normal children and adults, evoked early gamma oscillations are significantly enhanced for known items already stored in memory. ADHD children lack an early memory based classification, possibly resulting in an impaired ability to rapidly reallocate attentional resources to relevant information and to facilitate processing of relevant information based on early successful stimulus classification. This finding suggests that impaired early automatic stimulus classification in ADHD patients could be involved in deficits of selective and sustained attention. We can assume that this non-selective gamma synchrony evoked early (90-150 ms) in ADHD is related to a poor evoked N100 potential, which is also a marker for early selective attention. Consequently, lacking this early categorization might prevent a facilitated information processing and simultaneously boost the influence and processing of distracting information. Especially with respect to the limited attentional capacity, this filter deficit could have a major effect on the ability to turn and keep the attentional spotlight on necessary information, which could be associated with attentional problems reported among ADHD patients. The early deficit seems to be compensated for at a later processing stage, as evident in a higher differentiation between known and unknown items in the frontal negativity (late frontal negativity), a component that is also associated with memory access and classification processes. Lenz's suggestion is that ADHD patients miss an early differentiation of evoked gamma synchrony that originates from top-down modulations through higher cortical areas in healthy participants. This conclusion is similar to that of Mazaheri (2013) who demonstrated a malfunctioning top-down control from frontal (early theta synchrony) over perceptual parietal and motor central areas (alpha desynchronization). Kropotov (unpublished data; see Figure 30) has shown a lower event-related gamma synchronization in frontal areas between the cue and imperative stimulus in a go/no-go task in ADHD.

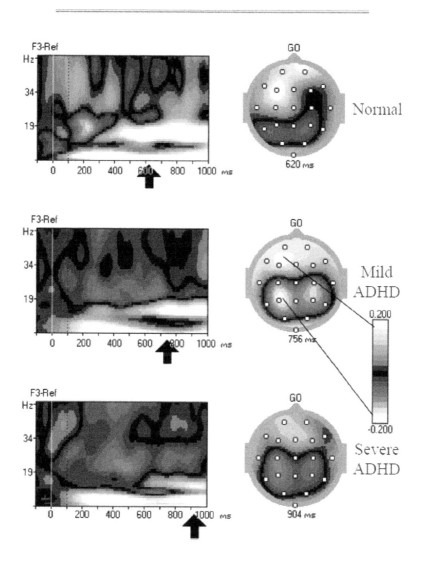

Figure 30. Wavelet analysis of the evoked EEG- the uppermost window shows the processed left frontal (F3) brain waves of a subject without ADHD following the Go stimulus in a Go/No-go task. The middle window shows the same conditions for a participant with moderate ADHD, and in the bottommost window for someone with severe ADHD. Time is on the x-axis; the y-axis represents the EEG frequency spectrum (1-40 Hz). The mappings on the right show the spread of beta activity at the moment indicated by the arrows at each window. Notice that for the uppermost subject, early intense beta activity is observed in left central and left frontal areas while in ADHD, beta activity appears later and is less intense. Notice the 'nested' gamma activity in the normal participant, which is less clear in the ADHD windows. (Image provided courtesy of Kropotov, unpublished).

Summary

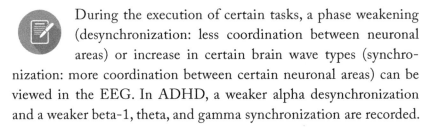During the execution of certain tasks, a phase weakening (desynchronization: less coordination between neuronal areas) or increase in certain brain wave types (synchronization: more coordination between certain neuronal areas) can be viewed in the EEG. In ADHD, a weaker alpha desynchronization and a weaker beta-1, theta, and gamma synchronization are recorded.

- The weaker frontal theta synchronization is an expression of weaker working memory.

- The weaker frontal gamma synchronization is an expression of weaker conscious processing (therefore weaker attention);

- The weaker parietal alpha synchronization is actually a weakening of multiple localized microscale alpha synchronizations, reflecting the weakening of cognitive processing in ADHD;

- The weaker beta synchronization in motor and frontal cerebral cortex indicates weakened motor planning.

The stronger parieto-occipital gamma synchronization could be indicative of the activation of additional neural resources in ADHD patients as a compensation for inefficient processing during early selective attention.

3.7 Phase and Coherence in the EEG

Measuring the coherence of certain frequency bands at different points on the scalp allows us to assess the degree of cooperation between different regions of the brain. Coherence is a measure of the extent of cooperation between two different areas of the cerebral cortex over certain frequency bands (delta, theta, alpha, and beta). The degree of coupling of specific frequency bands in certain phase relationships in the EEG signal can be precisely calculated over the measurement period. Coherence is maximal if two signals hold a constant phase angle in a distinct frequency band over the course of time. A very low coherence indicates functional independence of the two areas. Coherence between two areas that is lower than the one measured normally indicates insufficient integrative cooperation between these areas. Increased coherence indicates an inadequate degree of differentiation, often observed in people with low intelligence. In adulthood, coherence normally decreases. Thatcher (1998) demonstrated that coherence is typically higher in frontal rather than posterior areas, as might be expected from evidence that more local processing occurs in posterior areas together with more focal differentiation and short-range interaction.

Thatcher reasoned that the frontal cerebral cortex regulates the posterior cortex. He supported his suggestion further with an ecological model or a 'predator-prey' model of human cerebral development. Considering that increased coherence in frontal areas is frequently observed in ADHD, it is plausible that such frontal control of posterior areas (where higher integration of sensory information is processed) is less efficient.

Chabot (1996) found a hypercoherence of alpha and theta activity between the left and right frontal areas during rest states (such as is the case after a concussion) and between the frontal and temporal areas within each cerebral hemisphere in children with ADHD. This reflects a lack of differentiation in the processing performed in these brain areas, which may lead to attention difficulties. Barry's (2002) findings are slightly different, indicating increased coherence of delta and theta activity between left and right frontal areas but decreased alpha coherence. Over the past 15 years, the study of EEG coherence in ADHD has been carried out primarily by researchers of the Brain & Behaviour Research Institute and Department of Psychology at the University of Wollongong in Australia. The researchers have studied both intra- and interhemispheric coherence by considering short, medium, and long distances between electrodes. They have reported that ADHD subjects, compared to healthy controls, present higher intrahemispheric coherences in short/medium distances in delta, theta, and beta frequency bands. Barry (2011) demonstrated increased intra-hemispheric coherence in delta and theta at short-medium inter-electrode distances. Over longer inter-electrode distances, the AD/HD group had reduced intrahemispheric coherence in alpha. Following Thatcher's two-process model of coherence (Thatcher, 1986), the increased short-medium and decreased longer range coherences are both compatible with reduced cortical differentiation and cortical maturity. Increased coherence goes hand in hand with phase angle constancy for each frequency band. In high coherence, the phase difference is usually low because functional connections are flatter. In these cases, and probably also in ADHD, there is likely to be a decreased number of phase resettings: normally the phase relationship suddenly switches to another phase relationship at least once per second. This phase resetting plays another role in working memory (Rizutto, 2003); thus, a diminished number of phase resettings in ADHD might explain poorer working memory functioning in people with ADHD.

Summary

Coherence measures the cooperation of two different brain areas in certain EEG frequency bands. Increased coherence has been frequently observed in ADHD, which suggests insufficient differentiation between the brain areas concerned. If coherence is high, the phase angle between two frequency bands (each measured from a point on the scalp) remains longer, probably accompanied by less phase resettings, which may explain the existence of poor working memory, as in ADHD.

3.8 Cognitive/Event-Related Evoked Brain Potentials

Models of brain function in ADHD emphasize frontal/parietal interactions in deficits of attention and anterior cingulate/lateral prefrontal cortex interactions in behavioral disinhibition. Event-related brain potentials, as a test method, allow us to study these dysfunctions.

EEG techniques fall in two categories: time-frequency techniques extract the power of multiple frequency bands in the ongoing electroencephalogram (EEG) as a function of time, and event-related brain potential (ERP) techniques average epochs of EEG data associated with repeated events to reveal neural activity elicited by the event (the 'signal') from unrelated neural activity (the 'noise'). The averaging technique sums up EEG patterns time-locked to the stimulus presentation. Because trials are not time-locked to EEG oscillations and are presented randomly irrespective of the phase of the current EEG, negative and positive fluctuations preceding the stimulus cancel each other so that the prestimulus interval can be approximated by a straight line with an averaged zero potential.

Whenever a stimulus, such as a sound or light flash, is presented to an experimental subject within fractions of a second, evoked brain activity in the form of a wave pattern (potential) appears in the EEG. Evoked brain potentials are not often visible to the naked eye against the background of the present EEG waveforms. However, if hundred stimuli were presented one after the other, and the resulting short-coupled EEG fragment following each stimulus were measured, then the average EEG pattern could be calculated from all these fragments. The background EEG activity is smoothed, rendering the evoked potential (formed at exactly the same time after the stimulus) clearly visible. Potentials that are triggered purely by auditory, visual, or tactile stimuli are termed exogenous potentials, and they can reveal neurological injuries in the affected brain areas.

If a cognitive task ('event') is coupled with a stimulus, these potentials can allow the investigation of cognitive processes. All these potentials reveal different aspects of attentional and executive function processes, and all of them can be disturbed in people with ADHD. An ERP component reflects the response of a certain brain sub-system (such as monitoring neuronal network) to an adequate stimulus in an appropriate behavioral paradigm. The basic operations of the executive system, which can be tested with ERP components, are the maintenance of working memory and attention, the engagement operation, the inhibition of actions, and the monitoring operation.

3.8.1 The Odd Ball Test: Processing of Incoming Information

The best-known EEG cognitive test is the 'odd ball paradigm.' This test is used to obtain insight into processing of incoming information. Four stages have been distinguished in the central processing of incoming sensory information, each revealed by the characteristic electrical activity maximally measurable along the midline of the crown of the skull: N100, N200, P300, and LFN. In ADHD, lower amplitude or longer peak latencies appear.

In the most frequently used auditory variant of the odd ball and therefore the most standardized, a series of tones are randomly presented. Infrequently occurring targets (oddballs or deviants) are interspersed among frequently occurring standards. The evoked brain potentials provide information about cognitive capacities, such as various attention mechanisms that are important to the processing of incoming information. Overall, 150 tones are presented (120 low, 30 high tones), and the participants must actively listen to the tones while pressing a button after identifying an infrequent (high) tone. The brain activity that follows for half a second after each tone is measured.

3.8.1.1 Selective Attention: N100 (electrically negative brain wave after 100 ms)

The extent to which the amplitude of this wave increases (both after the frequent and infrequent tone) whenever an individual actively focuses on the series of tones is a measure of how well the individual selectively focuses on the listening task without being distracted by irrelevant stimuli. In passive states, these waves originate from the primary auditory temporal cerebral cortex; in active listening tasks, the auditory cortex is prepared for the stimuli. The frontal integrative association cortex also contributes to the amplitude of the N100 wave. Normally, the increase is greater than 20% while the increase is smaller in ADHD.

3.8.1.2 Automatic Discrimination: N200
(electrically negative wave after 200 ms)

N200 wave appears only after the onset of the infrequent tone in the active listening trial or during the first trial when the individual is not focused on the tones. This wave indicates how well an individual automatically notices an unexpected stimulus (therefore possibly important) outside the field of focused attention. Most events that occur outside the laboratory are unexpected, and the N200 provides a constant spur to explore the outside world. This wave originates in the auditory temporal association cortex and part of the frontal integrative association cortex. Normally, this wave will be at least 20% higher after infrequently rather than frequently presented tone. In ADHD, this amplitude difference has been found to be lower (Lazzaro, 2001; Satterfield, 1988).

3.8.1.3 Controlled Assignment of Meaning: P300
(P3b) (electropositive wave after 300 ms)

When an individual is asked to listen selectively for infrequent tones (or sometimes to count them), typically, a higher positive wave appears after the infrequent tones than after the more frequent low tones. This wave originates in the integrative temporoparietal and frontal integrative associative cortex. The wave's amplitude is an indication of the extent to which an individual succeeds in assigning a particular significance to the meaningful stimuli in a controlled manner.

The P300 component classifies brain activities underlying the revision of the mental representation induced by incoming stimuli (Donchin, 1981). After initial sensory processing, an attention-driven comparison process evaluates the representation of the previous event in working memory. If no stimulus attribute change is detected, the current mental model or 'schema' of the stimulus context is maintained, and only sensory evoked potentials are recorded (N100, P200, N200). If a new stimulus is detected, attentional processes govern a change or 'updating' of the stimulus representation that is concomitant with P300.

The once unitary phenomenon of P300 is now thought to be composed of several parts that reflect an information-processing cascade when attentional and memory mechanisms are engaged. The P3a, related to novelty detection, originates from stimulus-driven frontal attention mechanisms during task processing, whereas P3b originates from temporal-parietal activity associated with attention and appears to be related to the context updating and subsequent memory processing. Stimuli enter the processing system and a memory comparison process that determines whether the current stimulus is the same as or different from the previous stimulus (e.g. in the oddball task, whether a standard or a target stimulus was presented) is engaged. If the incoming stimulus is the same, the neural model of the stimulus environment remains unchanged, and sensory evoked potentials (N100, P200, N200) are obtained after signal averaging. If the incoming stimulus is not the same and the subject allocates attentional resources to the target, the neural representation of the stimulus environment will be changed or updated (contextual updating), such that a P300 (P3b) potential will be generated in addition to the sensory evoked potentials (Donchin, 1988; Polich, 2003).

Although the highest density of generators of the conventional P3b component are located in the parietal cortex and strictly speaking, in this respect, the P3b component belongs to ERP indices of attentional networks, a complex system that includes frontal/temporal/parietal areas together with the basal ganglia - thalamocortical circuits is involved in generation of the P3b component. In our daily life, we are always looking forward prepared to make further actions. However, the contextual content of the environment is rapidly changing, and in some cases, the prepared action must be suppressed. The inhibition of prepared action is performed by a complex brain circuit that involves partly the ventrolateral prefrontal. The prefrontal cortex receives the sensory information from the sensory systems (visual, auditory, and somatosensory), and depending on the results, it is in position to make decision on whether to respond. One can speculate that to inhibit a prepared action, the brain must first compare the current sensory situation with the sensory model and subsequently detect the mismatch. The comparison operations of sensory signals take place in the posterior sensory systems, and this process has been interpreted as context updating. We can further speculate that the result of these comparison operations is transferred to the prefrontal cortex to activate the circuits responsible for activation (engagement), that is, when deviant stimuli required actions (pressing a button), or inhibition (disengagement) of the prepared action. Although the control of sensory processing takes place in posterior regions of the cortex, these areas interact with the frontal parts of the cortex, which are traditionally associated with working memory. Indeed, attention and working memory are interconnected operations, since to keep the item in working memory, one must attend to it, and vice versa, to attend to some expected stimulus, one must keep it in memory. A network consisting of areas in the parietal and frontal cortex has been found to be activated in various visuospatial tasks that require attention and working memory. P3b amplitude is often lower, and its peak latency is often longer in ADHD. P300 latency correlates positively with increased rest theta activity in ADHD (Barry, 2003). Normalization of the P3b amplitude after a single dose of Ritalin accurately predicted the outcome in 81% of cases (Young, 1995).

3.8.1.4 Further Controlled Processing: LFN (late frontal negativity)

When the individual selectively attends to the listening task, a frontal increase of the late frontal negativity (at least 5 µV more negative) appears after presenting both the frequent and infrequent tone. The LFN is indicates the extent to which additional controlled processing of information occurs after stimulus recognition.

The presence of the LFN indicates the predominance of an internal control system that is able to inhibit the inflow of distracting or irrelevant information. This system is especially active in task situations in which attention is controlled from 'inside out' (for example, search processes in short-term memory in which consciousness knowingly directs attention to certain aspects of the environment). It is associated with intentional, controlled focusing of attention. A low LFN points to domination of an external control or orientation system, facilitating the influx of stimuli to the cerebral cortex. The external control system is especially activated during situations of 'attentional demand' or in association with orientation reactions. If there are weaknesses in divided attention, which may be clearly demonstrated by an increase in intrusive errors during the Stroop task, for example, the LFN will decrease (there is less controlled processing and therefore attention is more reactive to external control processes).

3.8.2 ERN and FRN and Frontal Midline Theta: Action Monitoring

3.8.2.1 The Go/No-Go Test: A Window on Behavioral Control

In recent years, research interest in ADHD has shifted from the processing of incoming information (for example as elucidated by the oddball test) to the study of the executive functions that control behavior (from attention deficit towards intention deficit). Self-monitoring of the consequences of action is an important self-regulatory function. The latter can be investigated using, for example, the 'go/no-go' test in which action monitoring and inhibition of inadequate responses can be observed. In the 'go/no-go' test, a series of visual or auditory stimulus pairs are presented. The first, forewarning stimulus, which has always the same value, enables the subject to prepare to respond as fast as possible after the second stimulus presentation at a fixed interval. The second stimulus can have either value. A series of hundred stimuli are presented with a fixed rhythm. Pairs of identical or different stimuli are presented in a random order, with half of the stimuli pairs being identical. In the go condition, participants must push a button only after a pair of identical stimuli; the other condition is termed no-go. Following the last stimulus in each pair, the evoked brain potentials, which are maximal at the front of the middle line of the scalp, are measured over half second periods. A negative potential (N2, at 235-255 ms), followed by a positive potential (P3, at 350-450 ms) measured maximally in frontal regions, appears after not pushing the button initially. Note that in the oddball paradigm, subjects also have to respond to some stimuli and avoid responding to other stimuli, but the low probability of deviant stimuli and small interstimulus intervals do not allow the subjects to prepare the action for each stimulus. Rather, standard stimuli in the oddball paradigm create a background on which deviant (go) stimuli rarely appear. However, Holroyd (2004) wondered whether the oddball N200 and the no-go N200/ERN might reflect different aspects of a common underlying cognitive process labeled conflict monitoring.

One method to locate the source of processed brain potentials (see figure 31) is LORETA (low-resolution brain electromagnetic tomography) (Pascual-Marqui, 1994). LORETA identifies the source generator of the electrical activity deep in the brain using mathematical computations of the strength of the processed brain potentials taken from the different scalp measurement points. Both potentials originate in the right ventrolateral prefrontal cortex (VLPFC) and in the dorsal anterior cingulate (dACC). N2 activity in the dorsal anterior cingulate strongly correlates with activity in the ventrolateral and dorsolateral prefrontal cortex, which indicates strong interconnections (Lavric, 2004).

The no-go N2 and P3 were originally attributed to (response) inhibition (Kok, 1986, 1999; Falkenstein, 1999), but recent studies suggest that they reflect a more general action monitoring or cognitive control process that is also present if no response needs to be inhibited (Donkers and van Boxtel, 2004; Nieuwenhuis, 2003). In a study by Nieuwenhuis (2003), an enhanced N2 was evoked in go trials when presenting 'go' infrequently in the frequent no-go trials. This observation indicated that the N2 might reflect conflict arising from the competition between the execution and the inhibition of a response. This suggestion was recently supported by an ERP study of a combined go/no-go and Stop-signal task (Enriquez-Geppert, 2010). In order to separate their underlying neural and functional mechanisms, conflict was manipulated by varying go-trial frequencies across blocks (75% vs. 25%). Motor inhibition was manipulated by using go, no-go, and stop trials, each representing a different load of inhibition. ERPs as well as current density reconstruction of fifteen healthy participants were analyzed. Overall, compared to frequent trials, infrequent trials evoked significantly more pronounced N2s, with the dACC as its source. With equalized no-go and go probabilities, the data become less consistent, but a trend towards more lateral frontal generators seems apparent (Lavric, 2004). The P3 predominantly revealed significant variations among trial types (go, no-go, stop). Estimated source activations of the dACC and right VLPFC supported the ERP results. N2-related effects were revealed in both regions, whereas the condition-specific variations of the P3 were observed only in the VLPFC. The results indicate that the N2 reflects primarily conflict-related effects whereas the P3 represents predominantly motor inhibition.

However, given P300's late onset, the frontal-midline P300 or delta band activity likely does not qualify for proper motor inhibition. In addition, other P3a-like potentials (e.g., the oddball novelty-P300), in contrast to target-related P3bs, usually occur also in contexts where the ERP-evoking events do not have to be followed by a response. Therefore, an integration with P300 findings from other domains suggests that this P300 signals evaluative and updating processes associated with the stimulus at hand. In case of a no-go stimulus, it may thus reflect the evaluation of the inhibitory process itself or its outcome. This interpretation is in accordance with functions ascribed to delta band activity, which is believed to reflect the evaluation of motivational relevance and saliency of a stimulus (Knyazev, 2012). The commonality of delta activity with the frontal-midline P300 has already been discussed (Başar-Eroglu, 1992; Demiralp, 2001). Early studies on spontaneous EEG oscillations localized delta to medio-frontal, orbito-frontal, and anterior insular cortices (Anderer, 2002; Michel, 1992).

Multiple operations involved in the task can explain the diversity of results regarding functional meaning of the N2 and P3 no-go waves. Kropotov (2011) separated action inhibition, conflict monitoring, and sensory mismatch into independent components of event related potentials in a go/no-go task. Three variants of the same stimulus task manipulated sensory mismatch, action inhibition, and conflict monitoring operations by varying stimulus-response associations. The anterior N2 and P3 waves were decomposed into components by means of independent component analysis (ICA). There is a general agreement that the averaged ERP in cognitive tasks can be represented as a sum of separate components generated by distinct sources in the cortex. The components are supposed to be generated by the distributed generators and associated with certain psychological operations (factors). It is presumed that the decomposed waveforms represent distinct psychological operations performed in specific cortical locations with specific time dynamics. Just as the background EEG is composed of several rhythmic components, evoked potentials represent sums of several components generated by different cortical areas at different time intervals. To be able to decompose different components, we need to know how potentials at electrodes correlate with each other. Indeed, we presume that the potentials of electrodes that peak up activity from generators of the one component correlate with each other much stronger compared to electrodes potentials belonging to two different generators. The independent component analysis (ICA) method is based on the assumption that the sources of components are statistically independent. This assumption seems to fit the nature of generators producing different components in ERPs. Indeed, the information flow in the brain induced by stimulus presentation sequentially activates different hierarchically organized cortical areas so that the generators of different components are activated in different time intervals and at different cortical locations. Components are constructed by optimizing the mutual independence of all activation time curves, leading to a natural and intuitive definition of an ERP component as a stable potential distributor, which cannot be further decomposed into independently activated sources. It is thought that different stages of information flow are associated with activities in distinct cortical areas and with different (and to some extent independent) time patterns.

Actually, the largest no-go component in terms of amplitude is generated in medial prefrontal and anterior cingulate cortical areas. It is a symmetrical positive component located centrally in the 2D space with maximum at Cz-Fz. The latency of the component changes significantly with age– from 370 ms at middle age to 420 ms at an early age and 460 ms at older age. The response inhibition P3 component has a latency of about 340 ms (increasing with aging), with generators widely distributed over premotor and motor cortical areas.

The action monitoring component is generated in the dACC, where the N2 has a similar functional meaning as the error-related negativity (ERN). In fact, Yeung (2004) proposed that the anterior N2 is actually the same as the error-related negativity (described later). The response inhibition N2 component is generated in the right VLPFC, which receives input from the dACC where the executed action is compared with a prepared one.

The concept of monitoring must be distinguished from the concept of attentional control. Attentional control refers to a top-down, limited resource cognitive mechanism that modulates sensory information processing while the monitoring of actions refers to a cognitive mechanism that evaluates the quality of executive control and activates the executive system in the case of mismatch between expected (planned) and executed actions. The point is that flexible adjustments of human and animal behavior require a continuous assessment of ongoing actions and the outcomes of these actions. The ability to monitor and compare ongoing actions and performance outcomes with internal goals and standards is critical for optimizing decision-making. The cingulate cortex (the core of the monitoring sub-system) receives the richest dopaminergic innervations of any cortical area. A meaningful stimulus releases a dopamine molecule from the vesicular carrier. Dopamine diffuses into the synaptic cleft and binds to the postsynaptic D2-receptor. In a normal brain, any behaviorally meaningful stimulus evokes a trace that is partly defined by the time during which dopamine is kept in the synaptic cleft. Less D2 receptors in ADHD would eventually shorten the 'trace' induced by a meaningful stimulus. This might in turn lead to: (1) poor working memory, (2) inability to concentrate on the action for a long time (inattention), (3) a fast switching between different motor actions (hyperactivity), (4) a fast switching between visual objects and sounds (distractibility), and (5) a constant alteration in thoughts (impulsivity).

In the combined subtype of ADHD (ADHD-C), smaller no-go-N2 amplitude is associated with more frequent false alarms (Bluschke, 2016). Regarding the P3, its amplitude was smaller in the ADHD-C compared with controls only in no-go trials. This modulation was due to alterations in the ACC (BA24). This finding is in line with source localization results on the no-go-P3 (Fallgätter, 2004).

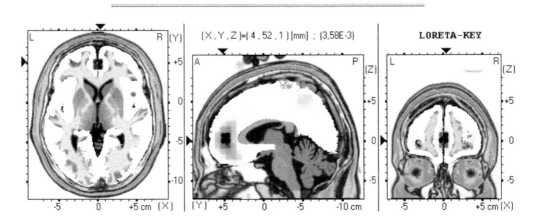

Figure 31. Source localization of the no-go P3 ERP (LORETA method): Maximal (dark shading) in the dorsal anterior cingulate in the frontal cortex. Left: Transverse section of the brain showing the dorsal anterior cingulate. Middle: A side view of the same level. Right: A frontal section of the brain through the same area. In this way, a three-dimensional reconstruction of brain activity is possible.

Banaschewski (2004) failed to find any deviations from normality in an ADHD group in the N2 component of ERPs in a variant of the go/no-go paradigm – the CPT-A-X task. In contrast, in another study (Pliszka, 2000), ERPs in another variant of the go/no-go paradigm – the Stop signal task - showed a remarkable decrease of the N2 component in the ADHD group compared to healthy subjects. In response to all Stop signals, control participants produced a large negative wave at 200 ms (N2) over the right inferior frontal cortex, which was markedly reduced in ADHD children. The N2 amplitude correlated significantly with the response–inhibition performance across subjects. The ERN was also found to be weaker in amplitude in ADHD (Liotti, 2005). The no-go P3 was also weaker in ADHD (Fallgätter, 2003, 2004, 2005; Kropotov, 2005).

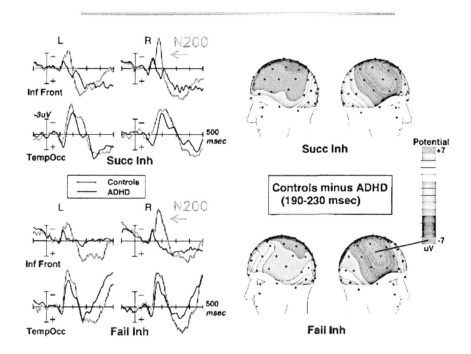

Figure 32. The no-go N2 in a group of children with ADHD and in typically developing children. Note on the left that both the N200 and the P300 are weaker in ADHD for the instances when the children were successful and the instances when they failed to inhibit a response to the stop signal. On the right, the differences in the N200 between the two groups are presented with a brain mapping. The maximum difference is in the right inferior frontal area. In ADHD, the N200 is weakest in this area. Reprinted from Biological Psychiatry, 48(3), Pliszka, Liotti, & Woldorff, Inhibitory control in children with attention deficit/hyperactivity disorder: Event-related potentials identify the processing component and timing of an impaired right-frontal response-inhibition mechanism, Copyright (2000), with permission from Elsevier.

Children with ADHD showed lower activity in the caudate nucleus during a go/no-go task compared to children with typical development (Vaidya, 1998). Comparative studies using fMRI of normal children and adults have shown that during response inhibition in a go/no-go task, activity in the caudate nucleus is stronger in children (Booth, 2003). The researchers interpreted this to be an expression of the insufficient maturation of the frontostriatal circuit in children, such that these children must put forth more effort to compensate. This suggests that the lower activity found by Vaidya (1998) (Figure 33) in children with ADHD can be interpreted as a lack of compensatory effort in comparison to typically developing children. Ritalin can improve the normal compensatory over-activity during response inhibition in the caudate nucleus and the putamen in children with ADHD. In normal, typically developing children, administration of Ritalin does not lead to this over-activity. It is interesting to note that a decreased caudate nucleus size is one of the most consistent findings in structural MRI ADHD research.

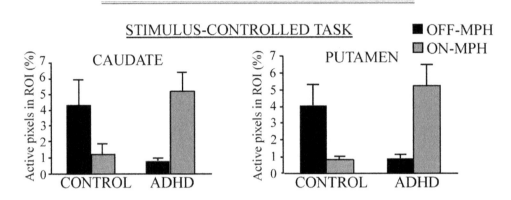

Figure 33. In ADHD during the go/no-go task, there is less activity in the caudate nucleus and the putamen, after the administration of Ritalin, the activity clearly increases (contrary to the result in the control group) (Vaidya et al., 1998). Copyright (1998) National Academy of Sciences, U.S.A.

In ADHD, the positive potential that follows the no-go condition is maximal at the central midline rather than the frontal midline, indicating weaker inhibition and action monitoring (Kropotov, 2005). Falgätter (2004; 2005) reported this 'no-go anteriorization' (NGA) of the no-go P3 as an index of action monitoring. Child and adult ADHD patients were characterized by reduced NGA values, indicating that this parameter might be an adequate endophenotypic marker for prefrontal dysfunction during the processes of response control in ADHD.

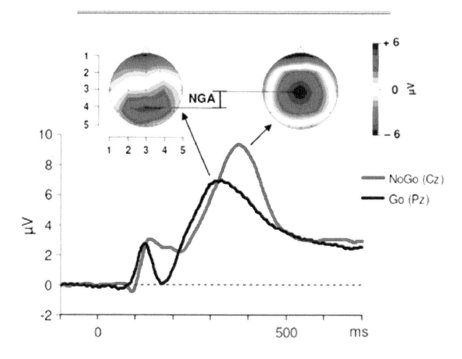

Figure 34. The no-go P3 anteriorization (NGA) (Dresler, 2010)

The source of the no-go P3 has been localized in the dACC (Falgätter, 2004). Correlation of a well-developed NGA with a normal functioning dopaminergic system has also been described (Dresler, 2010; Heinzel, 2013). Several authors have emphasized the functional similarity of the no-go N2 and the ERN, where both have the dACC as their source (Cavanagh, 2014). The no-go N2 and ERN are also considered a phase reset of frontal midline theta (Cavanagh, 2011).

Schiller (2013) demonstrated an inverse correlation between NGA and resting EEG delta, theta, and alpha 1 power in left middle frontal gyrus (BA9,44), as measured by 3-D source reconstruction (sLORETA). Resting delta, theta, and alpha activity are inverse indicators of cortical activation, meaning that higher baseline activation in the lateral prefrontal cortex predicts a larger NGA, that is, a better response inhibition capacity.

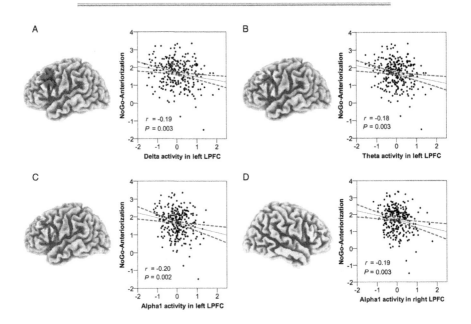

*Figure 35. Inverse correlation between NGA and resting delta, theta,
and alpha 1 activity in DLPFC (Schiller, 2013).*

Ritalin normalizes the no-go P3 in ADHD children only when there is a significant improvement in omission and commission errors in a continuous performance task, which is a classical go/no-go paradigm (Yan-ling and Xuan, 2013).

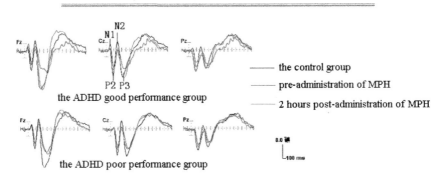

*Figure 36. A single dose of Ritalin normalizes the no-go P3 amplitude only in the ADHD subgroup
that shows an improved performance on a continuous performance task (Yan-ling and Xuan, 2013).*

More recent studies (Chatham, 2012) have challenged the traditional view of the right VLPFC as the no-go P3 component site for motor response inhibition by demonstrating that this component reflects cognitive control, more specifically the context monitoring in the service of goals, regardless of stopping demands. Inhibition is critical for enabling controlled behavior, as bad habits, unfamiliar situations, and dangerous environments often require stopping the default behaviors and performing more context-appropriate actions. Effective inhibitory control requires not only stopping the unwanted actions, thoughts, or emotions, but also the efficient detection of those contexts that indicate the need for these forms of stopping. Chatham illustrated the involvement of the rVLPFC in the detection and interpretation of behaviorally relevant stimuli to guide the selection of action. This context-monitoring role of rVLPFC may be understood as arising from the proximity of rVLPFC to the anterior insula, which appears to monitor interoceptive information, in some cases proactively. The anterior insula also shows greater hemodynamic responses to demands on action selection rather than to demands on motoric stopping, and it is thought to be tightly integrated with the rVLPFC. Thus, a basic mechanism in anterior insula for monitoring the internal significance of upcoming stimuli may have been evolutionarily adapted to monitor the goal-relevance of stimuli for action selection in the nearby rVLPFC. The context-monitoring account is also compatible with the recent revisions to a classical taxonomy of the effects of prefrontal insult in which the inhibitory deficits arising from right lateral prefrontal damage are now explained as monitoring deficits instead of deficits in target detection and action selection. Specifically, Chatham's results suggested that pathological impulse control deficits might reflect more effortful and prefrontal processes involved in context monitoring rather than a failure to stop in particular. ADHD may be associated with a monitoring deficit in which many stimuli, regardless of their behavioral relevance, are thought to warrant attention. The finding that ADHD is more strongly associated with increased reaction time variability, as might result from a context-monitoring deficit, rather than with deficits in tasks that require stopping supports this prediction. Relatedly, the resistance of response inhibition to improvement via training may indicate that monitoring context for contingent action selection, not the act of stopping, is the controlled process to be targeted for effective intervention. Chatham's proposal is in line with other studies (Cohen, 2013) on multiple forms of self-control and rVLPFC, where self-control is defined as 'the overriding or inhibiting of automatic, habitual, or innate behaviors, urges, emotions, or desires that would otherwise interfere with goal directed behavior' (Muraven, 2006). Interestingly, modern theorizing is largely consistent with a hypothesis proposed 140 years ago, in that 'the centers of inhibition being thus the essential factor of attention, constitute the organic basis of all the higher intellectual faculties' (Ferrier, 1876).

The paradigms on which response inhibition theories are based fail to distinguish between inhibitory and non-inhibitory cognitive demands, specifically since the stop-signal task and go/no-go task do not control for potentially confounding non-inhibitory cognitive demands. In the broader literature, it has been reported that the right inferior gyrus (rIFG) is recruited during a range of attentionally demanding conditions that have no obvious requirement for behavioral inhibition. Erika-Florence (2014) used four novel fMRI variants of the classic stop-signal task to test whether the inferior frontal cortex houses unique inhibitory modules. The results demonstrated that inferior frontal cortex sub-regions are not functionally unique in their sensitivities to inhibitory cognitive demands, but instead form components of spatially distributed networks. These networks are most strongly activated when infrequent stimuli are being processed, regardless of behavioral inhibitory demands, and when novel tasks are being acquired, as opposed to when routine responses must be suppressed. Erika-Florence proposed that there are no inhibitory modules within the frontal lobes and that behavioral inhibition is an emergent property of spatially distributed functional networks, each of which supports a broader class of cognitive demands. The findings suggest a general attentional role of the anterior insula, frontal operculum, and anterior cingulate network, and support the view that frontoparietal regions in general are strongly recruited during the learning of novel tasks as opposed to when inhibiting dominant behaviors.

In this context, there has been particular interest in the possibility that activation of the right inferior gyrus (rIFG), which is the largest part of the rVLPFC, might reflect the operation of attentional processes that are instigated by the presentation of the infrequent and salient stop cue rather than the subsequent process of response inhibition that is actually instructed by the stop cue. This has been addressed by measuring functional connectivity between brain areas using fMRI data and employing Granger causality analyses (Duann, 2009). According to Duann, rIFG is simply part of the ventral attention system – as has been defined by Corbetta and Shulman (2002) – activated in response to the detection of a salient target stimulus, particularly when the stimulus is behaviorally relevant. Therefore, rIFG might respond specifically to no-go stimuli, because these stimuli are highly salient and relevant. Right IFG only serves to detect no-go signals and subsequently 'energizes' pre-SMA, which then exerts inhibitory motor control via the subthalamic nucleus. Sharp (2010) came to a similar conclusion after using a stop-signal task designed to dissociate attentional capture, response inhibition, and error processing. Sharp argued that rIFG supports attentional capture, whereas pre-SMA inhibits the ongoing action. Corbetta and Shulman (2002) emphasized the attention reorientation role of rIFG, which detects unexpected targets. Response inhibition can but must not be one of the consequences, and the rIFG can be considered as a network reset area (Hampshire, 2010). A complete account of the rIFG function may require the integration of attentional processing and response control. Given the similar functional roles of the no-go N2 and P3 in the dACC and rIFG, one could wonder whether the cingulo-opercular network concept (Dosenbach, 2007), which includes both areas, might explain these similarities.

Decreased intrinsic segregation of the dorsal and ventral attention networks (the latter includes the rIFG) in ADHD may alter the information exchange threshold between the two systems, with VAN signals interrupting goal-directed task-relevant DAN activity (Sidlauskaite, 2015). This is consistent with the recent findings that increasingly point to VAN as the locus of attentional dyscontrol and enhanced distractibility in ADHD. Increased SN–VAN coupling in ADHD produces an altered saliency attribution mechanism, where the discrimination between environmental distractors and task-relevant stimuli is muted (Sidlauskaite, 2015). Therefore, in the context of ADHD, this might be hypothesized to relate to symptoms of distractibility and inability to ignore irrelevant stimuli.

Contradictory findings in the ADHD literature report both over- and under-activation of rIFG, as ADHD has been associated with poor response inhibition resulting either from insufficient activation of rIFG or from a requirement for larger frontal recruitment for optimal task performance. Nymberg (2013) demonstrated an association of ADHD symptoms with distinct fMRI activation profiles, depending on MAOA genotype. In A hemizygotes of the expression single nucleotide polymorphism rs12843268, which express lower levels of MAOA, ADHD symptoms are associated with lower ventral striatal BOLD response during the monetary incentive delay task and lower rIFG BOLD response during the stop signal task. In G hemizygotes that express higher levels of MAOA, ADHD symptoms are associated with increased rIFG BOLD response during the stop signal task in the presence of increased ventral striatal BOLD response during the monetary incentive delay task. The monoamine oxidase A gene (MAOA) is localized on the human X chromosome, and encodes a mitochondrial enzyme, which degrades monoamines, including norepinephrine, dopamine, and serotonin. A meta-analysis of 14 fMRI studies showed that psychostimulants most consistently enhanced rIFG/insula during inhibition (Rubia, 2014).

While modulations of theta oscillations are also important for response inhibition sub-processes in the N2 time range, Dippel (2015) investigated response inhibition related theta oscillations, which were also shown to have their source in the left temporo-parietal junction (TPJ). The no-go P3 also has sources in the TPJ, besides the anterior cingulate and insulae (Huster, 2013). The right TPJ is traditionally considered a critical area of the ventral attention network, a more recent findings imply also a role for the left TPJ. A review of the literature on TPJ function (Geng and Vossel, 2013) suggest that the TPJ processes task-relevant stimuli to update internal representations of the environmental context by means of sensory information to initiate appropriate actions, especially when these stimuli are unexpected. It seems that the rarity of events signalling the necessity to inhibit a response is crucial for the involvement of the left TPJ in theta band activity. It therefore seems that the left TPJ is an important element to consider in different response modes during response inhibition processes. Under conditions that provoke such a response mode, it may be necessary to intensify internal monitoring based on a 'surprise signal' (Cavanagh and Frank, 2014) to maximize the chances of detecting changes relevant to behavior. Dippel's data suggest that the surprise signal coded by theta band activity is important not only for response inhibition processes, but also for response execution processes. The reason is that theta power also increased on infrequent go but not on frequent no-go trials. As such, it seems that theta frequency power is enhanced whenever a predominating operation mode (i.e., responding or non-responding) needs to change into the opposite, rarely occurring operation mode. Regarding theta oscillations, it has been also suggested that they are important for 'attentional sampling' processes, i.e., the environment is periodically sampled to verify and update its contents to maximize the chances of detecting changes relevant to behavior (Vanrullen and Dubois, 2011). In this regard, modulations in theta frequency oscillations across response modes may reflect some form of contextual updating that is necessary to inform cognitive control and response inhibition. This concept appears to be closely related to the conception of a surprise signal, as an attentional sampling of the environment is necessary to detect rare events that are likely to induce surprise signals. It cannot be excluded that the differences between response modes described above reflect differences in the necessity or intensity of 'attentional sampling' processes that update internal task representations. This alternative interpretation also supports the role of the TPJ in attentional control processes (Geng and Vossel, 2013). A response mode that is susceptible to impulsive errors is associated with stronger theta band activity, suggesting that response modes differ in the encoding of surprise signals and related processes of attentional sampling to update internal task representations and to maximize the chances of detecting changes relevant to behavioral control. It would also be in line with the concept of the ventral attention network, which includes the TPJ. The right temporo-parietal junction (TPJ) is widely considered as part of the ventral attention network that reorients attention 'bottom-up' to unexpected but task-relevant stimuli. The TPJ and the ventral attentional network are suppressed during 'top-down guided attentional processes, but they are activated in order to 'circuit-break' the voluntary attentional control system to reorient attention to unexpected but relevant information (Corbetta and Shulman, 2002). Despite the prevalence of this theory in cognitive neuroscience, there is little direct evidence for the principal hypothesis that TPJ sends an early reorientation signal that 'circuit breaks' attentional processing in regions of the dorsal attentional network (e.g., the frontal eye fields) or is completely right lateralized during attentional processing. Instead, TPJ signals might reflect post-perceptual processes involved in contextual updating and adjustments of top-down expectations, in which the function of TPJ is to update internal models of the current behavioral context to generate appropriate actions (Geng and Vossel, 2013). A similar idea has long existed within the event-related potentials (ERP) literature with respect to the P300 component, which is thought to contain a number of neural sources, including TPJ (Donchin, 1988). The TPJ does not seem to play a role specifically in early stimulus-driven attentional reorienting, but it involves integrating internal representations of the task context with stimulus and response expectations.

3.8.2.2 The Feedback-Related Negativity (FRN)

The FRN paradigm is somewhat similar to the ERN paradigm. Feedback is presented after the subject's motor response. Unlike the ERN, which is time-locked to the response, the FRN occurs 250 to 300 ms after a negative feedback stimulus. The feedback-related negativity in EEG represents the RPE (reward prediction error), which is known to be encoded by mesencephalic dopamine neurons projecting to the striatum and frontal regions. Some have argued that the FRN represents salience prediction errors (Talmi, 2013). Hauser (2014) clarified the functional role of the FRN and determined the role of the dorsal anterior cingulate within the RPE network. The reinforcement learning theory of the error related negativity (ERN) proposes that the ERN and the FRN reflect the same reinforcement learning signal generated in response to unexpected negative outcomes (Nieuwenhuis, 2004). Specifically, ERNs and FRNs are associated with phasic decreases in dopamine activity, indicating that ongoing events are worse than expected. Both have their source in the dACC. Again, the FRN can be considered a case of conflict between the response that was made by the subject and the correct response that was indicated by the feedback.

3.8.2.3 Frontal Midline Theta and Cognitive Control

Cognitive control can be considered a set of processes that are responsible for goal-directed flexible behavior (Yeung, 2013). These processes can be conceptually divided into two broad classes, one of them forms a system of exertion of cognitive control itself and the other one forms a system to monitor the need to increase the level of cognitive control (Ridderinkhof, 2004). Exertion of cognitive control includes top-down attention to the task relevant sensory information; retention of relevant information, such as task rules, and the history of the previous task course in the working memory; integration of task-relevant neural processes that represent the sensory information, context, retrieved long-term memories, reward expectations and motor programs; facilitation of representations of the task-relevant actions; inhibition of representations of incorrect automatic or prepotent actions. The monitoring system signals the demand for increasing the cognitive control level in the situations, such as simultaneous activation of conflicting action representations; detection of erroneous response commissions; ambiguous task rules; change in the task rules; and discrepancy between the actual and the predicted reward.

The neural substrate of most aspects of cognitive control is represented by a number of structures in the prefrontal cortex linked to a highly interconnected network. Although their functions overlap, it is possible to distinguish relative contributions of these structures to cognitive control processes. Particularly, the lateral prefrontal cortex (DLPFC) is presumed to be largely involved in retention of task-relevant representations, and thus it participates in such functions as working memory, top-down attention, and creation of the behavioral bias towards correct responses consistent with the current task rules (Ridderinkhof, 2004; Yeung, 2013). The orbitofrontal cortex (OFC) is an important node in reward prediction and evaluation. The medial frontal cortex (MFC), and more precisely its part called the rostral cingulate zone (RCZ), is believed to be involved in such processes as monitoring the need for increasing cognitive control and producing behavioral adjustments by signaling this need to other cortical structures. The bursts of frontal midline theta power that occur around the presentation of stimuli and commission of responses are modulated by the conditions characterized by increased cognitive demands, such as errors, conflict, reward omissions, and task switching (Cavanagh and Frank, 2014). On this basis, theta activity is considered to be related to cognitive control, specifically, to the process of monitoring the need in the increased level of control.

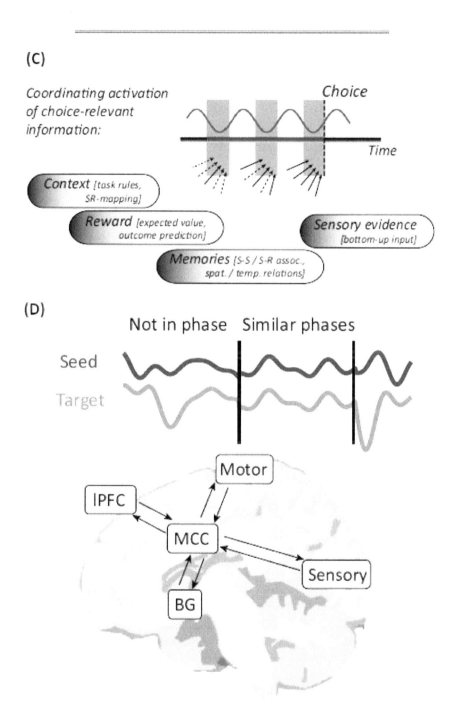

Figure 37. (C) Midfrontal theta is thought to reflect the synchronization of goal–relevant information around critical decision points, such as action selection. In this example, theta activities coordinate inputs across cortical areas (arrows), particularly at the trough of the oscillation (gray

bars). Action selection is likely to be executed when these sources of choice-relevant information (context, reward, memory, etc.) are successfully integrated (solid arrows). (D) Theta band phase consistency is thought to reflect the instantiation of transient functional networks (purple and green traces). For instance, intersite theta band phase consistency, following signals of the need for control, have been observed among sources modelled in MCC (dACC), lateral prefrontal cortex (lPFC), motor areas, and sensory (i.e., extrastriate visual) cortex. Theta activity may also implement communications between MCC and the basal ganglia (BG) (Cavanagh and Frank, 2014).

A growing consensus suggests that the dorsal anterior cingulate (dACC) is sensitive to both the elicitation of negative affect and the need for cognitive control, suggesting that the dACC implements a common, domain general process. A recent meta-analysis of functional imaging studies demonstrated that the elicitation of both negative affect and cognitive control is associated with activation of an overlapping region in the dACC (Shackman, 2011). This overlap is consistent with anatomical evidence suggesting that the dACC represents a hub where information about pain, threat, and other more abstract forms of potential punishment can be synthesized and used to modulate regions involved in expressing fear and anxiety, executing goal-directed behaviors, and biasing the focus of selective attention. Using meta-analytic techniques to synthesize the human electrophysiology literature, Cavanagh and Schackman (2015) provided evidence that anxious individuals show larger frontal midline theta control signals and that larger control signals are, in turn, associated with a more cautious or inhibited response set following errors and punishment. In their Adaptive Control Hypothesis, they claimed that dispositional anxiety correlates with frontal-midline theta, as a generic 'need for control' signal of the anterior midcingulate cortex. They argued that frontal-midline theta provides a neurophysiologically plausible mechanism for optimally adjusting behavior to uncertainty, a hallmark of situations that elicit anxiety and demand cognitive control. Collectively, these observations support the idea that frontal midline theta reflects a common mechanism, a 'lingua franca,' for implementing adaptive control in various contexts that involve uncertainty about actions and their motivationally-significant potential outcomes. Cavanagh proposed theta as a biophysical mechanism for organizing local and distal neurocomputational functions. Midfrontal theta is thought to reflect the synchronization of goal-relevant information around critical decision points, such as action selection.

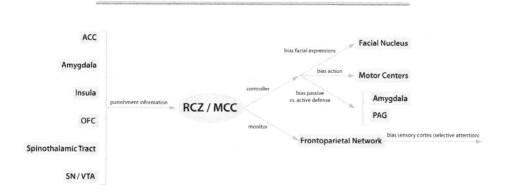

Figure 38. The Adaptive Control Hypothesis (Cavanagh and Shackman, 2015).

Based on brain imaging and anatomical evidence, it has been hypothesized that dACC activity reflects control processes that optimize responses made in the face of uncertainties about instrumental actions and their potentially aversive outcomes (Schackman, 2011).

Cavanagh and Schackman (2015) proposed the Adaptive Control Hypothesis. The dACC implements adaptive control by integrating information about punishment arriving from subcortical regions, insula, orbitofrontal cortex (OFC), and elsewhere in order to bias responding in situations where the optimal course of action is uncertain or entails competition between alternative courses. Control signals generated in dACC (MCC) and directed at the amygdala or periaqueductal gray (PAG) might serve to resolve conflict between passive and active defensive behaviors. Another possibility is that dACC (MCC) biases aversively motivated actions directly through its connections with motor centers, but biases selective attention indirectly through its connections with the frontoparietal network. In other words, the Adaptive Control Hypothesis suggests that anxiety and negative affect tend to involve the same processes described by the cognitive control theories to solve similar problems. Control processes are engaged when automatic or habitual responses are insufficient to support goal-directed behavior. This occurs when there is uncertainty about the optimal course of action (e.g., probabilistic learning), when potential actions are associated with the possibility of error or punishment, or when there is competition between alternative courses of action (e.g., flee/freeze, go/no-go). These features are hallmarks of dangerous environments, as in studies of fear, anxiety, and pain.

Luu's (2004) research results appear consistent with a body of research that has demonstrated a relationship between limbic theta activity and action regulation, including error monitoring and learning. Both the theta-band ERN and the amplitude of non-phase-locked post-response EEG were maximal at medial frontal recording sites, which is consistent with the notion that the ERN emerges in part from phase-alignment of frontal midline theta EEG processes. The scalp distributions of the theta-band ERN and remaining theta-band EEG were somewhat different, suggesting that different theta-producing EEG sources may be phase-locked to the motor response of different magnitudes, thus contributing in different proportions to the phase-locked (ERP) and non-phase-locked data portions. Although the ERN appears after the motor response, phase consistency of EEG theta activity starts before the button press. In the phase-locked data, 100 ms before error responses, frontal midline bursts became partially and more strongly phase-aligned to the button press than before correct responses. This is consistent with the interpretation that the theta-band portion of the ERN sums activity of EEG processes contributing to the frontal midline theta increase, rather than being a discrete, monophasic evoked response the generators of which are unrelated to the generation of other EEG activity.

Feedback related negativity (FRN) and frontal midline theta have both been proposed to index a dopamine-like reinforcement learning signal in the dACC, a signal that is differentially sensitive to reward versus error information for the purpose of adaptively modifying behavior and adaptive decision-making. Thus, for example, a signal that is larger for incorrect compared to correct outcomes but that is also larger for improbable compared to probable outcomes would confuse information related to errors with information related to probability, potentially biasing the system to avoid improbable events even when these events were unexpectedly good. Holroyd's team investigated these proposals by comparing FRN amplitude and theta power with respect to their sensitivities to outcome valence and probability in a previously collected EEG dataset (Hajihosseini and Holroyd, 2013). A dissociation was revealed between the two measures, with FRN amplitude mainly sensitive to valence and theta power mainly sensitive to probability. The valence of feedback indicates whether an outcome is rewarding (or correct) as opposed to non-rewarding (or incorrect). Further, FRN amplitude was correlated highly with the portion of theta power that is consistent in phase across trials (i.e., evoked theta power). These results suggest that although both measures provide valuable information about cognitive function of frontal midline cortex, FRN amplitude is specifically sensitive to dopamine reinforcement learning signals whereas theta power reflects the dACC response to unexpected events. In addition to error processing, frontal midline theta is associated with cognitive processes underlying working memory (Jensen & Tesche, 2002) and conflict monitoring. These observations have motivated the proposal that frontal midline theta reflects sensitivity to important cognitive events in general rather than to errors in particular (Cavanagh, 2012).

Interestingly, the baseline rest theta/beta at Cz is associated with decreased FRN amplitude and increased risk taking during a gambling task (Massar, 2012). There is a correlation between high resting theta and low FRN in the dorsal anterior cingulate in sLORETA. The correlation is mediated by sensitivity to punishment in conflict situations. Putman (2010) described the ways in which the theta/beta ratio reflects the extent to which the limbic motivational drives are not inhibited by neocortical cognitive control mechanisms. It correlates with risky decision making, propensity to seek rewards, and poor reinforcement learning. Moreover, Massar also localized the source resting theta in the dorsal anterior cingulate.

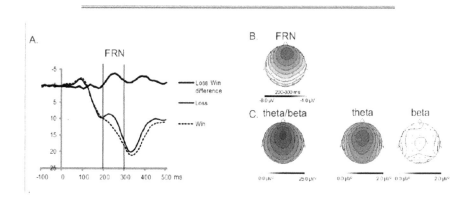

Figure 39. Correlation between FRN amplitude and central theta/beta ratio (Massar, 2012).

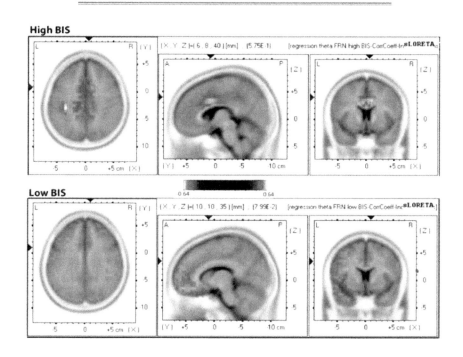

Figure 40. Correlation between high resting theta and FRN (associated with punishment sensitivity), which is found only in high BIS (behavioral inhibition system) subjects (Massar, 2012).

A normal dopaminergic activity in the reward circuit transfers error information to the dorsal anterior cingulate, causing its neurons to fire (disinhibition) whenever the outcome is worse than expected. A low dopaminergic activity in the reward circuit (as in ADHD) results in suboptimal error-feedback signaling, resulting in high resting theta and a low FRN (leading to high-risk taking). The FRN is thought to reflect activation of a reinforcement learning system that rapidly evaluates outcomes of decisions to guide reward-seeking behavior. The difference between expectations and actual outcome are encoded as a reward prediction error, which is used by the dorsal anterior cingulate to improve performance. The reward prediction error is reflecting a phasic dip in ventral tegmentum dopaminergic activity. ERN/FRN is the result of disinhibition of the dorsal anterior cingulate by dopaminergic neurons signaling events, which is worse than anticipated. Therefore, error signals are important for learning because they are used to predict future rewards and non-rewards and to modify ongoing behavior. FRN activity might represent just one-step in the decision making process. FRN may be a fast motivational or affective reaction to the reward prediction error. The further decision process might depend on cognitive control mechanisms related to beta activity, probably in the anterior cingulate and the dorsolateral prefrontal cortex.

The high theta activity in the dorsal anterior cingulate at rest might restrict phasic disinhibitory firing of the dorsal anterior cingulate in reaction to feedback information after error signals, while the phasic ventral tegmentum dopaminergic dip is less on the background of less tonic dopaminergic activity. In ADHD, the FRN is lower (Hauser, 2014), and impaired decision-making and learning mechanisms are driven by impaired reward prediction error processing in the dorsal anterior cingulate.

In the real world, we use our brains to learn about the ever-changing world to predict and thus modulate what will happen to us in both the short-term and the long-term. This learning process is superior to simplistic reinforcement learning models because the environment, and together with it the beliefs of the subjects, are changing much of the time. Flexible switching between exploratory (dorsolateral prefrontal cortex) and exploitation (medial orbitofrontal cortex) strategies is needed. A probabilistic learning reversal task is used to understand how the brain is handling such complex situations (Hauser, 2014). ADHD adolescents are using less differentiated, more simplistic learning patterns not sensitive to subtle changes in reward contingencies, such as changes in environmental volatility or their current beliefs, resulting in suboptimal decisions. They exploit the best option less frequently according to their current beliefs, although they behave in an exploratory way (not able to adjust it adequately) and examine the alternative option more frequently. fMRI, during such a probabilistic learning reversal task, localizes the decision making processes in the ventromedial prefrontal (orbitofrontal) cortex, the subgenual anterior cingulate, ventral striatum and posterior cingulate cortex, especially if one has to choose between several options and learn from errors. In ADHD, this activity is clearly less pronounced. The orbitofrontal cortex plays a role in decision making when there is uncertainty and value attribution when selecting between different response options. The posterior cingulate is the highest in hierarchy to change policy options.

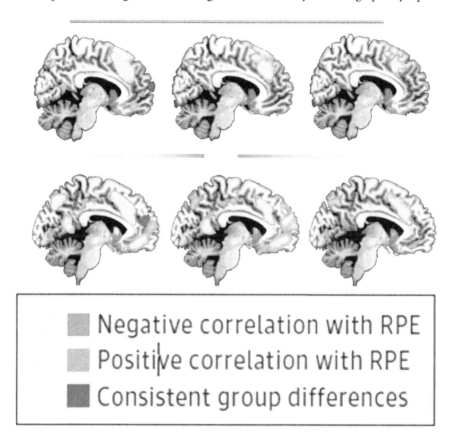

Figure 41. Correlations between reward prediction error (FRN) and fMRI BOLD signal activity: left in all, middle in control group, right in ADHD group (Hauser, 2014).

In a next study using effective connectivity measures (dynamic causing modeling, Friston, 2003), Hauser (2015) found that the FRN source region most probably receives direct reward prediction error inputs rather than signals, which are first processed in other areas of the reward prediction error network. The dACC is densely connected to areas, which process reward prediction errors, such as DLPFC, VMPFC, the amygdalae, and striatum. These findings are in line with the recent theory suggesting that dopaminergic neurons also encode reward prediction error-like salience signals, which are most probably also projected to the dACC.

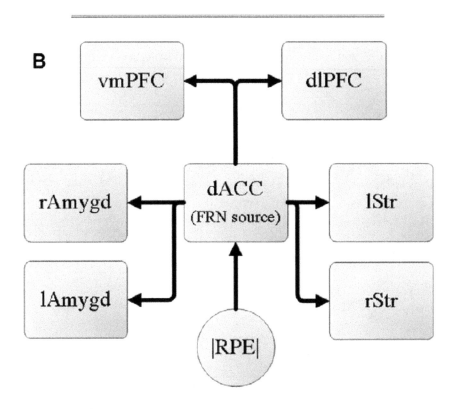

Figure 42. Reward prediction error network (Hauser, 2015).

Goal-directed decisions have their basis in a value signal encoded in the ventrome-dial prefrontal cortex (VMPFC). The value signal is the net result computed by weight-ing several behavior options, especially in uncertain situations. The DLPFC influences self-control by modulating the value signal computed in the VMPFC (Hare, 2009). The VMPFC originally evolved to forecast the short-term value of stimuli, and humans developed the ability to incorporate long-term considerations into values by giving struc-tures, such as the DLPFC, the ability to modulate the basic value signal. Hare's results are consistent with previous theories on the role of DLPFC in cognitive control, which posit that it sends signals to other brain regions to promote task-relevant processing and suppress irrelevant activity.

This proposal is consistent with ideas about the role of the VMPFC in actor–critic models of hierarchical reinforcement learning (Holroyd and Yeung, 2011, 2012). According to these theories, the VMPFC, acting in parallel or in series with the ventral striatum, serves as the critic, providing information necessary to compute a 'state value,' which is, in turn, required by downstream areas, such as the midbrain, to calculate reward prediction errors. These errors serve as teaching signals to facilitate the acquisition of rules or policies in other regions - such as the dorsolateral striatum and DLPFC - that drive behavior. This idea of state value is comparable to the outcome expectancies that are signaled by the VMPFC. In the actor-critic model, the actor component (dACC, DLPFC, dorsal striatum) selects and executes behaviors. A critic (VMPFC, ventral striatum) evaluates the appropriateness of those actions. The excitatory effect of the dACC option selection on DLFC policy implementation provides an important route by which the dACC can be said to energize or motivate behavior. The critic route (VMPFC) receives information about and assigns value to options received as 'efference copy' from the dACC. An efference copy of selected actions elicits value signals in the VMPFC that are broadcasted via the ventral tegmentum area dopamine system to facilitate option selection by the dACC and policy implementation by the DLPFC and dorsolateral striatum.

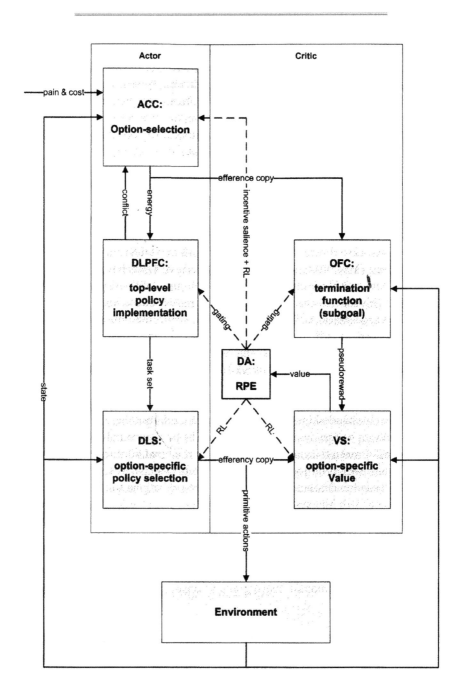

Figure 43. The Actor-Critic Hierarchical Reinforcement Learning Model (Holroyd and Yeung, 2011).

Reinforcement learning algorithms provide a simple but powerful framework for understanding how agents learn to behave in complex and uncertain environments. Standard reinforcement learning approaches find an intuitive and influential implementation in actor–critic architectures, which propose a division of labor between two components of the learning system, an actor that selects actions according to their weighted associations with the current state of the world (termed a policy) and a critic that generates an estimate of the long-term reward associated with each world state (termed a value function). The policy of the actor and the value function of the critic are both learned through experience, specifically through computation by the critic of a reward prediction error that indicates whether ongoing events are better or worse than expected. However, standard reinforcement learning algorithms become increasingly inefficient, as the world becomes more complex in terms of the number of possible states and available actions. The resulting combinatorial explosion renders standard reinforcement learning infeasible in even moderately complex tasks. Hierarchical reinforcement learning algorithms attempt to address this scaling problem by grouping together interrelated states and actions (policies) to form higher-level behavioral plans – termed options – that comprise structured sequences of actions directed towards specified subgoals. Options can be considered as coherent, temporally extended steps towards the overall goal, reducing the complexity of the learning task. Importantly, learning occurs via straightforward extensions of standard reinforcement learning, where options that lead to better-than-expected outcomes are reinforced, whereas successful completion of a chosen option serves as a pseudoreward that reinforces preceding lower-level actions according to the same reinforcement learning principles. In effect, the learning task is solved simultaneously at different levels of abstraction, identifying both low-level actions and high-level options that most efficiently achieve their respective goals. The increased computational efficiency of hierarchical reinforcement learning results from the ability to learn and organize sequences of behavior at the option level rather than at the level of primitive actions. Specifically, Holroyd and Yeung proposed that dACC selects and maintains options, that dorsolateral prefrontal cortex (DLPFC) and motor structures in the dorsal striatum (which together comprise the actor) execute those options, and that orbitofrontal cortex and the ventral striatum (which together comprise the critic) evaluate progress toward the goal states of the options.

3.8.3 CNV (Contingent Negative Variation)

Another important cognitive brain potential is the 'contingent negative variation' (CNV), which is a slow, electrically negative wave maximally measurable at the vertex (Cz) that follows a stimulus warning and precedes a target stimulus. Then, in 2 to 5 seconds, a second command stimulus will occur. At that point, participants must press a button. CNV amplitude is correlated with BOLD activation of a thalamo-corticostriatal network, including the middle frontal gyrus, superior frontal gyrus, superior parietal lobule, pre-SMA, ACC, thalamus, and basal ganglia (Fan, 2007). Studies have suggested that the ACC, superior frontal cortex, and cortical regions along the intraparietal sulcus are involved in cued task-set implementation and in holding information on-line during response anticipation. In addition, prefrontal and parietal regions are involved in sustaining attention during response anticipation. The ACC, along with the prefrontal cortex and basal ganglia, which are interconnected in corticobasal ganglionic loops, have been implicated in volitional action.

Reduced CNV amplitude has been reported in ADHD subjects in several experimental designs (Banaschewski, 2003, 2008; Barry, 2009; Broyd, 2005). These findings are frequently interpreted as consistent with impaired resource allocation to attentional orienting cues in subjects with ADHD and often persist into adulthood (McLoughlin, 2010). This electrophysiological index predicts the behavioral performance of ADHD or non-ADHD child. The reduced amplitude of CNV in ADHD seems consistent with ADHD deficits in executive function. This component shows reliable differences between children and young adults (Flores, 2009). Thus, the reduction in CNV amplitude observed in ADHD children could result from the documented delay in regional cortical maturation that affects most prominently the prefrontal regions in this developmental disorder (Shaw, 2007). Similarly, the frontoparietal networks related to attention and working memory have also been described as the main contributors to the CNV component (Gomez, 2007). Nevertheless, a delay in maturation of frontal structures has an alternative explanation. Reduced CNV amplitudes could also be interpreted as evidence of a deficiency in energy pools, pointing specifically to reduced effort to meet task demands (Benikos and Johnstone, 2009). Again, a deficit in inhibition of the default mode network during the expectancy period might also underlie a reduced CNV and a poorer performance (Aboitiz and Castellanos, 2011; Sonuga-Barke and Castellanos, 2007). In either case, smaller CNV amplitudes have been consistently reported in ADHD children and adults (Banaschewski, 2008; Doehnert, 2010; McLoughlin, 2010; Valko, 2009).

The PINV (postimperative negative variation) component, as the ERN, is an important marker of movement/action monitoring processes, representing the individual's uncertainty about the correctness of a given answer. Especially schizophrenic and depressive individuals show elevated PINV amplitudes, representing the uncertainty about the appropriate response. PINV amplitude is sensitive to ambiguous contingencies and is thought to reflect an unexpected outcome, which causes performance uncertainty. PINV usually shows a prefrontal maximum; therefore, generators in the prefrontal cortex have been postulated. An increased PINV was found in a group of 18 ADHD (combined type) children (Werner, 2011). Children with ADHD are likely to be more uncertain about the correctness of their performance. The increased PINV over the ventrolateral prefrontal cortex can indicate compensatory mechanisms for a deficit in the evaluation of contingencies. After the intake of Ritalin, PINV amplitudes of ADHD children normalized. The increased PINV amplitude over the VLPFC could be interpreted as a compensatory mechanism in the response monitoring process, which is deficient (as marked by a low ERN). Thus, the deficits in error detection could be compensated by increased evaluation processing in other brain areas. As the ACC and the VLPFC represent important parts of a monitoring network responsible for the evaluation of the correctness of a given answer and the impairment of cognitive control in case of failure, the two cortex areas interact dynamically with each other and thus ensure the permanent self-monitoring and adjustment of all target-oriented actions. Particularly the VLPFC is thought to be involved in the processing of negative feedback to correct action with the objective of optimization of performance; it is implicated in contingency detection and in the evaluation of stimuli. An overall right-sided preponderance of PINV has been found also in previous studies and points towards a preferential involvement of the right hemisphere in contingency evaluation. The increased compensatory efforts for self-monitoring and contingency detection, represented by the enhanced PINV amplitude, may contribute to ADHD children's inability to concentrate on relevant stimuli in their environment.

Like the ERN and CRN, the PINV has a fronto-central maximum and may be associated with regions, such as the ACC and dorsolateral prefrontal cortex (DLPFC), which are implicated in ERN and CRN modulation. Uncertainty about the appropriateness of a response may increase ERN and CRN amplitude by mechanisms similar to those by which it increases PINV amplitude. In cases of loss of control, the PINV is a marker of restitution of control resulting in reduction of response-outcome uncertainty (Diener, 2010). Under conditions of response ineffectiveness or ambiguity, the PINV subsequent to the motor response shows enhanced negativity. Elbert (1982) proposed that the PINV indicates a reappraisal mechanism for stored contingencies whenever learned response-outcome contingencies contradict current observations. PINV is considered as an index of response-outcome ambiguity processing. In forewarned S1–S2 paradigms, enhanced PINV magnitudes have consistently been found over frontal and fronto-central recording sites during an unexpected change from control to uncontrollability and during ambiguous response-outcome relations in general.

Healthy adults were instructed to respond to S2 onset by pressing the correct (left vs. right) button in order to avoid aversive 1 ms electrical stimulation to the index finger of the non-dominant hand following termination of the imperative stimulus S2. To permit the assessment of both the effects of loss of control and subsequent regain of control, controllability of the aversive stimulus varied across three successive conditions of 40 trials each. During initial control, the aversive stimulus could be avoided by pressing either the right or the left button (counterbalanced across subjects). In the following condition of loss of control, the response-outcome contingencies were withdrawn without warning, and the subjects randomly received the electrical stimulus in half of the trials. In the third condition, control was re-established, again without warning. The left vs. right button press as effective response was switched between the conditions of controllability and restitution of control.

Several EEG and one imaging study have suggested that prefrontal regions, including the ACC and temporal regions – presumably including limbic structures, such as the hippocampus, the amygdala, and the mammillary bodies – are responsive to loss of control after successful response-outcome contingency learning.

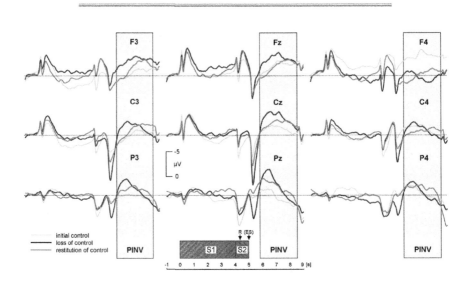

Figure 44. CNV and PINV in 3 conditions. S1: warning stimulus; S2: imperative stimulus; R: reaction (left versus right button press); ES: electrical stimulation (Diener, 2010).

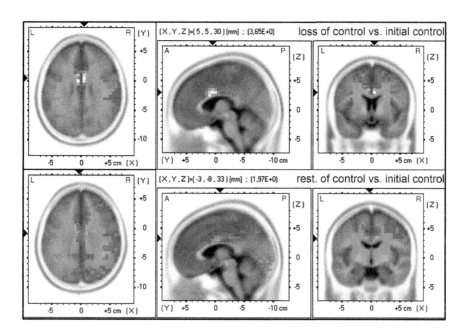

Figure 45. sLORETA visualizes in comparison to initial control, activation in the dorsal anterior cingulate is enhanced during loss of control (Diener, 2010).

Diener's study focused on the cortical generation of the PINV, an index of cognitive processing provoked by changing response-outcome contingencies during instrumental learning. During loss of control, parietal activity was enlarged over the left and right BA 7, and it extended laterally to the left BA 40. Likewise, dispersed activity was found in the left and right medial frontal BA 6. Maximal activity during loss of control emerged in the left middle temporal BA 21 accompanied by substantial activity in the left caudal precentral (BA 6), inferior frontal (BA 45), and rostral frontal cortex (BA 10). During the loss of control, the participants showed enhanced activity in the left VLPFC (BA 45), including BA 10. The VLPFC activation may reflect the detection of the presence or absence of the aversive stimulus during contingency evaluation. This view would be in line with the findings that show the VLPFC to be important for contingency reversal learning. However, the VLPFC is also thought to encode the intensity of emotional responses, and one cannot rule out that aversive stimulation during loss of control induced negative emotions. Enhanced activity both during loss of control and initial control was found in parietal areas (BA7). Parietal activity intensified and extended to BA 40 during loss of control. In the context of motor planning and execution, parietal areas have been discussed as the core regions in the 'top down' processing of attentional control signals. Hence, parietal areas might support attentional mechanisms during response-outcome evaluation, which are especially enhanced during loss of control.

Most remarkably, by contrasting the experimental conditions, Diener found that loss of control over aversive stimulation caused marked activity increases in the ACC (BA 24). In the present study, withdrawal of control induced continuous uncertainty response; therefore, the pattern of ACC activation may correspond to response conflict detection, as proposed by recent theories of ACC function. As the ACC is thought to detect conflicts between plans of action and consecutively recruit cognitive control in lateral prefrontal structures (predominantly including the DLPFC), activation in the rostral and VLPFC found during loss of control is likely to reflect neuronal effort to resolve response conflict.

Summary

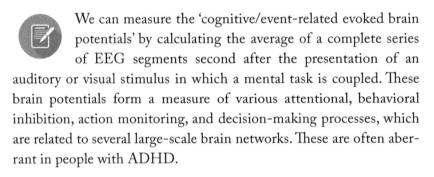
We can measure the 'cognitive/event-related evoked brain potentials' by calculating the average of a complete series of EEG segments second after the presentation of an auditory or visual stimulus in which a mental task is coupled. These brain potentials form a measure of various attentional, behavioral inhibition, action monitoring, and decision-making processes, which are related to several large-scale brain networks. These are often aberrant in people with ADHD.

CHAPTER 4
Self-Regulation, Executive Functions Embedded in Motivation, and Their Dysregulation in ADHD

4.1 Error-Related Negativity as a Window for Conflict/Action Monitoring and Reinforcement Learning

RESEARCH ON THE Error Related Negativity (ERN) provides a clearer understanding of how frontal executive functions are intertwined with emotional and motivational processes in the limbic system. Although it has long been known that important pathways exist between the frontal regions and the limbic structures (Nauta, 1971), research that is more recent delivers fresh insight into the mechanisms of self-regulation of executive functions, such as monitoring and planning.

An exhilarating development in contemporary EEG research is that it illuminates the way in which motivational and emotional processes are interwoven with the executive functions and explains the self-regulatory processes. This research provides answers to a quintessential question: What underlies the adaptive, motivational control of cognition? Whilst emotion and self-regulation are now popular research topics in cognitive neuroscience, concepts of motivational control are poorly developed within the theoretical framework of cognitive science. Behavioral theories of learning hit their peak in the 1940-1950 period. Subsequently, cognitive psychology rejected this behavioral dogma and, based on a model of computers, described cognitive processes, such as observation, attention, and memory, as objective, as definable information processing tasks. Consequently, behavioral fields of study, such as motivation, rewards, and learning, lost in popularity.

Remarkably, cognitive models of self-regulation and feedback control developed out of computer science inspired by Wiener's (1948) cybernetics (literally meaning: the science of control) research. It is even more remarkable that Wiener was inspired directly by Canon's studies (1915) of physiological homeostasis that investigated changes in physiological standard (or baseline) values ('set points,' such as body temperature, acid base balance, and oxygen concentration), which lead to adaptive regulation mechanisms. The word 'homeostasis' means 'the same state' and describes stabilization of internal states. Pribram (1960) was the first to apply cybernetic ideas of homeostasis to human planning and self-regulation, shortly followed by Nauta (1971). In Pribram's model, various motivational conditions replace homeostatic set points.

The concepts of behavioral control and executive functions have been described in classical cognitive psychology without clear distinctions, so that the two constructs are entwined. In this tradition, executive functions are described as high-level processes that exercise cognitive control over more elementary mental operations. A supervisory attentional system was introduced to bind behavior in situations where routine responses are inadequate (Norman, 1986). The cognitive psychological model of executive functions runs the risk of being confused with an external agent rather than being understood as an integral part of bodily, self-regulatory functions. Moreover, these cognitive models of executive functions are inappropriately invoked to explain how dysfunctions in executive functions can cause psychopathologies of mood, motivation, and attention (such as ADHD). Rather, these pathologies suggest fundamental changes in the internal goals and regulatory set points that guide self-control rather than a problem with a remote supervisory source.

The study of ERN allows for the monitoring of actions as an elementary component of executive functions to be examined in the wider context of action regulation. Behavior is evaluated in the context of expectations (proposed to be a context for actions). Electrophysiological responses are frequently observed when the execution of actions fall short of expectations: an ERN emerges when actual actions are discrepant with planned action goals. McEwen (2000) argued that because the ERN and related mediofrontal negative brain potentials seem to reflect various regulatory points, they may be important set points in frontal and limbic mechanisms for various homeostatic and allostatic processes.

Action monitoring is a crucial executive function that by definition monitors the divergence between expectations and outcomes. The measurement of the ERN provides a window into this process of 'fault detection'. Everyone makes mistakes, especially if we work quickly - we push the wrong button or almost knock something flying. It is astonishing that this 'Oops' reaction has a distinctive pattern of brain activity: the ERN. The most popular research paradigm employs the following methodology:

> *The participant sits at a computer screen and must respond using one of two buttons: one on the left and one on the right. A series of five letters like HHHHH, SSHSS, SSSSS, or HHSHH appears on the screen. The participant must react to the middle*

letter in each five-letter group as quickly as possible with a left push for an H and a right push for an S. This is known as the 'flanker task' in which the outlying letters are both identical to the middle letter and helpful or not helpful to the task. The 'incongruent' flanker letters more often lead to a wrong button push. The averaged EEG potentials from correct and incorrect responses are calculated separately. The resulting difference curve gives the best image of the ERN.

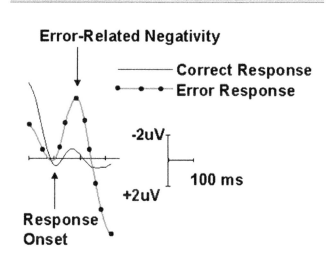

Figure 46. Error-Related Negativity.

The error related brain activity appears 50-100ms after the button push ('response onset'). That is quite fast. We 'know' that we are making a mistake just before the erroneous response movement is made (the brain has already registered: it is a preconscious response). The error related brain activity is evoked in the anterior cingulate, which forms a part of a control network that includes the prefrontal cortex, the basal ganglia, and the limbic areas. The anterior cingulate has been described as an 'interface' and relay station among cognition, motor control, motivation, and arousal of activation state (Paus, 2001). Using alcohol or sedatives, such as lorazepam (brand name Temesta), leads to a smaller ERN, whereas dextroamphetamine creates a larger ERN. In people with ADHD, a decreased ERN is observed while in those with obsessive-compulsive disorder (OCD), an increased ERN is noted, mirroring overactive action evaluations (Fitzgerald; 2005; Hajcak, 2002; Hehring, 2000; Johannes, 2001). OCD is not only a disorder of action monitoring, but also one of 'evaluation.' Although the affective evaluation of the ERN is a relatively new development (Luu, 2004), it can be a useful alternative to error detection and conflict monitoring. In Luu's model, functional affective control via the anterior cingulate is central to self-regulation.

ERN research techniques allow the examination of conscious 'executive attention' (Posner, 1994) that develops out of elementary and frequently conscious corticolimbic processes, and it is associated with activity in the dorsal region of the anterior cingulate. Recently, fMRI research has found that the anterior cingulate is linked to certain limbic areas and plays a role in the evaluation (or more precisely detection) of when cognitive control is required while the dorsolateral prefrontal cortex (DLPFC) is involved in the strategic control of task performance (MacDonald, 2000). The anterior cingulate plays a part in the representation of adaptive goals, such as motivationally or emotionally important 'set points.' In fact, Luu's model (2004) treats motivational processes as an integral part of every behavior, from controlling simple actions to the most complex forms of executive self-regulation. The anterior cingulate's ability to identify appropriate actions in a given motivational context is emphasized, as it monitors the action outcome and switches to another series of actions when that outcome falls short of the desired goal. In this theoretical framework, the anterior cingulate is a part of a circuit with the amygdala. This circuit reflects the encephalization of the homeostatic motivation system from the mesencephalon (midbrain) in the brain stem and the hypothalamus in the diencephalon (the brain between mesencephalon and telencephalon). Encephalization permits greater behavioral complexity in the form of complex representations of motivational goals that can be consolidated in memory and used to guide action planning.

This discovery of higher levels of integration allows us to form global concepts about the integration of mental levels (Ey, 1952). Chapter 3 explores and brings into perspective their reflection in the global EEG pattern (Bente, 1964). This perspective allows us to understand that sleep deprivation leads to an erratic EEG due to a lower degree of integration of mental processing and lowered activity in the frontal cortex. Sleep deprivation also results in a lower ERN (Tsai, 2005). In this way, ADHD can be better understood by linking an unstable EEG, a lowered ERN, problems with executive functions and with motivational processes, and fMRI data that shows lowered activity in frontal areas, such as the anterior cingulate, during certain neuropsychological tasks. In this way, it helps to understand how successful neurofeedback training can normalize this lowered frontal activity in the EEG (Beauregard, 2006).

According to Luu (2004), fault detector and conflict monitoring theories are too narrow because they do not take into account the ways in which motivation, goals, and context contribute to adaptive adjustment of behavior. Set points can form motivational expectations. Brains of humans and those of higher vertebrates are not simply passive generators of reflexes, but also continuous predictors that guide interactions with their environment. Luu argued that cognitive neurosciences could do more than chart isolated mental operations because they can address the self-regulation of the whole organism.

The ERN amplitude in ADHD increased after Ritalin but also after the subject received rewards for not making errors or penalties for making errors (Groom, 2013): motivation improves adaptive adjustment of behavior. A similar amplitude increase has been shown for the oddball P300 when given a reward as well as higher default mode network deactivation during the go/no-go task (Liddle, 2011). These findings are in line with the triple core network model for ADHD (Chen, 2015).

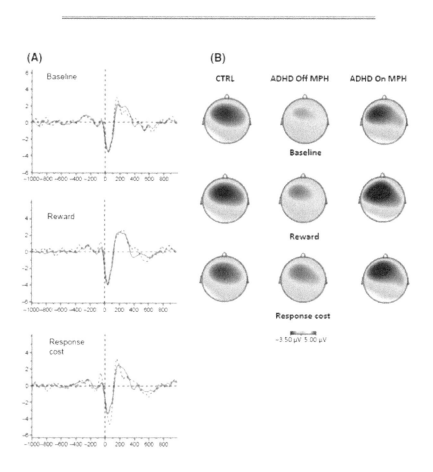

Figure 47. ERN amplitude increase in ADHD when given rewards for not making errors or when given penalties (response cost) for making errors (Groom, 2013).

Holroyd (2002) described that the ERN represents not only conflict and action monitoring, but also reinforcement learning (learning from errors). When humans com-mit errors in reaction time tasks, the mesencephalic dopamine system (which is related to reinforcement learning) conveys a negative reinforcement learning signal to the frontal cortex, where it generates the ERN. It reflects a phasic decrease in dopamine (reward prediction error) when the system detects that ongoing events are worse than expected. Since then, it was emphasized that reinforcement learning is not occurring so much by rewards, but by reward prediction errors. People are learning more from errors. In ADHD, ERN is weaker, implying a less pronounced phasic decrease in dopamine.

Later, Holroyd and Yeung (2012) reconciled the views of the role of the dorsal anterior cingulate in motivation and its contribution to cognitive control and reinforcement learning by developing a model of hierarchic reinforcement learning. In this model, the dorsal anterior cingulate supports the selection and maintenance of 'options' (high level behavior plans: extended, context-specific sequences of behavior directed toward particular goals) that are learned through a process of hierarchic reinforcement learning. This view holds that the dorsal anterior cingulate integrates rewards and punishments across time to learn not whether individual actions are worth performing, but rather whether the task itself is worth carrying out, thus motivating subjects to engage in and complete a task. An option selected by the dorsal anterior cingulate is executed by the dorsolateral prefrontal cortex and dorsal striatum ('the actor'). In a parallel way, the orbitofrontal cortex and ventral striatum ('the critic') determine whether the individual actions are consistent with the goal.

4.2 Delay Aversion and Motivation Deficits in ADHD

The ability to learn contingencies between actions and outcomes in a dynamic environment is critical for flexible, adaptive behavior. Goal-directed actions adapt to changes in action-outcome contingencies as well as to changes in the reward-value of the outcome. When networks involved in reward processing and contingency learning are maladaptive, this fundamental ability can be lost, with negative consequences for decision-making. ADHD is characterized by symptoms of inattention, hyperactivity, and impulsivity, consistent with dysregulation of top-down control processes modulating goal-directed control. A number of researchers have argued that ADHD is a motivational problem, whereby individuals are unable to use intrinsic motivation to guide choice performance (Douglas, 1989; Sergeant, 2000). This is supported by evidence that children with ADHD perform well on continuous reinforcement schedules, whereas their performance deteriorates on partial reinforcement schedules where the consistent extrinsic motivation of reward is not provided (Luman, 2008; Parry and Douglas, 1983).

An altered response to reinforcement has been demonstrated in children with ADHD and has been proposed as a mechanism underlying particular symptoms of ADHD by several authors (Sagvolden, 2005; Sonuga-Barke, 2003; Tripp and Wickens, 2008). Historically, children with ADHD have been described as less able to delay gratification and as failing to respond to discipline (Haenlein and Caul, 1987; Wender, 1971, 1972, 1974). Like executive function deficits, altered reinforcement mechanisms are not specific to ADHD and need not be present in all cases. They may, however, explain a number of ADHD symptoms. Dopamine cell firing activity is normally associated with reinforcing events and with the transfers of established rewards to reward predicting cues at earlier time-points in the behavioral sequence, as reinforcement becomes more predictable (Schultz, 2007). Thus, the repeated experience of a cue followed by a reinforcer leads to a transfer of dopamine cell responses from established reinforcers (e.g., praise or attention to earlier cues in the behavioral sequence that predict the later delivery of reinforcement). When this process occurs normally, it provides a mechanism to ensure that the timing of the dopamine signal at the cellular level is immediate and continuous even when behavioral reinforcement is delayed or discontinuous. This immediate and continuous dopamine signal ensures that even in a natural environment in which reinforcers fluctuate according to the circumstances, the cellular mechanism is able to engage effectively and maintain reinforced behavior.

Tripp and Wickens (2009, 2012) discussed the ways in which a failure of this transfer to reward predicting cues may give rise to many symptoms of ADHD, and they proposed that Ritalin might compensate for the proposed dopamine transfer deficit. In particular, they assumed that the phasic dopamine cell response to cues that predict reinforcement is reduced in amplitude to the point of being ineffective (i.e., the mechanism that normally comes to excite the dopamine cells in response to cues that repeatedly and persistently precede reinforcement fails).

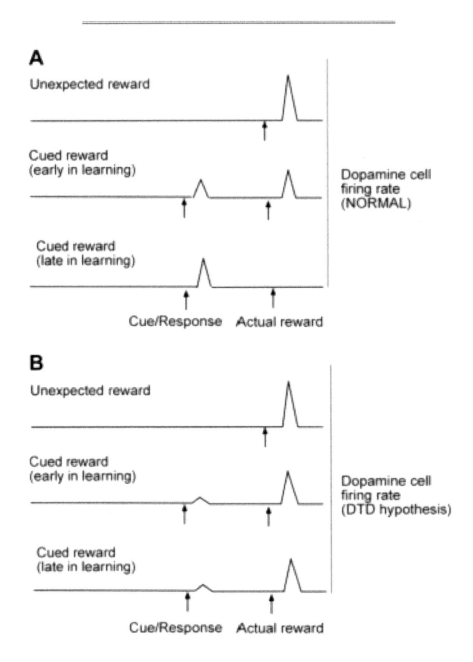

Figure 48. Transfer of dopamine cell signaling to predictive cues and behaviors.
A. Normal transfer of dopamine cell firing. Unexpected reward is a potent stimulus for dopamine
cell firing activity. Early in learning, dopamine cell firing responses transfer to cues that predict
later reinforcers. They may also transfer to responses, which can act as cues that predict reinforcers.
Later in learning, responses to cues may dominate the responses to actual reinforcers. B. Dopamine

cell firing in dopamine transfer deficit (DTD) hypothesis. There is a failure of the dopamine cell firing to transfer to earlier cues that predict positive reinforcers (Tripps and Wickens, 2009).

Altered dopamine receptor function, a consequence of genetic polymorphisms in these molecular mechanisms, could disrupt the transfer process. Other possibilities to explain the dopamine transfer deficit also exist, such as abnormalities in the systems that are afferent to the dopamine cells, which may include prefrontal cortical mechanisms. Winstanley (2004) argued that the medial orbitofrontal cortex (OFC) is involved in revising the representation of the incentive value of a response, as the outcome associated with that response changes. It is important to note that BOLD activation during evaluation has been reported within both the lateral and medial portions of the OFC. There is, however, evidence for cytoarchitectural and functional heterogeneity within the OFC (Carmichael and Price, 1995; Elliott., 2000; Kahnt, 2012), suggesting that studies using reward-predictive cues are utilizing alternate or additional learning processes. Though there is still considerable debate on this topic, a converging view is that the medial OFC, together with the basolateral amygdala, is involved in updating the expected values of different experienced outcomes, whereas the lateral OFC is responsible for the formation and updating of values derived from the Pavlovian stimulus-outcome associations. The value of an action is a product of its contingency with a particular outcome and the desirability of that outcome. Studies using trial-and-error action-based learning tasks have reported action value-related signals in the supplementary motor area, where actions are presumably planned before the execution. In contrast, BOLD activity in the medial OFC is modulated by the expected reward signal of the chosen action, suggesting that this region provides the agents with feedback about the consequences of their actions to guide future choices (Gläscher, 2009; Wunderlich, 2009; FitzGerald, 2012; Hunt, 2013). Camille (2011) found that humans with dorsal anterior cingulate cortex (dACC) damage were unable to consistently make the correct choice between actions after positive feedback, suggesting that this region is critically involved in updating action values, perhaps passing feedback from the medial OFC to the action planning areas in the supplementary motor areas via the anterior caudate nucleus.

Top-down cognitive control exerted by such structures as the DLPFC and dACC may also modulate the integration of value and contingency and its conversion into performance. Kim and Shadlen (1999) and Wallis and Miller (2003) found DLPFC neurons that encoded both reward value and the forthcoming response, whereas Kim (2008) found neurons that ramped up or down in their firing rate with increasing or decreasing action values until a choice was made. In the ACC, neural signals resembling the difference between action values or a combination of movement intention and reward expectation have been reported (Matsumoto, 2007; Seo and Lee, 2007; Wunderlich, 2009).

A study using fMRI in human adolescents with ADHD demonstrated reduced activation of the ventral striatum in reward anticipation relative to controls (Scheres, 2007). In a different study, Plichta (2009) compared brain activation in adult patients with ADHD and healthy control subjects during a series of choices between two monetary reward options that varied by delay to delivery. Reduced responsiveness of the ventral striatum to rewards was seen in ADHD patients. In a study of adults with ADHD, a monetary incentive delay task decreased activation in the ventral striatum in anticipation gain (Strohle, 2008). A recent review by Plichta and Scheres (2014) summarized consistent evidence from functional imaging studies on reward anticipation in ADHD, indicating that particularly the ventral striatum shows lower activation during reward anticipation in ADHD compared to controls, which may be related to hyperactive-impulsive symptom severity rather than inattention. Wilbertz (2012) found increased OFC activation during outcome delivery consistent with increased excitation to reward.

Balancing behaviors that provide a reward NOW versus behaviors that provide an advantage LATER are critical for survival. Volkow (2015) proposed a model in which dopamine can favor NOW processes through phasic signaling in reward (salience) circuits or LATER processes through tonic signaling in control circuits. At the same time, through its modulation of the orbitofrontal cortex, which processes salience attribution, dopamine also enables shifting from NOW to LATER while its modulation of the insula, which processes interoceptive information, influences the probability of selecting NOW vs LATER actions based on an individual's physiological state.

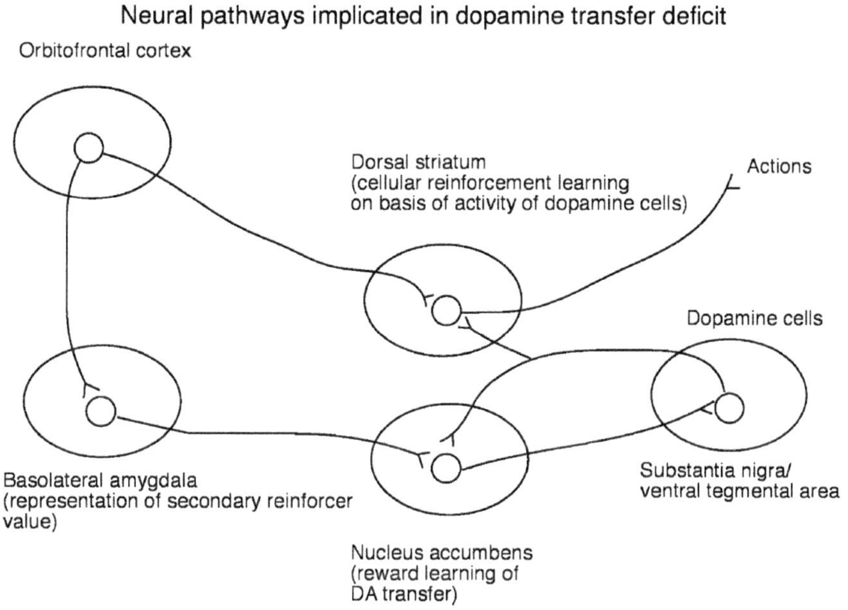

Neural pathways implicated in dopamine transfer deficit

Orbitofrontal cortex

Dorsal striatum
(cellular reinforcement learning
on basis of activity of dopamine cells)

Actions

Dopamine cells

Basolateral amygdala
(representation of secondary reinforcer
value)

Substantia nigra/
ventral tegmental area

Nucleus accumbens
(reward learning of
DA transfer)

Figure 49. Neural pathways implicated in anticipation of reinforcement. Schematic diagram indicating connections important in transferring dopamine cell firing response to predictive cues and reinforcement learning based on the dopamine cell activity. Not only the OFC, but also the DLPFC (not included in this scheme) has a top-down influence on the nucleus accumbens (ventral striatum) (Tripps and Wickens, 2008).

It has been demonstrated that Ritalin increases tonic as well as phasic dopamine availability in the synaptic cleft in ventral striatum and caudate. In the context of the dopamine transfer deficit theory, Ritalin facilitates the response to predictive cues, suggesting a possible basis for its therapeutic effects in children with ADHD. Specifically, Ritalin should reduce the effect of delay of reinforcement by amplifying the effects of 'bridging' cues.

Summary

Internal control circuits in the brain determine what information is processed, taking into account intention, motivation, and experiences. Following an orientation response, the executive functions of the frontal cerebral cortex direct selective attention and suppress certain responses in the context of wider evaluative functions. At the same time, meaningful stimuli are evaluated automatically and consequently, the behavioral response is further refined by the executive functions (i.e., working memory plus planning and sense of time), regulation of emotion, and activation state.

After sleep deprivation, all of these cognitive functions are poorly regulated in typical individuals and show some similarities to the regulation of these functions in ADHD. More recent theoretical concepts have emphasized the role of self-regulation in the context of variable homeostasis in which motivational factors determine the degree of variability of regulatory set points. The frontal executive functions in this approach are thought to be entwined with emotional and motivational processes, and higher executive functions can be seen in terms of a complex development of motivational processes in action regulation that produces adaptive behavior. In ADHD, these processes, and so also adaptive behavior, are constrained to a certain degree.

ADHD symptoms are consistent with dysregulation of top-down control processes modulating goal-directed control. The dopamine transfer deficit theory proposes that in ADHD, there is no transfer from established reinforcers to cues at earlier time-points in the behavioral sequence. Contingency learning processes are thought to occur in the medial OFC, and they are relayed to the anterior caudate to mediate control of action selection. Reward information is also relayed to the ventral striatum to provide motivational drive for the performance of instrumental behaviors. The DLPFC and dorsal anterior cingulate cortex (dACC) play a role in comparing action values, and they can exert a modulatory influence over circuits involving prefrontal and anterior caudate activity. Together, the contingency and evaluative circuits allow for the acquisition of goal-directed behaviors. The lateral OFC and the basolateral amygdala encode the value assigned to reward predictive stimuli, which the ventral striatum uses to mediate instrumental performance. In ADHD, these systems are malfunctioning, which could explain the dopamine transfer deficit that is hypothesized to explain delay aversion in ADHD.

CHAPTER 5
Dynamic Metastable Organization of Vigilance in EEG

5.1 'Cyclic Alternating Patterns' and Alpha Fluctuations

I N 1964, THE Berlin psychiatrist Bente developed a dynamic psychiatric model of the EEG in which the concept of vigilance formed an integral part. The stringent definition, which defined vigilance as the quality and degree of an individual's adaptive interaction with the environment, formed by the London neurologist Head in 1923 stimulated this work. Bente was additionally inspired by a model of sleep deprivation, which he developed based on his inspiration by the French psychiatrist Ey, to understand mental disintegration states. Bente applied both these concepts to build an understanding of EEG, and described vigilance as a function of the dynamic state of the central nervous system, as mirrored in EEG. Later, Ulrich (1994, 2013) further developed the model.

Predominantly an alpha rhythm in posterior areas with fluctuating spindle formation characterizes an optimal EEG during the waking state with eyes closed. This is observed in about 80% of healthy subjects, while an EEG dominated by beta is obtained in 5-10% of subjects, and an EEG with very low voltage is observed in 4-9% of subjects (Gallinat, 1988). During the transition to sleep, alpha activity frequently takes hold first, as this activity is more monomorphic (shows less fluctuation). Often, the anterior amplitude is greater on the left than on the right (A-state). A state with predominately beta-2 activity (20-30 Hz), which may or may not mix with theta activity (B-state), follows. Bente took sleep deprivation states as a model. Bente and Ulrich noticed types A and B EEG in psychiatric patients during wakefulness, just as in healthy sleep deprived subjects. Type A indicates a 'rigid' vigilance, type B a 'labile' form. The B type is seen most often in people with ADHD, however, a minority exhibits the A type. The B type with too few sleep spindles during sleep and SMR rhythms during wakefulness also typified Sterman's epilepsy patients. The sleep spindles have a vigilance-stabilizing influence on sleep states, specifically, when they are deficient (as it is often the case in ADHD), sleep states are fragmented.

The classic spectrum analysis of the EEG (using Fast Fourier transform) gives the averaged EEG spectrum over a specific period. This method views the EEG as a super-position of sinusoidal frequencies, as if it were a stable state. In reality, neural networks cause spontaneous cyclic changes in EEG that are lost in classical statistical frequency analysis. The sleep spindles produced cyclically in sleep provide an example. A traditional spectrum analysis certainly indicates the absolute quantity of sleep spindles, but yields no information about their periodicity (the average time between occurrences). Periodicities make a major contribution to the organization of the EEG, and traditional statistical frequency analyses cannot fully quantify them. Evans (1993) found an inverse proportional relationship between manifestations of sleep spindles in a sleep EEG and 'cyclic alternating patterns' (CAP), as described by Terzano (1988). These recurring sequences are 3 to 7 minutes long and comprise periods lasting on average 40 (range 2-60) seconds. If the complete sequence is described as a CAP, the interval between two periods cannot exceed a minute. Each CAP period is characterized by a shorter phase A and a longer phase B. Phase A is a short (2-60 s) phasic EEG paroxysm, an EEG phenomenon that contrasts sharply with the background activity of the EEG. It is followed by a longer lasting deactivated interval (phase B). A normal quantity indicates sleep phase stability, but a heightened quantity is the expression of vigilance instability: in the latter case, they occur especially just before or after a sleep phase transition. The CAPs are also associated with adaptive dynamic responses to environmental conditions. If there are not too many external disturbances, they guarantee sleep stability in a healthy person while a greater number of external disturbances pave the way to sleep phase transition. Undoubtedly, such external factors can modulate CAPs with a certain endogenous oscillatory rhythm, just as they modulate, on a different time scale, the day-night rhythm and the basic rest activity cycle (BRAC) of our organism.

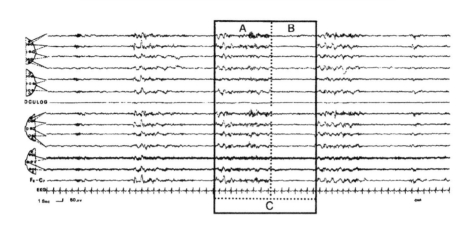

Figure 50. CAP during sleep phase II consists of two phases (A: paroxysmal, B: deactivated phase). Reprinted from Sleep Medicine, 2(6), Terzano et al., Atlas, rules and recording techniques for the scoring of cyclic alternating patterns (CAP) in human sleep, Copyright (2001), with permission from Elsevier.

An alternation of phases A and B is observed during the transition from wakefulness to the first phase of sleep. In sleep phase A, there is a rigid, monomorphic alpha activity. In sleep phase B, a low voltage beta-2 activity eventually mixes with theta activity. Terzano (2001) pointed out that sleep phase A, in terms of reactivity of vigilance, displays similarities with CAP phase A (low reactivity) while sleep phase B has similarities with CAP phase B (induced by external or internal factors induce a phase A reaction). Evans suggested that these alternations in wake-sleep phase transitions are analogous to a CAP. Terzano himself suggested that an intermittent continuous alpha series are analogous to the CAP during waking state. This is in agreement with recent findings (Tirsch, 2000).

The CAP cycle was originally considered an activation phenomenon, but in recent years, no unique relationship has been uncovered in clinical correlations of sleep disorders. Recently, an alternative and more nuanced conceptualization has formed, describing CAPs as a process that encompasses both sleep maintenance and sleep fragmentation. This broader perspective was formed when the paroxysmal A phase of CAP sleep was subdivided into either type A1 or types A2 and A3. The A1 phase type is a paroxysm (upsurge) of synchronous EEG activity, such as delta waves, alpha waves, and K complex (an upsurge of a higher voltage biphasic wave occurring in sleep stage 2, which may or may not be accompanied by a sleep spindle followed by a segment of not less than 20% of desynchronized low voltage activity).

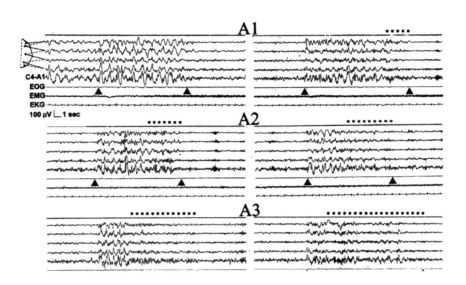

*Figure 51. The three CAP phase A types: the first type (**A1**) is characterized by a short upsurge of synchronized EEG activity and has sleep stabilizing and integrating functions; the two other types (**A2** and **A3**) occur after the upsurge and consist of a segment of desynchronized activity with microarousals. Reprinted from Sleep Medicine, 2(6), Terzano et al., Atlas, rules and recording techniques for the scoring of cyclic alternating patterns (CAP) in human sleep, Copyright (2001), with permission from Elsevier.*

The phase types A2 and A3 are similarly paroxysmal, but they are followed respectively by either 20-50% or by more than 50% of low voltage desynchronized EEG activity (Terzano, 2002).

CAP phase A1 occurs predominantly during light NREM sleep stages 1-2 during the progression towards REM sleep and deep NREM sleep stages 3-4. CAP phases A2-A3 occurs most often during the progression of deep sleep towards phases of lighter NREM sleep stages 1-2. In physiologically healthy states, sleep stabilizing subtype A1 prevails. The distribution of subtypes is associated with definite strategic functions, and it is certainly not based on chance, as evidenced by the role they play in the synchronization or resynchronization of the EEG.

CAP phase A1 (paroxysmal high voltage synchronization, such as delta waves, alpha waves, or a K complex with or without a sleep spindle) is an expression of the effort made by the brain to maintain light sleep despite the presence of internal or external stimuli. In this case, discrete destabilization accompanies a gradual increase in arousal;

thus, increasing stabilization and consequently sleep maintenance. Bizarrely, the light instability of sleep stage 1-2 guarantees sleep maintenance. If this effort fails, because too few CAP phase types A1 are produced, real arousal occurs in the form of CAP phase types A2-A3 (paroxysmal low voltage desynchronization).

CAP phase type A1 is therefore a sleep stabilization phenomenon, which currently considers K complexes followed by sleep spindles as a subtype of sleep stabilizing CAP. CAP phase type A1 plays an integrating role in transient large-scale cooperation of multiple brain areas, and it has a similar cortical distribution as sleep spindles and delta waves of slow wave sleep (Ferri, 2005).

CAP phase types A2-A3 are recognized as microarousals and are more frequently observed in epilepsy, periodic muscle twitches of the lower limbs (classically with a periodicity of 2-60 Hz), sleep apnea, and bruxism (teeth grinding), among others. CAPs have a period of 2-60 seconds, within which sleep spindles are about the fastest, with a rhythm of 0.1 to 0.2 Hz.

Miano (2006) found a lowered quantity of CAPs, especially CAP phase type A1, in 20 sleeping children with ADHD (in comparison with a group of 20 children without ADHD). This suggests that during light NREM sleep stages, no discrete increase of arousal occurs in response to internal or external stimuli; therefore, no compensatory sleep maintenance processes are launched to stabilize sleep in the children with ADHD. The same study observed shorter sleep duration and an increased number of sleep phase transitions in the ADHD group. This supports an earlier small-scale sleep study of children with ADHD (Kahn, 1978). However, Prihodova (2012) did not find CAP anomalies in 14 sleeping children with ADHD, but possibly other CAP scoring methods were involved. The CAPs were associated with 'infraslow' EEG rhythms of 0.02 Hz (waves with duration of about 50 seconds), which are an expression of very slow cyclical cortical and subcortical stimulus sensitivity.

Slow waves recruit large neuronal networks that generate functional connectivity between cortical and subcortical structures through rhythmic coupling (Buzsaki, 2004; Vanhatalo, 2004). During sleep, the changing activation/ deactivation of a CAP cycle generates a 'brain beat' that can drive synchronization between neuronal groups; thus, providing for progression between different sleep stages. Further, there are indications that faster EEG rhythms synchronize infraslow EEG rhythms, which are responsible for a slower cyclic modulation of cortical sensitivity. A routine sleep EEG does not measure infraslow EEG rhythms because the apparatus is not calibrated for frequencies lower than 0.5 Hz.

CAP patterns with a frequency of 0.02 Hz are embedded in an even slower cycle within the NREM/REM 90-minute cycle. The 'brain beat' of the sleep stabilizing CAPs, of which the sleep spindles are a special subtype, contributes to the progression of these cycles. CAPs decrease around sleep phase transitions.

Sleep deprivation disrupts the performance of the sleep wake cyclical rhythm, resulting in EEG similar to the EEG of a person with ADHD. On the night following sleep deprivation, fewer sleep spindles and increased sleep fragmentation are present, as in ADHD.

Considering that during the daytime, a 'basic rest activity cycle' with cycle duration of ninety minutes also exists, it is plausible that these same principles apply to wakefulness, in good agreement with Terzano's hypothesis that CAPs in the form of slow cyclic alpha wave fluctuations occur during wakefulness. Tirsch (2000) investigated the cyclic nature of alpha energy fluctuations over the course of at least a minute in order to gain a better understanding of fine structure in the EEG, taking into account the never static nature of EEG. He examined the time course of occipital alpha energy for EEG data from eight healthy adult participants. A sliding window analysis was employed in which the alpha energy of partially overlapping fragments of 2.56 seconds duration was calculated to obtain 230 'windows.' The windows were arranged in a time series and a frequency spectrum was calculated from the resultant time series. An alpha peak occurred on average every 50 (+/-20) seconds, with an average rhythm of 0.02 Hz. It is striking that the duration of this period concurs with the CAP. This dynamic method of spectrum analysis can clearly reveal the cyclic fluctuations that the clinician sometimes suspects in the raw EEG. The relative absence of these fluctuations is often discernable even by inspection of the raw EEG of someone with ADHD, which expresses either a too labile EEG (with too many alpha fluctuations or too little) or sometimes a too rigid EEG (too much alpha activity with too few fluctuations). Systematic fluctuations over the course of 50-60 seconds are of course difficult to detect visually from the raw EEG. Later, Tirsch (2004) demonstrated an inverse relationship between the energy of the alpha fragment and the corresponding nonlinear 'correlation dimension.' The nonlinear correlation dimension of alpha time series in an EEG is a mathematical reconstruction of the extent to which nonlinear correlations occur in the time course of alpha series. A higher nonlinear correlation dimension is an indicator of increased system complexity. Thus, Tirsch established that a high degree of alpha synchronization reflects less complexity in the system. His interpretation was that the brain, with its reactivity to internal or external stimuli, periodically changes its activation state and the degree of 'synergy' between different parallel information processing systems. He assumed that a central pattern generator ('pacemaker,' 'cyclic modulator,' 'self-organized rhythmicity') in the reticular formation of the brain stem or thalamus drives these synchronized cyclic changes in the degree of synchronization.

This makes us think of the sleep spindles and other cyclic alternating patterns in sleep that play a cyclic modulating role, originate in the reticular nucleus of the thalamus, and are themselves modulated by cholinergic reticular formation neurons in the brain stem. The reticular formation is known to play a major role in consciousness and wakefulness.

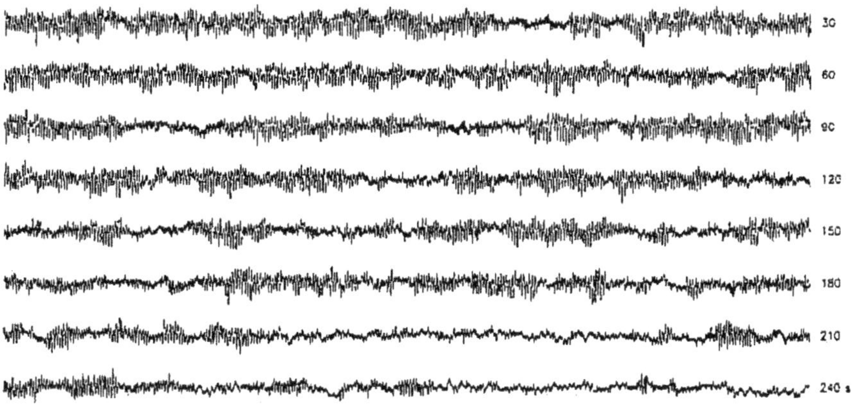

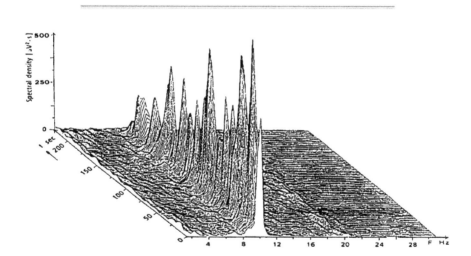

Figure 52. Raw occipital EEG of 4-minute duration (240s) from a normal adult participant in 8 consecutive fragments of about 30s. With kind permission from Springer Science+Business Media: Biological Cybernetics, Inverse covariation of spectral density and correlation dimension in cyclic EEG dynamics of the human brain, 82(1), 2000, Tirsch, Keidel, Perz, Scherb, & Sommer, fig. 1.

Figure 53. The course of the occipital frequency spectrum of the EEG from the previous figure over 4 minutes (240 s) in which the 50-60s cyclic fluctuations of alpha peaks are clearly seen. With kind permission from Springer Science+Business Media: Biological Cybernetics, Inverse covariation of spectral density and correlation dimension in cyclic EEG dynamics of the human brain, 82(1), 2000, Tirsch, Keidel, Perz, Scherb, & Sommer, fig. 3.

Possibly, this 'pacemaker' or 'cyclic modulator' in the brain stem also contributes to the generation of hippocampal theta rhythms implicated in working memory and integrative functions of REM sleep. Noradrenalin input from the locus coeruleus in the brainstem to the hippocampus also contributes to these processes.

An optimal fluctuating system provides adaptive responses to internal or external stimuli, and this is potentially reflected in a well-developed event related desynchronization (Kaiser, 2001). Kaiser noted that ERD-ERS cycles run continuously in waking states, and their sequential flow reflects cognitive responses to internal and external stimuli as well as the subsequent restoration of a state of readiness for further inputs. Moreover, reaction times during an attention task are slower at moments of alpha synchronization when the evoked ERD is often weaker (Sterman, 1996). Sustained fine regulation of the brain's reactivity to internal and external stimuli leads to maintenance of a certain intermediate level; thus, avoiding extreme habituation and over-excitability (possibly leading to epilepsy). This mechanism can also decide on optimal attentional regulation. The cycle duration of 50 to 60 seconds is, at the behavioral level, expressed in attentional tasks, fully promoting a more efficient global functioning of the system.

Tirsch assumed that lower alpha energy fragments (and thus possessing a higher correlation dimension) reflect faster parallel information processing in independently active brain areas. The highest energy fragment (and thus with the lowest correlation dimension) would therefore express synchronized data transfer over higher association cortex areas. These CAPs, formed from series with average 50-second duration, illuminate the brains' integrative functions in which parallel and central information processing modes alternate with each other. From the evidence for decreased quantities of sleep spindles and CAPs during sleep as well as a lowered quantity of SMR rhythm during wakefulness, one may suspect that these fluctuations in daytime will show a different pattern in disorders, such as ADHD.

Tirsch's research into this cyclic pattern of occipital alpha activity has been described here in detail, but it should be mentioned that he also demonstrated the same 50-60 Hz cycle in sensorimotor beta rhythm in EEG (Tirsch, 2004). Moreover, this phenomenon has been observed in all physiological phenomena, such as attentional quality, motor performance, and normal physiological resting tremor (Tirsch, 1995).

The discovery that fluctuations that occur in the physiological resting tremor are similar to those in the EEG strengthen the hypothesis that a pacemaker plays a moderating role in the brain stem both in ascending paths (towards the brain stem) and descending paths (towards the backbone) in which other rhythmic structures are also involved. All these discoveries persuaded Tirsch that 'injuries' in temporal structure could be identified earlier than structural injuries. In the future, this new approach may be a practical method for diagnosing pathology. On the other hand, it might be that cyclic alternating patterns in the EEG do not need a 'pacemaker;' instead, they can be explained by self-organizing criticality (see next section).

Summary

 As in behavioral regulation, a cyclic modulating pattern with a period of 50-60 seconds exists in the EEG, probably playing a 'pacesetter' role. The evidence indicates that this cyclic pattern may originate in the mesencephalic reticular formation of the thalamus and may be similar, in some ways, to the cyclic alternating patterns (CAPs) in the EEG that are responsible for optimization of global functioning of the EEG. It is very likely that this integrating pattern is disturbed in ADHD, which might explain global disturbance in the vigilance system.

5.2 Pink Noise and 'Self-Organized Criticality' in Behavior

Slow cycles, lasting 30-60 seconds in EEG and in behavior (such as the physiological resting tremor), are also found in other behaviors. A far-reaching phenomenon in both behavior and EEG is that both have time series (for example the occipital alpha waves and the sensorimotor beta-1 waves), which fluctuate in a scale-free manner, that is, the degree of fluctuation over short time scales is identical to the fluctuation over longer time scales. It is not yet known whether infraslow EEG waves also show similar scale free fluctuations.

A time series can be constructed by plotting consecutive reaction times from simple reaction time on vertical strips for each serial position and sketching a connecting curve through the end-points. Traditionally, the average reaction time and standard deviation are then calculated for these tasks. Although rearranging the order of the original reaction times does not alter either the average reaction time or the standard deviation, it does destroy the fine structure of the original time series, as it can leave out much valuable information about functional behavior. If a frequency spectrum is obtained from the curve formed by the time series of reaction times, the slowest frequencies have the highest energy. The spectrum slope is best evaluated by plotting the x-axis (frequency) and y-axis (amount of energy in each frequency) on a logarithmic scale (Figure 54) (Van Orden, 2002).

The slope of the energy spectrum is steepest during simple tasks (less dependent on external noise). Consequently, pink noise is much more visible in a very simple behavioral task in which participants are asked to press a button whenever they subjectively feel that a second has passed for a period lasting ten minutes (Gilden, 1995). This task is self-paced, without the necessity to react to an external stimulus, giving rise to a very clear behavior. The introduction of an external stimulus is responsible for the appearance of more white noise; therefore, it produces a slope that is less steep compared to that of the frequency spectrum. As tasks become more complex, more white noise combines with pink noise and the slope becomes less steep. In pathological cases, the slope is even flatter during complex tasks. That could suggest that there is too little response to external circumstances (associated with white noise); thus, indicating that organization is no more complex than during simple tasks. In summary, if the time series of reaction times mix randomly, the average reaction time and the standard deviation remain unchanged, and white noise replaces pink noise in the time series frequency spectrum.

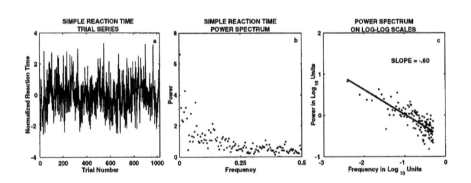

Figure 54. **Left**: *A series of a 1000 reaction times from a healthy participant.* **Middle**: *Frequency spectrum of these reaction times.* **Right**: *Logarithmic treatment of the frequency spectrum. There is a 1/f relation (pink noise in which the longest frequency has the most energy). Reprinted from Ecological Psychology, 14(1), Van Orden, Intentional contents and self-control, Copyright (2002), with permission from Taylor & Francis – http://www.informaworld.com.*

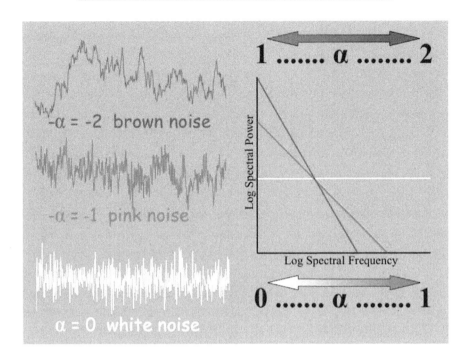

Figure 55. Summary characteristics of brown (or "red", "random walk"), pink and white noises. Data series appear on the left (together with their characteristic alpha values for 1/f^α) and spectral slopes appear on the right. Philosophy of Complex Systems. Handbook of the Philosophy of Science, Vol. 10 (Elsevier) 2011 Van Orden, Kloos, Wallot, Living in the pink: Intentionality, wellbeing, and complexity.

The noise in such systems is thus not completely disorganized. Completely disorganized noise is white noise, analogous to the visible light spectrum in which white light consists of all component colors. Every measurement in the series is thus completely independent of the values at every other point. This is also termed uncorrelated noise. Pink noise can be observed in Figure 54, in analogy with visible pink light comprising mostly long wavelength (lower frequency) light with other subcomponents present in exponentially decreasing amounts. An inverse proportional relationship exists between energy and frequency band (1/f), and this is termed correlated noise. Background noise, like pink noise, is expected to occur in a self-organizing behavioral system over the course of time. Pink noise indicates the internal source of variability and refers to the brain's intrinsic dynamics and mechanisms of alternation between cognitive processes. Pink noise is the signature of goal directed behavior arising from self-organization. When 'surrogate data,' created from a series of measurements by placing data fragments side-by-side white noise, is obtained in place of pink noise, then absolutely no interrelationships survive. Thus, a 1/f relationship in which f has a negative exponent (with a value of roughly -1) indicated by the gradient of the slope characterizes pink noise. Pink noise occupies the space between white noise and brown noise. White noise yields a horizontal line when the logarithm of the density is plotted against the logarithm of the frequency, thus each frequency contains on average the same amount of energy. White noise is characteristic of a stable time series that randomly fluctuates around an average value where f has an exponent of 0 in the 1/f time series. Brownian noise (Brown noise, named not after a color in the electromagnetic spectrum but after Brownian motion described by the botanist Brown) is also known as red noise (because the curve gradient is steeper than in pink noise) and is defined as the cumulative sum of a series of random movements, often said to resemble a drunkard's walk. The exponent of f in the expression 1/f is 2 for Brown noise. Pink noise is independent of time scale since on a logarithmic scale, the 2-4 Hz band possesses the same energy as the 20-40 Hz frequency band. Incidentally, human hearing also functions in accordance with this principle, which explains why every octave perceived contains the same quantity of energy. Acoustic engineering often utilizes pink noise because the human auditory system perceives approximately the same volume at all acoustic frequencies.

Based on reaction time experiments, Van Orden (2002) hypothesized that goal directed cognitive performance develops via 1/f organization. The internal complexity and especially the personal internal history of such a system permit better adaptability to various situations via a smooth transition from one organizational state to another.

A well-developed pink noise system is constantly balanced between unpredictability and over-determination, a critical balance that Bak (1988) termed 'self-organized criticality' or SOC. Out of a full range of subsystems within the global system, self-organization spontaneously establishes the critical equilibrium state optimally favorable to task adaptive behavior. The theory of SOC suggests that a system self-organizes into a complex system with fractal features (fractal: approximately the same degree of organization is found for all time scales). A sand heap provides a canonical example in that additional sand added to the top of the existing heap may suddenly subside along different break lines. Another example would be a snow avalanche that leads to further sudden shifts as further snow accumulations. According to this theory, fractal organization develops in a simple unbalanced system. An SOC system has a number of important characteristics: 1) the degree of complexity arises from self-organization and is not determined by a regulating control parameter; 2) a scale free (fractal) pattern of organization exists (the same pattern is expressed on both a small and a large scale); and 3) SOC and pink noise arise through the interaction of many systems from which a global system arises spontaneously with its own dynamic that can no longer be reduced to the specific input of subsystems.

Van Orden (2002) observed that in classical linear 'Newtonian' cognitive psychology, cognitive phenomena are explained using computer models in which measurements of human behavior are directly linked to assumed brain components. The products of psychological processes are not distinct from the processes themselves (attention, perception, thought, speech, and walking, among others). Van Orden named this classic approach the 'component dominant dynamic.' He stressed that concepts, such as free will, reflex, and automaticity, were developed in the seventeenth century as classificatory designations, but over time, they became laden with philosophical, physiological, and psychological associations with causal implications. In this connection, Van Orden cited Fearing wrote an article in 1930 in an attempt to distinguish the knee jerk reflex from 'voluntary' movement of the lower leg. Fearing thought that the 'voluntary' movement was a higher and the knee reflex a lower form of reflex. However, Fearing (1970) warned that these reflex hypotheses and related data generated from the 17th and 18th centuries should be considered as provisional, and therefore should be viewed with caution.

Van Orden (2002) suggested an 'interaction dominant dynamic' in which interactions between neighboring processes change each other. Internal and external processes hold behavior within certain boundaries, leading to emergent behavior. The interplay between component systems over different time scales is the source of correlated noise. The behavior of subcomponents reflects the behavior of the whole system because of their underlying system dependence. Likewise, variation in the subsystems reflects variation in the whole. Goal directed intentional behavior therefore arises from self-organization in a system that, at its critical point, is strongly determined by internal and external circumstances. Choice and self-control are emergent properties arising from interactions between the organism and the environment.

Accordingly, Van Orden (2002) argued that the indications of correlated 'pink noise' are the signature of goal directed behavior. The characteristics of goal directed behavior, such as self-control and choice, are context dependent. Classical science saw noise (for example in a reaction time experiment) as an irritating side effect. In the 'interaction dominant dynamic' approach, noise represents precise information worthwhile of study because pink noise is an 'n' indication of the system's organizational pattern.

If we equate the brain's pink noise with the brain's intrinsic dynamics, then we can argue that these dynamics are responsible for the global emergence of behavior. However, isolation of certain causal mechanisms in a 'component dominant dynamic' of the brain requires certain behavioral parameters that are expressed on specific scales. Composition of pink noise does not support these characteristic scales, raising the question if we will ever be able to reduce the causes of human behavior to activity within specific brain areas.

Similarly, pink noise curves have been obtained, and the resulting frequency spectrum have been calculated from an experiment in which participants were asked to rate their mood every day over a two-year period (Gottschalk, 1995). In healthy participants, the logarithmic curve is steeper than in people with bipolar disorder.

Another study examined the frequency spectrum of the time series formed from consecutive participants' own ratings of 'self-esteem' assessed twice daily over 729 days (Delignières, 2005). Here too a remarkably similar pattern formed, which the authors labeled as 'self-image' emerging from the nervous system in a self-organized manner.

Notice that self-organized refers not to the individual 'self' but to the automatic interaction among many system components. Delignières (2005) concluded that this pattern not only demonstrated stability in an individual with a healthy self-image, but also possessed enough flexibility to adapt to changing circumstances. This can be possibly achieved through adequate 'criticality.'

Marks-Tarlow (1999) predicted that we might observe more white noise in patients with a hysterical personality disorder (which we might assume is the case in ADHD) and more brown noise in rigid obsessive-compulsive personality types. Nowak (2000) demonstrated that self-image is an emergent property from a complex dynamic system composed of a flow of specific, linked self-thoughts. From this vantage point, the self can emerge as a coherent structure, and the process of preservation, when exposed to incongruent elements, can be understood as a process of self-organization based on multiple interactions within the system. A robust system exhibits pink noise, which means that the energy contained within every frequency of the energy spectrum of the time series is proportional to the oscillation period. Thus, energy does not concentrate within any time scale but, instead, spreads over the entire spectrum. Therefore, fluctuations in one time scale only loosely connect to fluctuations in another time scale. The relative independence of the underlying processes that are active on different time scales implies that a localized disturbance within a time scale does not necessarily change the stability of the entire system. In other words, pink noise (1/f) produces a system that is both stable and adaptable to internal and external disturbances. However, Delignières (2005) remarked that in principle, these kinds of analyses apply only to the adaptation of a stationary time series so that the fractal analysis of self-image is just a first step in the characterization of its nonlinear properties. He assumed that dynamic changes characterize non-stationary processes, which happens in depressive or very anxious patients. Meanwhile, methods for analyzing non-stationary time series may be applied to the current approach.

Healthy undergraduates completing mental rotation tasks showed a large amount of 1/f noise in their reaction time series, whereas subjects with ADHD-like symptoms did not show this pattern (Gilden, 2007). Instead, their data was characterized by a large amount (92%) of white noise in combination with 8% of 'brown noise' ('random walk model') in which a given reaction time is merely a preceding trial's reaction time plus a random increment. Gilden concluded that 1/f noise is a phenomenon generated by the process that enables attentional vigilance.

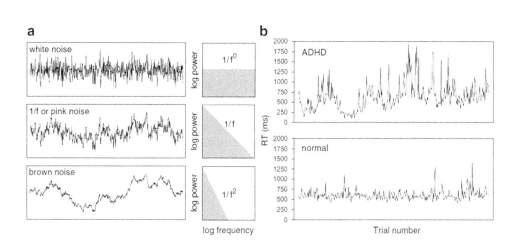

Figure 56. 1/f noise and a reaction time series of an individual with ADHD.
(a) From Gilden (2001) (b) from Gilden and Hancock (2007).

5.3 Pink Noise in the EEG

Brain dynamics switches constantly between the complex and the unpredictable. Friston (2000) stressed the importance of momentary transitions in the 'labile brain.' This switching element provides the most efficient manner for the brain to detect change in the body and in the surroundings while at the same time, maintaining autonomous self-generated internal organization. This self-generating mechanism arises at the microscopic level from neuronal discharge and synaptic activity and keeps building up to the macroscopic level of a complex organized system at multiple coordinates of time and space within the brain. Pink noise (1/f) allows a system to be predictable (maintaining stability) but also flexible enough to adapt to unpredicted events. This is the definition of a 'critical' system.

A logarithmic x, y plot of the Fourier spectrum in the EEG follows a 'power law' (1/f) in which the energy of the system is inversely proportional to the signal. The slowest frequencies contain the most energy. This is the essence of a scale free system. The brain generates a full series of EEG rhythms that allow processing and predicting of events on multiple time scales. The inverse relationship between EEG frequency and energy indicates that the interference at low frequencies is responsible for a chain reaction of energy shifts at all frequencies. It is assumed that these dynamics form the essence of a global temporal organization of the cerebral cortex. The fact that the same 1/f phenomenon occurs on every time scale is an important argument for self-organization. The speed with which energy drops from slow to fast frequencies in the EEG is a measure of the strength of the correlations and of the statistical memory of the signal. If no relationship existed among different frequency bands, the energy density over specific EEG frequency distributions would be constant and the spectrum would be flat (in other words, it would show white noise). The 1/f behavior of the EEG is the golden mean between disorder and high information maintenance on the one hand and the predictability of low information maintenance on the other. This golden mean represents the 'self-organized criticality.' The fact that different frequency levels depend on each other explains the fact that slow frequency disturbances lead to power changes at all frequency levels. During slow rhythms, slow axonal conductions and slow synaptic processes also contribute to the activity, consequently larger neuron groupings can participate in faster EEG rhythms. This shows a 1/f phenomenon. Such correlated pink noise has important consequences and advantages for perception and behavior. From this viewpoint, the brain does not demonstrate just large-scale long-term patterns because these self-organized collective patterns guide the very neuronal behavior that contributed to the existence of these patterns. The effect of properties of emergent higher levels on lower levels of organization contributes to 'circular causality' (Haken, 1996; Kelso, 1995). The corollary is that the firing patterns of single neurons occurring at any given moment do not depend solely on the external input, but also on the firing pattern history and the state of the network in which they are imbedded.

The fact that the 1/f network is independent of scale implies that the macroscopic EEG patterns, which on a large scale describe the functioning of neural networks as a unified whole, are, as a globally functioning system, independent of the details of those dynamic processes that ultimately guide the sub-components towards unification. It does not follow that these rules are applicable at all times to all scales in time and space. On the one hand, a small local disturbance can influence a great part of the network and exert long lasting effects. On the other, the functional history of the network limits neuronal firing patterns. The 1/f 'power law' implies that for the better part of the time, the brain's dynamics is in a state of 'self-organized criticality.' This unequivocal complex state is mathematically defined, and it occupies the border between predictable periodic behavior and unpredictable chaos. It enables the cerebral cortex to show transient states during certain perceptions or cognitions, allowing fast and flexible responses to inputs. In addition to response flexibility, this cerebral cortex metastability enables dynamic reorganization in response to even the smallest and weakest disturbances. The occurrence of an event related desynchronization (ERD) in the EEG after a sensory, motor, or cognitive event is a clear example of a disturbance in the brain's critical state. The ability to switch quickly from metastable pink noise to a strong predictable rhythmic EEG state is quite possibly the most important characteristic of the dynamics of the cerebral cortex. By switching to a rhythmic state, the brain immediately creates a state with linear characteristics that are a fundamental physiological necessity for the psychological processes described as 'expectation,' 'prediction,' and 'anticipation.' During these short transition processes, a linear time scale needs to provide stability in order to maintain and compare information within a certain time, allowing behavioral predictions on the time scale.

To describe the present state of the brain, it is necessary to know its recent history embodied in the time correlation and represented by the $1/f$ memory of scale free systems. The term '$1/f$ memory' is a statistical concept and does not necessarily relate to human memory directly. However, the $1/f$ statistical measure can indicate a link between the dynamics of the cerebral cortex and behavior. Cerebral cortex dynamics constantly alternate between complex metastable pink noise and very predictable rhythmic states. In recent years, an additional role of pink noise has been observed, that is, an increase in the continuously present noise in some nonlinear systems has been found to counterintuitively increase the sensitivity of signal detection. In the somatosensory cortex, a signal in the form of a just detectable pulse of electric current delivered to a nerve receptor in the hand was perceived better when alpha activity with pink noise characteristics was present in the cortex. This is known as stochastic resonance. Traditional thinking would suggest that low noise accompanies better signal detection. At present, it seems that noise resonates, so to speak, in SOC systems, picking up and strengthening weak signals. Linkenkaer-Hansen (2004) described how this pink noise can be discovered in a time series of organization of occipital alpha waves (10Hz) and of sensorimotor beta waves (20 Hz). Alpha and beta activities were filtered from the MEG (magnetoencephalography), the fluctuations in their amplitude were investigated by placing an 'amplitude envelope' around the filtered signal, and the frequency spectrum from these envelopes was calculated. The resultant spectrum showed the characteristics of pink noise. The highest energy was observed at low frequencies and the lowest energy at the fastest frequencies of the amplitude envelope.

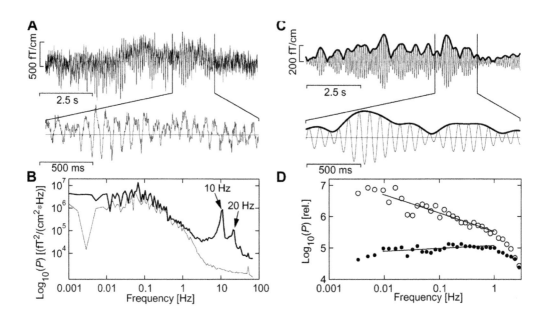

Figure 57. The frequency content of broadband signals and of the amplitude envelope of narrow frequency-band neural oscillations. (A) A representative epoch of the broadband signal as obtained from a single MEG channel at the acquisition (0.1-100 Hz) is shown at two time scales. Note from the upper trace that the high-amplitude 10-Hz oscillations are riding on slow fluctuations (< 1 Hz). (B) The slow fluctuations in the broadband signals are likely to originate mainly from environmental noise, as it can be inferred from B showing the spectral density of the entire 20-min long signal in A (thick line) and reference data from the same channel (thin line). The neural signals clearly dominate at frequencies above but not below 1 Hz, with prominent peaks at 10 and 20 Hz (see arrows). (C) The signal shown in A has been filtered at 10 Hz with a Morlet wavelet (passband 6.7–13.3 Hz). The thin lines are the real part and the amplitude envelopes (thick lines) are the modulus of the wavelet transform. (D) The power spectrum of the amplitude envelope of the neural data at 10 Hz exhibits a $1/f^\beta$ power spectrum (circles) with $\beta = 0.58$ in the range from 0.01 to 1 Hz, thereby indicating that the fluctuations of the amplitude envelope of these oscillations correlate at time scales of 1–100 s. On the contrary, the 10-Hz amplitude envelope of the reference data gave rise to a white-noise spectrum characteristic of a temporally uncorrelated process (dots). Reprinted from European Journal of Neuroscience, 19, Linkenkaer-Hansen, Nikulin, Palva, Kaila, & Limoniemi, Stimulus-induced change in long-range temporal correlations and scaling behaviour of sensorimotor oscillations, Copyright (2004), with permission from John Wiley and Sons.

Plotted on a logarithmic scale, the frequency spectrum is an oblique line with high values lying to the left and low to the right (high in slow and low in fast frequencies). Calculating the negative exponent of 'f' in the 1/f expression gives us a measure of the curve gradient, that is, steeper curve indicates more pink noise and higher degree of self-organized criticality. This way, the pink noise for different frequency patterns has been calculated (such as theta, alpha, beta, gamma) (Freeman, 2000; Linkenkaer-Hansen, Nikulin, Palva, Kaila, and Limoniemi, 2004; Stam, 2004) indicating that the energy of the frequency band is at its highest at slow frequencies of the time series spectrum for these different frequency bands.

It is not yet clear whether the 0.02 Hz slow EEG waves, such as CAPs, participate in the scale free pink noise modulation of theta, alpha, and beta waves. The fact that they increase in the neighborhood of sleep phase transitions is certainly an indication that they correlate with these even slower cycles (an NREM/REM cycle lasts 90 minutes) of which the sleep wake cycle is an example.

We know that the highest amplitude SMR-bursts occur roughly every 50 seconds (Tirsch, 2004) and that this phenomenon is similar to a CAP (cyclic alternating pattern), which has a stabilizing function. This slow cycle is only discernable with a chronospectrogram (see Figure 53). Sterman and Lubar noticed, by visual inspection, that in normal children, the SMR rhythm (which is defined as a burst with a minimum duration of 0.5 s and an amplitude of at least 10 ☒V) occurs predominantly around 10-20 times per minute. Smaller and more frequent short bursts of 12-15 Hz are also plainly visible in the EEG.

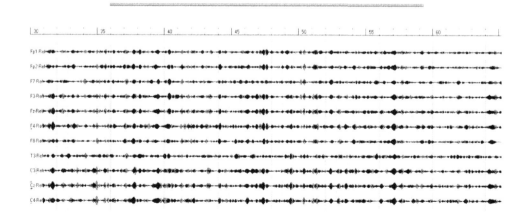

Figure 58. 12–20 Hz filtered EEG, 50 µV gain, speed 7.5 mm/ s. Smaller and shorter bursts are clearly discernable between the bigger, longer bursts described by Sterman and Lubar. Image created by WinEEG, Mitsar Co. Ltd.

This may be linked to the 1/f pink noise phenomenon. The evidence that fewer SMR bursts (and possibly less cycling alternating patterns of 0.02 Hz) are present in ADHD, as Sterman and Lubar suggested, could therefore be interpreted as a manifestation of a disruption in intrinsic organization with the presence of less pink noise.

Robert Thatcher (personal communication) thinks that we could expect increased burst duration in a homeostatically regulated system. The burst duration of any frequency, not just SMR, represents a type of rapidly opening and closing 'shutter' in which action potentials occur on the falling phase of each rhythm of local field potentials (LFP; excitability cycles representing a discrete action potential probability distribution; see Buzsaki's review, 2006). If bursts are too short, then more bursts per second compensate for the need to process information, which resembles the shutter opening and closing. When burst duration increases, then there is a more sustained period for processing information and for cross-frequency synchronization to occur. The hypothesis is that in people with ADHD, the SMR rhythms (cyclic alternating patterns with a vigilance stabilizing function) contain less slow fluctuations of 0.02 Hz. Moreover, as Lubar demonstrated, the strongest SMR-bursts with a minimum duration of 0.5 s usually occur 10 to 20 times per minute in normal children and have probably a vigilance-stabilizing role.

From a different perspective, recent research has revealed that the amplitude envelope of delta, theta, alpha, beta, and gamma rhythms also correlates with slow fluctuations measurable by fMRI. These slow (0.01-0.1 Hz) blood oxygenation level-dependent functional imaging signal-fluctuations are topographically organized in discrete brain networks. During passive rest states, the 'default network' that controls internally focused processes, such as introspection, is active. This network links the bilateral inferior parietal lobules (mainly the angular gyrus), the precuneus / posterior cingulate, bilateral superior frontal gyri, and medial frontal gyrus. The latter network is called the 'default' network because fMRI research indicates that it is active during the passive condition (no cognitive tasks or other functions) or, more cogently, because this network is deactivated during cognitive tasks. However, the 'default' network is not in itself at rest. It reflects brain activity during introspection (medial frontal gyrus) as well as proprioception (parietal cortex), among others.

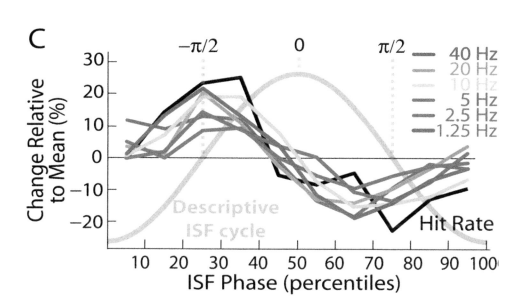

Figure 59. The amplitude envelopes of the traditional EEG-frequency bands (measured at Fz, probably with source in the medial prefrontal cortex), as well as the hit rate of a behavioral task, fluctuate synchronously and in phase (45°) with the infraslow fluctuations of the fMRI BOLD signal of the default mode network, as if the latter were a conductor of an orchestra (Monto S., 2008).

The default network has a peak frequency of 0.013 Hz in slow fMRI-signal fluctuations, which is similar to that of the slow fluctuations in the occipital alpha and the sensorimotor beta rhythms that were demonstrated during rest (Tirsch, 2004), which in turn show similarities to a CAP (cyclic alternating pattern).

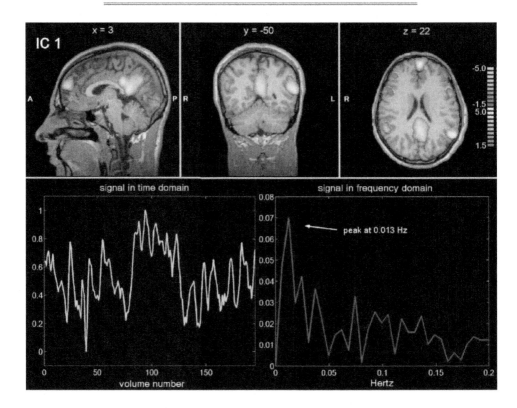

Figure 60. **Left bottom:** *fMRI BOLD signal fluctuations in the time domain.* **Right bottom:** *frequency spectrum of the infraslow signal fluctuations in the left picture, showing 1/f pink noise.* **Top:** *fMRI BOLD signal of the default mode network (Mantini, PANS 2007).*

During cognitive tasks, the default network (especially the medial prefrontal cortex) in people with ADHD is insufficiently suppressed (Broyd, 2011; Fassbender, 2009; Sonuga-Barke, 2007), which could explain increased distractibility. Sonuga-Barke advanced the hypothesis that the slow cycles of increased variability in reaction time tasks in people with ADHD may be linked to slow fluctuations of the fMRI signal of the default network. These slow default network fluctuations during attentional tasks are ineffectually suppressed. They may also correlate with slow fluctuations in reaction time variability in ADHD.

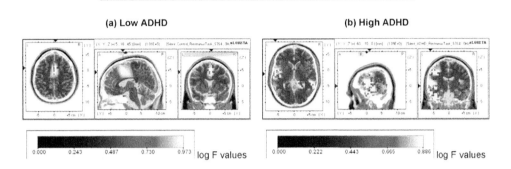

Figure 61. Deactivation of infraslow EEG oscillations in sLORETA during attentive task in ADHD (Broyd, 2011).

Summary

The discovery that frequency patterns in the EEG and also frequency patterns of time series consisting of the consecutive intensities from certain EEG wave frequency bands exhibit pink noise characteristics provide new insights into nonlinear relationships in the EEG. In analogy with the visible light spectrum, white noise describes the circumstance when all frequencies are present in the EEG frequency spectrum while pink noise displays more energy in the low rather than the high frequency bands of the spectrum. This indicates that the noise correlates and denotes a degree of order in the system called the 'self-organized criticality.' In such systems, fractal organization (the same pattern is repeated on every time scale) gives rise to the self-organization, as the system reaches a critical threshold in which flexible state transitions are possible. This system arises purely through self-organization in which reciprocal causality is established between the global macrosystem and the activity of multiple subsystems. Such a system integrates stability with flexibility, which is necessary for optimal 'critical' functioning. There are indications that people with ADHD exhibit relatively less pink noise and relatively more white noise, which would suggest a lower degree of self-organized criticality. The system is consequently less flexible and less stable, demonstrating less adequate event related desynchronization in the EEG.

5.4 EEG Phase Resetting, 1/f Organization of Phase and Brain States

Behavioral studies have shown that poor brain state regulation plays a fundamental role in ADHD, which may explain the lack of task adaptive behavior. Nowadays, we can provide a better insight into the meaning of the brain state and the determination of its organizational level.

Brain state level indeed determines attention, actions, and perceptions. At the behavioral level, sleep and wakefulness are two different states in the brain. In the first state, we are not conscious of our environment, but we are aware of our environment in the second state. However, there is also a subtler variation of motor and cognitive capabilities over periods lasting minutes, seconds, and even smaller time scales. This happens without an 'executive network' playing a supervisory role. We have already mentioned that variability in behavioral response does not arise from white noise in the brain, which itself is a consequence of the brain's imperfections, but from pink noise dynamic in brain activity. This indicates that the spontaneous activity of 'brain states' characterizes neither stationary nor white noise. The 1/f organization of the brain is responsible for continuous phase transitions that enable the brain to react to external stimuli as effectively as possible. Brain state changes are difficult to deduce from moment-to-moment overt behavior. Nevertheless, EEG changes can be precisely monitored and associated with each other, at least temporarily. Classical research on the brain's cognitive evoked potentials assumed that the underlying activity in the EEG represents random noise, which is smoothed by calculating the average values of the curve. Consequently, only the stimulus and resultant mental processing seem to determine the evoked activity following stimulus presentation. However, more recently, it has been found that after stimulus presentation, a phase reset occurs in the brain rhythm.

Makeig (2002) performed an experiment asking participants to press a button only when a stimulus appeared inside a small green square displayed on a monitor, not if it appeared at other location. The response generated to the ignored stimuli was analyzed. If alpha waves were not present prior to stimulus presentation, alpha response was not triggered. If background alpha activity was high, then the amplitude of the evoked response was also high. The latency of the individually evoked responses varied systematically as a function of the phase of the ongoing alpha rhythm. In connection with the neglected stimuli, a different degree of phase adjustment was found each time.

Palva (2005) examined the functional importance of background EEG activity in a study of the effect of a barely perceptible electrical stimulus on the skin of the index finger. The stimulus was just perceptible not just in the somatosensory, but also in the parietal and frontal cerebral cortex whenever sufficient alpha and theta activity preceded and followed the stimulus and whenever stimulus presentation occurred simultaneously with a certain phase of the ongoing rhythm. A phase reset was measurable in the EEG only under the perception of stimulus. Stimulus perception therefore depended on transient, spontaneous, rhythmic activity states in the frontoparietal network. Perception of the stimulus depended on the disturbance of spontaneous brain rhythms so that the stimulus itself only partly determined the brain activity associated with stimulus perception. The consistent finding that both movement initiation and reaction times systematically vary as a function of alpha rhythm phase further supports the functional behavioral importance of phase resets (Bates, 1951; Lansing, 1959). In movement initiation and reaction times, there is no evoked phase reset, so we can argue that the relevance of behavioral activity that evolves during certain EEG phases or phase reset is the same for spontaneous and for evoked EEG activity. MEG (magnetoencephalogram) responses were measured in the cerebral cortex of participants performing a working memory task (Rizzuto, 2003) and in the hippocampus (Tesche, 2000). A string of digits was presented on a monitor after which the participant had to recall the digits. A theta phase reset followed the stimuli, and its duration increased with memory load, with an upper limit of around 60ms corresponding to 5-7 remembered digits. The firing patterns of neurons in the cerebral cortex and hippocampus were grouped together in the trough of local alpha and theta activity. One can expect that in ADHD, usually with increased hypercoherence between frontal areas, phase lock would take longer. Too few phase resets may result in less adaptive behavior, that is, they may be over-reactive to intense or exciting stimuli and under-reactive to weak or boring stimuli. This would also provide an explanation for poorer working memory in people with ADHD, as they frequently cannot accurately recall 5-7 digits. We might suspect that the time series of phase values may demonstrate a less marked 1/f pink noise pattern in ADHD, which would correlate with less pronounced 1/f pink noise in the reaction time series. This would imply that in ADHD behavior, behavior is less task adaptive but also less exact. Phase resetting in an EEG rhythm can usefully create an optimal temporal relationship between the discharge of neuronal groups and information about stimulus related activity. If information is allocated to opposite phases of the cyclic rhythm randomly without the ability to adjust neuronal group timing, the effect induced by the stimulus might be amplified or ignored. Therefore, phase resetting can strengthen the incoming signals selectively.

A very strong or salient stimulus can influence the activities of many more neurons than can self-generate rhythms. Such salient stimuli not only exploit ongoing brain dynamics, but also alter brain state so that the newly created dynamic may be very different from the one preceding the stimulus. Sudden transition from alpha and mu to gamma rhythms during event related desynchronization is a characteristic example of such state changes in the activity of brain networks following the presentation of meaningful stimuli. People with ADHD often experience the stimulus as less salient, unquestionably because the brain dynamics of the phase rhythms exhibits less pink noise, resulting in less marked phase transitions and inadequate brain state (in this case in the form of event related desynchronization).

Similar phenomena have been described in macaques (Liang, 2002) after they initiated the task sequence. After they pulled a handle, either diamond or a line appeared on a monitor, and correct identification of the visual stimulus was rewarded. The energy and phase coherence of the 5-12 Hz band in the prefrontal cerebral cortex correlated highly with both amplitude and latency of the evoked potential in occipital cerebral cortex as well as with motor reaction time. These observations support the hypothesis that the brain state of the prefrontal cortex is able to prepare sensory cortical areas for efficient processing of stimuli.

In general, psychological theories about selective attention have attempted to interpret all of these findings as reflecting a top-down executive mechanism accompanied by gamma and theta rhythms. A logical consequence of this hypothesis would be that in order to maintain optimal selective attention, we must maintain our brains in an optimal condition and generate sufficient alpha and gamma rhythms. However, the brain does not operate in this way, at least not for long periods. This hypothetical executive mechanism would not be able to retain control over the long term. In the absence of a strong external stimulus, such as overwhelming tiredness experienced during a long car ride, the brain falls into its internally programmed rhythms, and these rhythms result in fluctuating performance levels. Consequently, there is no simple way to maintain voluntary attention, perception, memory, or motor actions over long periods. This applies even more to people with ADHD, which gives an impression that they possess a weaker will compared to other people.

Another indication that an internal mechanism is responsible for fluctuations in the state of readiness for perception and action is that the gamma and theta rhythms at the scalp demonstrate a 1/f pink noise pattern. The structural basis of this brain dynamics might be the multiple parallel neuronal circuits that deliver feedback over long time scales because of progressively longer conduction times and synaptic transmission durations in longer circuits. This may indicate that these multiple systems are responsible for the global 1/f pink noise. On the other hand, following the principle of reciprocal causality, the global 1/f dynamic maintains a certain degree of order in these subsystems. These multiple scales in time and space embody the contextual dependence of input disturbance in the 'situated' environment of task adaptive behavior and vigilance. This context itself is determined through the historical associations of the input and the previous responses of the brain to that input. The signal measured in the EEG after input may well contain more information about the brain of the perceiver than about the input because perception is an 'interpretation' by neuronal circuits over multiple scales in time and space in the brain rather than the aggregate of a number of unvarying physical characteristics.

Thatcher (2005) found a correlation between high intelligence and short frontal phase locking. Probably, based on this correlation with intelligence, the quantity of phase resetting counts is higher. Moreover, it is clear that there is a link between alpha and theta waves and working memory. Since working memory in ADHD is often rather limited, we may suspect that phase resetting is less frequent.

Phase resetting occurs regularly and spontaneously; therefore, it is for the most part internally generated even though it is certainly triggered and modulated by internal and external stimuli. Abrupt accelerations or decelerations in the temporal course of the phase relationship between beta waves (12-30 Hz) measured between two EEG measuring points occur several times a second (with intervals corresponding to theta- alpha waves) (Freeman, 2004). Freeman demonstrated the role of the phase resetting in sensory perception. Rizzuto (2003) observed such phase resetting in 12-16 Hz waves, especially during tasks involving working memory.

Makeig (2004) proposed a model in which phase resetting in alpha and theta waves occurs with each pulse from the septohippocampal pacemaker and that this temporal adjustment of neurotransmitter systems marks the beginning of a period of retention and analysis of information that lasts around 80 ms to 250 ms. This process is continuously repeated and the peaks of the alpha and theta rhythms reflect the phase resetting process. The stepwise phase resetting of working memory occurs at the 7-16 Hz EEG frequency. A great number of cortical EEG rhythms have their pacemaker in the thalamus so that consciousness is involved in other processes in addition to working memory. It is intriguing to think that the absence of consciousness in deep sleep or anesthesia is associated with a global uncoupling of the hippocampal cingulate complex from the thalamus and cerebral cortex. Phase resetting is still present in these states, even if at very low voltage. Perhaps, the powerful coordination between the septohippocampal cingulate and the thalamocortical system supports a central coupling between the past (as memory) and the present during consciousness expressed in the phase resetting. In ADHD, there are indications of less phase resetting, which in this framework can be interpreted as a discrete lowering of consciousness (in the sense of vigilance, optimal adaption of responses to circumstances) and a decreased working memory capacity.

The phase resetting involves abrupt adjustments of the phase relationship within a frequency band between EEG measuring points, which is seen clearly when studying the curve of the first derivative of the progress of the phase difference. The first derivative gives a measure of the speed of change. The second derivative is a measure of the speed of the change of the first derivative. Thinking about reading the speedometer when driving the car can help us understand this concept. The speedometer denotes the first derivative, i.e., the rate of distance change per unit time (km/hour). If we suddenly break, we feel our body falling forward towards the steering wheel, referred to as the second derivative. Galileo discovered the importance of the second derivative in physics. Newton wrote it in his famous equation F=m·a (force equals mass times acceleration). The EEG is fundamentally an electromagnetic process to which all the physical laws of energy and electricity apply. An interesting property of phase resetting is that it requires only a minimal amount of energy to adjust oscillators already in motion. The phase resetting can synchronize neural networks over long distances.

When we look at the first derivative of the phase shifts in the EEG, we can see moments when simultaneous phase resettings at all 19 points are measurable separately. Between the phase resettings, we see flat segments where the first derivative is zero, signifying that the phase coupling is constant.

The frequency spectrum of the first derivative of the phase shift shows 1/f 'pink noise' distribution. The lowest frequencies have the most energy while the highest frequencies have the least. Using this 1/f principle, Freeman (2004) explained the way in which we may achieve long distance synchronization of neural networks. This principle points to the phenomenon of self-organized criticality, indicating that self-organization occurs across the smallest to the largest time scale, guaranteeing stability of the global system and simultaneously the flexibility of adaptive responses to internal and external stimuli. The pink noise indicates the existence of mutual causality between the relative degree of phase update on short and on long time scales, involving also phase resettings of the longer sleep wake cycle. A night's sleep deprivation is a phase resetting on a grand scale, which will likely have consequences for short time scale phase resettings.

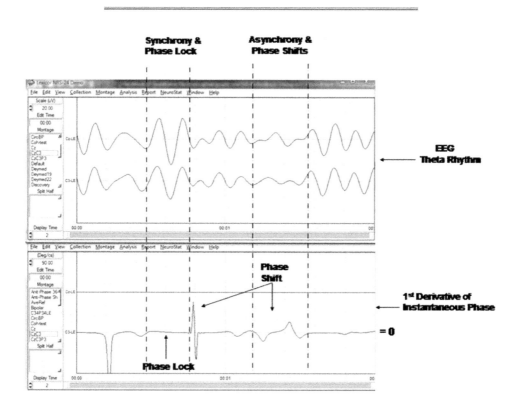

Figure 62. In the upper curves, the EEG at Cz and C4. We notice a theta phase synchrony between the two first vertical dashed lines, what is translated in the bottom curves as a phase locking (first derivative of the instantaneous phases of the upper curves), meaning that the phase difference remains stable. After the second vertical dashed line, there is phase shift between the two upper curves. Notice also that during the first phase–locking period, theta at Cz and C4 are also stronger in amplitude, which indicates a strong theta synchrony not only between both sites, but also on each site. From Neuroguide: www.appliedneuroscience.com.

Summary

The phase delay of EEG waves in distinct frequency bands between each electrodes pair is reset regularly, both spontaneously and in reaction to external stimuli. This enables the brain system to react to internal or external inputs in an adaptive way, allowing the history of the complex brain system to determine the evoked brain activity. A 'supervisor' does not control attention, certainly not over a long time. Attention arises through spontaneous self-organization via interaction with the internal and external environment to which the brain responds through its 'being situated' in an adapted way.

The phase and the phase resetting of EEG waves demonstrate a 1/f pink noise distribution, signifying that smooth brain state changes occur, as the situation requires, in the form of event related desynchronization. In ADHD, there are probably less phase resetting, and the time series probably demonstrate less pink noise. Consequently, we may expect a less efficient task adaptive functioning. Less phase resetting is characteristic of decreased, unstable vigilance and decreased working memory.

5.5 The Arousal, Balance, and Breadth of Attention Model

The posterior cingulate (PCC) is the highest hub in the hierarchy of policy-making, intervening when the anterior cingulate policy is no longer effective when external conditions are changing importantly. This topic has been discussed in the chapter on the electrophysiology of the anterior cingulate (ERN, FRN, No-Go N2 and P3). The PCC is hypothesized to play a chief regulatory role in focusing internal and external attention. It is involved in both integrating memories of experiences and initiating a signal to change behavioral strategies.

Leech and Sharp (2014) developed the ABBA Model (Arousal, Balance and Breadth of Attention), where the PCC is playing a crucial role in controlling the state of these parameters. This model emphasizes the PCC as a dynamic network rather than a fixed and unchanging structure. For an organism to react flexibly to a changing environment, information processed in functionally distinct brain networks needs to be integrated by the PCC hub. Using fMRI, Leech and Sharp showed this type of complex functional architecture, where echoes of activity of multiple other brain networks are seen in separate yet overlapping subregions. A predominantly ventral region shows strong functional connectivity to the rest of the DMN, whereas two subregions within the dorsal PCC show high connectivity to frontoparietal networks involved in cognitive control. PCC subregions show distinct patterns of activity modulation during the performance of an attentionally demanding task, suggesting that parts of the dorsal PCC interact with frontoparietal networks to regulate the balance between internally and externally directed cognition.

The frontoparietal networks are connected to the PCC during task-negative periods ('echo'). This activity change in the PCC might reflect varying levels of information gathering in different phases of task performance. If the dorsal PCC is playing a role in environmental change detection, interaction with attentional networks might be expected to be high during periods of fixation, when cues for action are awaited and broad, unfocused information is required. Once focused task has started, this type of interaction becomes less relevant, so PCC activity falls in preference for the specific attentional demands during task performance. As task difficulty increases, the ventral PCC shows reduced integration within the DMN and decreased anticorrelation with the cognitive control network (FPCN) activated by the task. The dorsal PCC shows an opposite pattern, with increased DMN integration and anticorrelation. At rest, the dorsal PCC also shows functional connectivity with both the DMN and attentional networks. As expected, these results provide evidence that the PCC is involved in supporting internally directed thought, as the region is more highly integrated with the DMN at low task demands. In contrast, the task-dependent increases in connectivity between the dorsal PCC and the FPCN are consistent with this region's role in modulating the dynamic interaction between these two networks when controlling the efficient allocation of attention.

The more widespread intrinsic functional connectivity of the dorsal PCC suggests that this region may be an interface between the DMN and FPCN. The dorsal PCC signals environmental change and the need to alter behavior. This leads to the hypothesis that the dorsal PCC is involved in broad information gathering, which is necessary to control responses to a rapidly changing environment. The ability of an organism to react flexibly to change requires the integration of information from functionally distinct brain networks. If the dorsal PCC acts as a cortical hub, integrating information across different functional networks, its brain activity should show a complex and dynamic pattern that partially reflects activity in other networks.

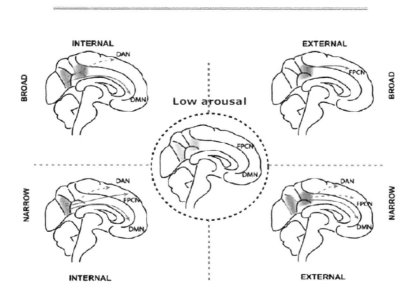

Figure 63. The arousal, balance, and breadth of attention (ABBA) model. The central panel illustrates the PCC during a low state of arousal, where there is little interaction with other networks. Each panel surrounding this illustrates one of four possible states from the interaction of an internal/external and a broad/narrow focus of attention. Interaction between the PCC and intrinsic connectivity networks is shown using arrows: solid arrows signify increased functional connectivity, broken arrows greater anti-correlation. Red areas within the PCC signify relatively increased neural activity, blue areas relatively decreased activity (Leech and Sharp, 2014).

The PCC represents a state of readiness, allowing an exploratory cognitive state and the efficient response to changing external events. This state of readiness is a metastable state, with an optimal balance between integration and segregation of information processing. The predictions of the model can be tested within the framework of complex dynamic systems theory. The dorsal PCC is proposed to influence attentional focus by 'tuning' whole-brain metastability; thus, it adjusts stability of brain network activity is over time.

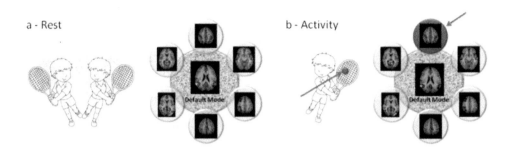

Figure 64. Allegorical illustration of rest–state versus active state: a) during rest, the state is in a multistable regime, exploring different available mental states (microstates), like a tennis player who jumps from left to right while waiting for the service of his opponent; b) in this way, upon receiving a stimulus, the brain can react and engage the regions in charge of processing the stimulus (Cabral, Thesis: Brain Activity during Rest, 2012).

Metastability is becoming recognized as an important dynamical mechanism for understanding brain and behavioral coordination. Etymologically, 'metastability' comes from the Latin 'meta' (beyond) and 'stabilis' (able to stand). In coordination dynamics, metastability is not just a word. It is the simultaneous realization of two competing tendencies: the tendency of the individual components to couple together and the tendency of the components to express their independent behavior.

The FPCN/DAN and DMN have opposing actions on attention: 1) activation of the FPCN/DAN increases global synchrony and decreases metastability; 2) DMN has the opposite effects; 3) these results suggest that the balance of activity in the FPCN/DAN and DMN might control metastability, providing a mechanistic explanation of how attentional state shifts between an unfocused/exploratory and a focused/constrained mode characterized by a low metastability.

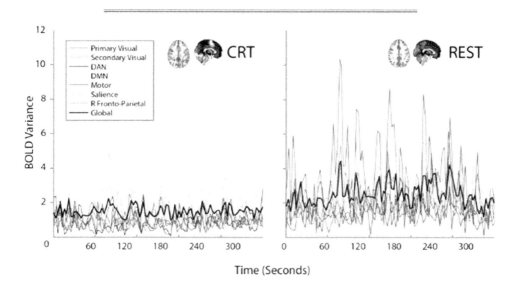

Figure 65. The results from a single illustrative subject. The global (i.e., all 66 regions) and local (i.e., specific ICNs) time series of fMRI BOLD signal synchrony during a choice reaction test CRT (on the left) or at rest (on the right). Greater variability in synchrony (metastability) can be seen at rest (Hellyer, 2014).

We, of course, recognize the metastable pattern of an optimal EEG vigilance, as described by Bente and Ulrich, where a rigid and labile vigilance pattern is maladaptive. It is well known that the source of alpha is the precuneus/PCC. In the chapter on large-scale brain systems (Chapter 2), we already described how the functional stability of the precuneus/PCC depends on the salience network activity and how a less effective salience network is characterized by rest state theta activity in the EEG, with its source in the dorsal anterior cingulate. We assume that the labile EEG vigilance of ADHD implies a less optimal metastability.

Leech and Sharp's converging computational and empirical work suggests that global neural dynamics are 'tuned' by varying levels of activity within the FPCN and DMN, which have the ability to shift the system into a more or less metastable state. This is consistent with theoretical and experimental work suggesting that the brain exists in a critical state, at a 'tipping point' between order and disorder. The scaling parameters used in the simulations were chosen to simultaneously maximize both metastability and synchrony, features that would be consistent with a critical system.

Therefore, tuning of criticality within the brain by selective activation of functional networks may increase or decrease the information capacity of the system, depending on the behavioral context. For example, the information capacity of the system is maximized at rest with activated DMN at the expense of network stability while during active attentional states, FPCN/DAN activation results in increased stability of the network but reduced information capacity. The DMN is typically more active during stimulus-independent thought and while maintaining a broad attentional state. These types of behavior share the lack of behavioral focus, which could be thought of as 'releasing' neural activity, allowing it to take on multiple different network configurations over time. This variability in network configuration would result in relatively low synchrony and increased metastability when measured across the whole brain.

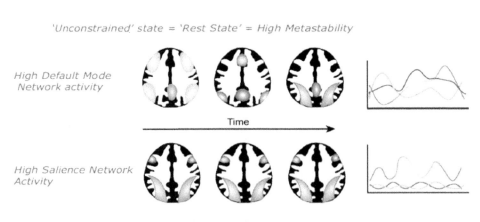

Figure 66. fMRI BOLD signal fluctuations of the DMN (blue), FPCN (green), and DAN (orange) during metastable rest state (upper figures) and during constrained focused task performance (lower figures) (Leech and Sharp, 2014).

According to this hypothesis, the FPCN/DAN can influence sustained attention through stabilization (reduced metastability and increased synchrony) of the temporal dynamics of the whole system. Similarly, the simulation of DMN activation provides a possible mechanistic explanation of the functional role of the DMN in 'permitting' the system to move into a more unconstrained state. In this state, the brain shows higher metastability and lower synchrony, exhibiting more labile dynamics spontaneously passing between different states that would facilitate both mind wandering and maintaining a broad attentional cognitive state. The balance of activity between the FPCN/DAN and the DMN acts to tune global brain metastability, which influences the consistency of brain network over time.

The dynamics of the instabilities of perceptual mind wandering bears the hallmark of a complex adaptive system. Mind wandering is proposed to be useful for integrating perceptual information with its context. The 1/f scaling behavior characteristic of complexity has been observed in amplitude fluctuations of 10 and 20 Hz EEG oscillation (Linkenkaer-Hansen, 2001), reflecting metastability within a cortical area. A similar 1/f behavior has been described for alpha phase synchrony, reflecting metastability of information communication between long-distance neural assemblies. Gong (2007) showed that this behavior could be attributed to a critical threshold phenomenon indicating that dynamic synchronization with 1/f characteristics in the durations of synchrony occurs in a system of coupled oscillators when the coupling strength between the oscillators is at the critical threshold of mutual entrainment.

Fagerholm (2015) investigated the EEG dynamics in healthy people during resting state and during a focused attentional choice reaction task. EEG events are termed neuronal avalanches or cascades due to their qualitative similarity with the sand pile collapses observed in the Bak-Tang-Wiesenfeld model (Bak, 1988). The characteristics of the probability size distributions of these avalanches can be used as markers of self-organized criticality. In resting state EEG, cascades are associated with approximate power law form, suggesting that the resting state is associated with near-critical dynamics in which a high dynamic range and a large repertoire of brain states may be advantageous. In contrast, a focused cognitive task induces subcritical dynamics associated with a lower dynamic range, which in turn may reduce elements of interference affecting task performance. The fastest reaction times in the choice reaction task however occurred when the EEG cascade distributions resembled power law form, a result that at first may seem at odds with the finding that the task performance is associated with subcritical dynamics. However, this result may reflect similarly counterintuitive findings that have been reported using more standard neuroimaging analyses. In particular, optimal performance (in terms of speed and accuracy) occurs when subjects are 'in the zone,' a state characterized by being task focused while performing a relatively automatic task. fMRI measures of BOLD activity suggest that being in the zone is associated with increased activity in the DMN, which typically deactivates during task. This implies that some level of activation within the DMN is necessary to be in the zone, but that excessive deactivation leads to suboptimal task performance. In a similar way, these results reflect an in-the-zone phenomenon, where optimal performance is associated with dynamics that, while still subcritical, are close to those observed at rest. Therefore, optimal performance may occur in a (slightly) subcritical regime; however, being in an overly subcritical state may harm performance possibly due to excessively restricted dynamic range and information transmission.

5.6 Metastability, Pink Noise, and Small-Worldness

Kelso and Tognoli (2007) argued that the fundamental property of complex systems that operate in a metastable dynamical regime is the duality of large-scale processing by sets of distributed, interconnected areas and local processing within those areas. Such local-global dynamics are promoted by modular small-world connectivity. Small-world networks are characterized as having a high clustering coefficient but with a short characteristic path length. A small-world network is also modular if it can be partitioned into sets of nodes (modules) that have dense within module connections but are only sparsely connected to other modules. Clustering and modularity tend to favor localized processing while a short characteristic path length enables easy connectivity between arbitrary sites. A balance of these two properties promotes local-global dynamics that is the hallmark of metastability. Not only modular small-world structure promotes the transient formation of synchronous oscillations through metastable dynamics, but also the modular small-world topology required to support these dynamics naturally arises through synaptic plasticity. The interaction of these oscillating neural populations with different intrinsic frequencies leads to complex dynamics. Acting in concert with synaptic plasticity, these dynamics naturally result in the restructuring of the network topology, yielding small-world connectivity, which in turn heightens levels of metastability in the system.

The relationship between small-worldness of the structural connectome and metastability makes intuitive sense. Short overall path lengths facilitate increased global synchronization while local modular architecture (high clustering) provide some reservoir of different states, preventing the system from getting 'stuck' in a synchronized state. This suggests a mechanistic link between reduction in small-worldness and neural dynamics. Within the framework of self-organized criticality, an alteration in metastability may accompany a shift away from the critical state associated with a decrease in efficiency of information storage or processing capacity of the brain (e.g., processing speed, cognitive flexibility, and associative memory).

Anatomical brain structure is a major constraint on the functional complexity (and metastability) of neural systems. Evidence of localized clustering as well as low characteristic path length between sites has been found in the network structure of large-scale cortical systems (Sporns, 2000). These findings, characteristic of modular small-world connectivity, have since been substantiated and extended (Bullmore and Sporns, 2009). In addition, Sporns (2013) reported on a growing body of work that draws attention to the essential role of the balance between structural segregation and integration in the operation of the brain networks underlying cognitive function. Functional activity is thought to reflect underlying anatomical structure, and correlations between structural and functional connectivity have been found.

Homeostatic plasticity (adaptivity) by local inhibition tunes spatio-temporal dynamics in such a way that an efficient neural functioning with optimized information transfer (processing) occurs (functional connectivity with small-world characteristics (Hellyer, 2016). For example, dopamine has been shown to alter the balance of neural excitation/inhibition and modulate criticality (Stewart, 2006), which is important for cognitive performance, and it has been implicated in many neuropsychiatric conditions. Macroscopic models incorporating dopamine pathways and variation in receptor densities could be used to understand how dopamine modulates plasticity, resulting in altered dynamics. One speculative example is that the level of regional dopamine may modulate the level of firing rate and provide a mechanism to alter the richness of the dynamical regime, as action potentials create feedback loops of neuronal activity that self-organize into larger traveling waves. Traveling waves are an observable realization of emergent constraints in motor coordination, perception, and cognition. Reduced dopamine in the brain reduces the capacity of traveling waves to coordinate, which in turn affects cognitive functions, motor coordination, and the dynamics of physiology.

These dynamics are similar to those of evolution. We think of evolution in terms of how things change, but in reality, it is much more about how living systems are peculiar in their ability to stay the same, to keep on surviving, rebuilding themselves day after day, and regenerating. Organisms evolve and learn by changing within a stable enough context that they can survive evolution's trial and error process. For any lineage to survive, a metastable platform on which adaptations can accumulate must be present. It has to be stable enough to persist but metastable (plastic or flexible) enough to allow trial and error. Some have pointed out that the brain's fundamental raison d'être is to deal with informational complexity surrounding the organism. William James (1890) already used a metaphor of the stream of consciousness as the flight of a bird the life journey of which consists of 'perchings' (phase gathering, integrative tendencies) and 'flights' (phase scattering, segregative tendencies), similar to phase locking (synchrony) and phase shifts in EEG phase reset. Both tendencies appear to be crucial for a dynamic brain in action. In a metastable system, phase alignment increases and decreases intermittently as a result of the continuous transactions between segregative and integrative tendencies (Kelso, 2014). When EEG patterns have misaligned phase relationships, their population signal cancels and disappears from the upper scales. The result resembles a state transition regime, although it is more plausible that a single spatiotemporally metastable regime without state transitions spans the entire episode. The microscopic signal hints at spatio-temporally metastable dynamics, the segregative tendencies of which result in intermittent disappearance of the meso- and macroscopic observables. The more recent neuropercolation model assumes that the level of self-organized criticality in a system can be tuned by control parameters, much like the temperature can serve as a macroscopic control parameter in non-equilibrium thermodynamic systems (Kozma, 2009, 2015). In a system where phase resettings ('neural avalanches,' which show a power-law distribution) are occurring less frequently, dopamine can increase the rate of these resettings.

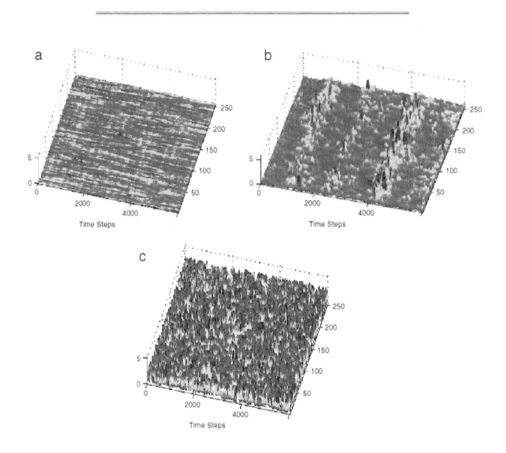

Figure 67. Intermittent synchronization in the neuropercolation model as the function of the system noise level: The noise changes from 13%, 15%, and 16% in Figures (a), (b), and (c), respectively. Intermittent synchronization is seen at critical noise level 15% in figure (b) (Kozma, 2009).

Meisel (2013) investigated the level of pink noise (criticality) in EEG after sleep deprivation. During sustained wakefulness, a progressive disturbance of 1/f during wake is observed, which is restored by sleep. The distribution of alpha phase lock intervals has less 1/f characteristics and a decrease in variability of alpha synchronization is noted. Sleep restores the critical state, resulting in recovered power-law characteristics in activity and variability of synchronization. These findings support the intriguing hypothesis that sleep may be important to reorganize cortical network dynamics to a critical state, thereby assuring optimal computational capabilities needed for optimal information processing during the following time awake. As has been discussed in the previous section, one can assume that dopamine, as a tuning control parameter in the system, improves the occurrence of phase resetting and its power-law distribution. It could explain the improvement of metastability/vigilance in ADHD after the treatment with dopaminergic psychostimulants as well as the improvement of conflict and action monitoring (ERN).

CHAPTER 6
Neurofeedback (EEG-Biofeedback)

6.1 Lessons from Neurophysiological Effects of Ritalin™ and Dextroamphetamine

FOR OVER 60 years, and increasingly more since the1990s, Ritalin and dextroamphetamine have been used to treat ADHD worldwide. The scientific literature generally describes them as safe and effective (with a beneficial effect in 70-80% of cases), provided the correct diagnosis (Barkley, 1997). These medicines increase the availability of dopamine and noradrenalin in the synaptic junction between connecting neurons in the caudate nucleus, resulting in improvements in attention, hyperactivity, impulsivity, and in the 'executive functions,' including working memory, sense of time, planning and organization, and problem solving ability, among others. Moreover, they improve adaptive motivation and decrease mood swings and irritability.

In ADHD, reaction times are longer for boring tasks and decrease in response to stimulating complex tasks. Such findings in people with ADHD persuaded the Canadian psychologist Virginia Douglas (1972) to speculate that the core deficit is an impoverished ability to adapt to changing situations and task specific requirements. Ritalin bolsters the ability of children with ADHD to maintain attention when they make mistakes or when they are uncertain of their performance as task requirements change. Ritalin facilitates intensive information processing to challenging subtasks, reflecting better regulation. During Ritalin treatment, the EEG shows normalization of the theta/beta-1 'distractibility index' and an increase in sleep spindles during sleep. The improvements in attention and behavior seem much greater if this index is initially more aberrant. If Ritalin does not normalize this EEG index, no effect on behavior is generally observed (Loo, 1999). Most studies on the effects of Ritalin on EEG power spectra are uncontrolled, with EEG recorded off and on medication. These studies show mostly decreases in theta activity (Clarke, 2002; Clarke, 2003; Song, 2005; Swartwood, 1998) and/or increases in beta activity with Ritalin (Clarke, 2002; Clarke, 2003; Song, 2005). Furthermore, clinical responders seem to be characterized by increased theta activity at baseline compared to nonresponders (Clarke, 2002; Loo, 1999; Ogrim, 2014). One double-blind placebo-controlled study demonstrated that Ritalin administration increased parietal alpha activity during the rest condition, but had no effects on theta (Loo, 2004). Ritalin works predominantly by increasing the availability of dopamine in the ventral striatum and caudate nucleus, which form part of circuits that include the orbitofrontal cortex (OFC), dorsal anterior cingulate (dACC), and dorsolateral prefrontal cortex (DLPFC). Thus, it improves the functioning in these circuits. Studies have shown that D2/D3 postsynaptic receptors are less available in the caudate nucleus and ventral striatum of people with ADHD (Volkow, 2012). Ritalin blocks the presynaptic dopamine transporter protein receptors of the dopamine releasing neuron, increasing the level of dopamine available to stimulate dopamine receptor positions on the postsynaptic neuron.

In ADHD, during inhibition tasks, fMRI studies showed a decreased activation in right inferior frontal gyrus extending into the insula, SMA, and cognitive division of the ACC, and in the left caudate extending into the putamen and insula. During attention tasks, a decreased activation in the right DLPFC, left putamen and globus pallidus, caudate tail ending into the posterior insula, right inferior parietal lobe, and the precuneus and superior temporal lobe has been noted (Hart, 2013). Ritalin normalizes the activity in the right inferior frontal gyrus and the right rostral/dorsal anterior cingulate (Rubia, 2014). During attention, Ritalin results in an increased suppression of default mode activity in precuneus and anteromedial prefrontal cortex (Peterson, 2009). A single dose of Ritalin also enhances activation in the medial orbitofrontal cortex, anterior cingulate, and caudate during reward processing (Rubia, 2009).

Accordingly, we need to consider its 'total effect.' Adults and children with ADHD are not only more attentive and calmer, but their moods stabilize, impulsivity and emotional reactivity decrease, boring chores become easier to initiate (motivation improves), and organization skills become more fluent. Nevertheless, according to various articles in the popular press, medication with Ritalin remains controversial. One root of this controversy is the difficulty of our society to understand the true nature of ADHD. Our society often attributes motivational and self-regulation difficulties to psychological causes ('he can do it when he wants to') or to the consequences of upbringing.

Another misapprehension is that Ritalin is a drug comparable to cocaine. There is indeed some similarity to cocaine in terms of their functioning but otherwise, Ritalin is unique in its speed, in its mode of action in the brain, and in normalizing these poorly functioning mechanisms. In contrast to cocaine, individuals experience longer lasting action but no high, immediate, or intense flash effect. Thus, Ritalin is not addictive. It is certainly true that people without ADHD can misuse Ritalin in order to work through the night, for example. Thus, misuse can lead to exhaustion phenomena, even depression and psychosis. Precisely for this reason, prior accurate diagnosis is a necessity.

Another myth is that Ritalin decreases creativity. It normalizes impulsivity and mood changes. Awareness of time also increases so that the momentary enthusiasms are less powerful. This can give the impression that the medicated individual is less inspired. In reality, the creativity of someone with ADHD is somewhat anarchic. Healthy creativity needs to be somewhat streamlined to keep the goal in mind. In fact, Ritalin has been shown to increase creativity in verbal tasks in people with ADHD.

Of course, Ritalin cannot 'cure' ADHD, as the symptoms reappear upon ceasing medication. There may be unwelcome side effects and, as already mentioned, Ritalin does not work for everyone. The effects of long-term Ritalin use are unknown. These are all good reasons for the need to discover alternative treatments that would have as good an effect on the mechanisms underlying ADHD as Ritalin. Increasing understanding of these mechanisms has led to the development of neurofeedback therapy.

Summary

Psychostimulants, such as Ritalin, normalize the theta/beta-1 ratio in the EEG of someone with ADHD and increase sleep spindles in the sleep EEG. This improves self-regulation, attention, and executive functions, overall resulting in more flexible, stable behavioral patterns.

6.2 Neurofeedback: Method and EEG Modifications

During a neurofeedback session, a child (or an adult) with metal electrodes glued to the scalp, sits before a computer screen displaying a simple computer game that is responsive to the moments when the targeted EEG activity is reached. Every now and then, a feedback reward signal appears onscreen when the stabilizing beta-1 or SMR activity exceeds a predetermined threshold and, at the same time, theta activity stays below a predetermined threshold. This is certainly the best-studied training protocol for people with ADHD and best suited to the most common abnormal QEEG patterns in ADHD.

Figure 68. On the left of the screen, a column indicates the theta wave strength moment by moment; on the right, a column indicates momentary variations in the strength of SMR activity (or slows beta waves). The threshold value is marked on both columns. The instant that theta waves stay under the threshold while SMR waves stay above the threshold, the game score increases.

In neurofeedback therapy, positive feedback is given the moment theta waves stay strictly under a threshold and SMR or beta-1-waves are clearly above threshold. This constitutes the process of operant conditioning, that is, certain 'operations' ('behaviors' in the EEG) are rewarded immediately following the desired behavioral change. In this way, it is hoped to achieve a progressive and eventually permanent improvement in EEG 'behaviors' and reorganization of the associated behaviors. Each session lasts about half an hour. The game score is tracked in a table and the theta/beta-1 ratio is obtained in order to monitor progress over 20-40 sessions. After the completion of a successful course of training, some further monthly sessions are recommended for consolidation.

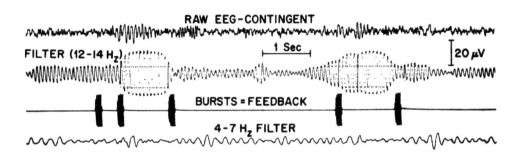

Figure 69. The raw EEG signal with the resultant filtered
12-14HZ and 4-7 Hz rhythms displayed below.

The first research studies applied SMR (sensorimotor rhythm, 12-15 Hz) neurofeedback (EEG-biofeedback) to cats in the late 1960s (Wyrwicka and Sterman, 1968) and found that the trained cats became more vigilant and less vulnerable to epilepsy. The first clinical treatment was given to people with epilepsy in the 1970s. In 1976, Lubar described the first clinical application to ADHD. Wider use in clinical practice did not occur until the 1990s almost exclusively in the United States. Availability of computers enabled this broad dissemination, which was applied primarily to ADHD because since 1976 (Lubar, 2000), an increasing number of published research studies focused on this issue. The origin and early dissemination of neurofeedback were independent of QEEG. In those early years, practical applications of neurofeedback were based on loose, simple clinical models, and training protocols were applied without evaluating the EEG. Since 1995, the trend has been to use QEEG in the development and evaluation of the training protocol. The utility of QEEG has remained limited, since the frequency spectrum analysis enabled only certain EEG waves to be selected and strengthened or weakened by the training. Many neurofeedback therapists hold the rather simple view that the EEG pattern thus marked for modification relates directly to behavioral change. A targeted reduction in theta activity is from this perspective interpreted as an expression of improved alertness. Another hypothesis is that the thalamocortical dysrhythmia is corrected based on a dysfunctional caudate nucleus. Lubar (1997) advocated another perspective, suggesting that training at the vertex (Cz) triggers an improvement in dorsal anterior cingulate functioning along the midline. This area plays a key role in 'executive attention' (Posner and Dehaene, 1994) and activates the frontal areas (in which executive functions are thought to arise) and subsequently other areas. The dorsal anterior cingulate also plays a central role in response inhibition and stimulus conflict monitoring.

While some reports have indicated that subjects are able to learn to increase the amplitude of SMR, almost no studies have described the concomitant effects on a resting EEG preceding and/or following neurofeedback. Doppelmayr (2009) investigated amplitude changes after 25 SMR neurofeedback sessions in 12 healthy subjects and compared the results with those of 8 healthy subjects who received sham-neurofeedback. EEG was recorded at C3 and C4 during the training as well as in resting conditions preceding and following each session. Inhibit bands were used to prevent subjects from manipulating EEG amplitude by eye blinks or from modulating amplitude estimates by voluntary muscle contraction (e.g., m. masseter or temporalis). The frequency bands for these inhibit bands were adjusted for 3 -5 Hz (eye blinks), 22-30 Hz, and 45-60 Hz (muscle artefacts). With respect to amplitude changes, SMR amplitude significantly increased in the experimental group during training, whereas it remained unchanged over time in the sham training. The strongest effects of training can be achieved in approximately 12 to 15 sessions, although further training continuously improves the performance.

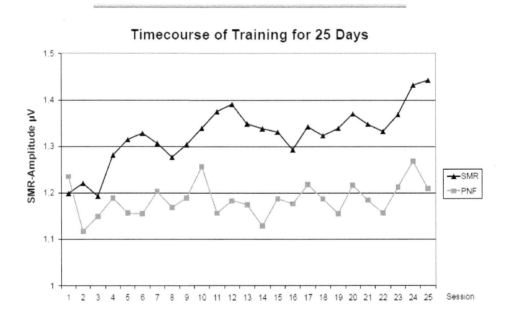

Figure 70. SMR amplitudes across all 25 sessions for the SMR group and the pseudo neurofeedback (PNF) group (Doppelmayer, 2009).

In a next study, Doppelmayer and Weber (2011) demonstrated that after successful SMR neurofeedback, healthy adults showed improved performance in the number of correctly answered items in a spatial rotation task as well in the simple and choice reaction time tasks. A control group that received neurofeedback with daily changing frequency bands did not show improved performance in these tasks.

Not all healthy subjects are able to increase SMR amplitude by neurofeedback. After 11 sessions, Weber (2011) was able to predict, which subjects would go on to increase SMR amplitude until the 25th session. Those who showed a steady increase over the first 11 sessions were the good performers. Those with enormously varying increasing or decreasing amplitudes over the first 11 sessions were the bad performers. The most critical point that prevented clear predictions at an earlier stage was the high intraindividual variance of the EEG. For the 27 healthy adult participants, 13 were performers and 14 were nonperformers.

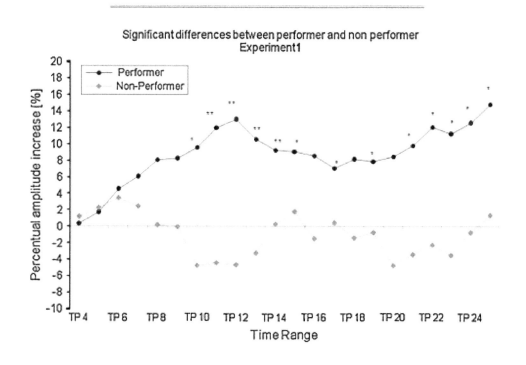

Figure 71. Performers and non-performers in a group of healthy subjects over 25 sessions of SMR neurofeedback (Weber, 2011).

Gevensleben (2009b) investigated EEG spectral changes after 18 sessions of beta-1/ theta neurofeedback in 46 ADHD children and compared them to those observed in 26 ADHD children who followed 18 sessions attentional skill training. This was the first randomized controlled neurofeedback trial in children with ADHD conducted with a sufficiently large sample size to reliably detect at least medium effects. After the treatment, the researcher found a decrease of midline central and parietal theta only in the neurofeedback group. At the behavioral level (parent and teacher ratings), neurofeedback was superior to the control training in terms of ADHD core symptomatology and associated domains (e.g., oppositional behavior). Superiority of the NF group was still evident at a 6-month follow-up (Gevensleben, 2010). Behavioral outcome also correlated with the amount of pre-treatment midline centroposterior theta, which implies that this measure has predictive value for neurofeedback treatment response. Monastra (2002) employed preselection of participants based on deviating theta/beta ratios. This study was excluded from a meta-analysis (Arns, 2009) because it showed the highest effect size for inattention (2.22) and hyperactivity (1.22); therefore, it contributed most to the heterogeneity of variance, suggesting this study showed higher efficacy due to the preselection of deviating theta/beta ratio (Arns, 2009). This large study demonstrated that QEEG-based preselection could potentially improve the therapeutic outcome, as was confirmed in Gevensleben's study. Arns (2011) replicated Monastra's findings that applying SMR/theta neurofeedback to ADHD children with an increased theta/beta ratio resulted in a better clinical outcome. In 21 ADHD children with an increased theta/beta ratio outtake, 76% of the subjects could be considered a responder (> 50% decrease on one or more subscales of the ADHD rating scales), 14% a non-responder, and 10% a drop-out. The ES was 1.78 for inattention and 1.22 for impulsivity/hyperactivity. The presented results are similar to the results of Monastra (2002), and the ESs are substantially larger compared to those obtained in the meta-analysis. Monastra's study also demonstrated reductions in theta from pre- to posttreatment. Doehnert (2008) also reported effects in the resting EEG, namely a reduction of the ⊠/⊠ ratio at Cz in children with combined-type ADHD.

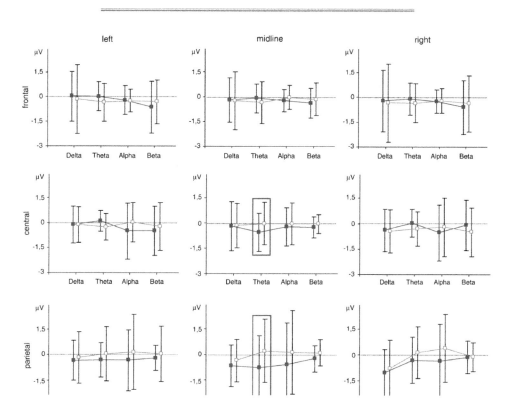

Figure 72. EEG change (post-training minus pre-training) measures. For each group (neurofeedback: blue, filled squares; attention skills training: gray, open squares), mean value ± standard deviation of changes (post-training minus pre-training) in the EEG frequency bands (delta, theta, alpha, beta) over different brain regions are plotted. In the NF group, there was a decrease of theta activity at central-midline and parietal-midline electrodes (Gevensleben, 2009b).

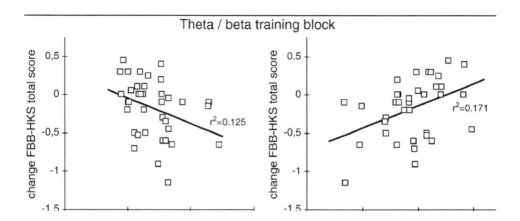

Figure 73. Theta/beta training block. **Left**: *change of the symptom (FBB-HKS) total score vs. theta activity measured at baseline over parietal-midline electrodes.* **Right**: *change of the FBB-HKS total score vs. change of theta activity over parietal-midline electrodes (Gevensleben, 2009b).*

Theta/beta has originally been interpreted as a marker for central nervous system arousal; however, this proposition has been increasingly challenged. Studies have failed to find a relation between theta/beta and skin conductance level, which is considered as the gold-standard index of arousal. Barry (2009b) suggested that elevated theta/beta in ADHD may not reflect an arousal deficit but rather an activation or processing deficit, as theta/beta is related to task performance. However, this hypothesis does not readily explain elevated theta/beta in ADHD during resting condition. The vigilance hypothesis (Head, 1923; Bente, 1969), proposed to explain the elevated theta/beta in ADHD, seems to be more valid but has not been embraced in the scientific world just because the EEG vigilance model in general is not well known.

Although positive objective behavioral changes have often been observed, and multiple studies have measured a normalization of the trained EEG frequencies (Monastra, 2002; Gevensleben, 2009b; Doehnert, 2008), changes in the EEG or other EEG alterations that were not directly trained were not always objective. Multiple explanations have been suggested. One view is that the EEG trains the mechanisms rather than static changes; therefore, static QEEG measurements cannot always show these (Othmer, 1999; Egner, 2004). Another, more nuanced argument, which is compatible with the EEG vigilance model, is that training brings about wider changes in EEG patterns (Cinciripini, 1984; Delorme, 2002; Rossiter, 2002; Sterman and Shouse, 1980; Tansey, 1991), and this can better explain the behavioral changes. The goal of the most popular training protocol is to increase the number of SMRsrendering the overly rigid EEG system more variable. At the same time, the SMR system can prevent derailment of the rhythm of the system. Sterman and Shouse (1980) and Tansey (1991) demonstrated that the global EEG spectrum normalized in this way, showing an increase in alpha and beta-1 activity and a decrease in theta and beta-2 activity. Rossiter (2002) also found that successful training increased alpha activity and decreased beta activity. Likewise, Cinciripini (1984) demonstrated an increase in alpha waves after SMR training. All findings regarding EEG spectrum normalization can be understood within Bente's interpretive framework, which interprets such EEG stabilization as an optimization of 'vigilance.' In Bente's terms, this represents optimization of the individual's functional ability to adapt to internal and external changes in various circumstances. This understanding is therefore more complete compared to the one based on 'activation level,' which suggests that frontal modulation of the EEG via inhibitory neuronal circuits optimizes 'vigilance.'

In a very recent study, EEG power spectra were studied before and after the treatment in 112 ADHD children who were randomized into three interventions: neurofeedback (n = 39), Ritalin (n = 36) and physical activity (n = 37). Overall, 103 children completed the study (Janssen, 2016). EEG power spectra measures were available for 81 children at pre- and post-intervention (n = 29 neurofeedback, n = 25 Ritalin, n = physical activity). The results were similar to those by Gevensleben (2009b) in respect to three main findings: (a) neurofeedback induced a reduction in theta power during an EO resting condition compared to an active control group, (b) higher baseline theta power at pre-intervention was predictive of greater ADHD symptom reduction from pre- to post-intervention, and (c) greater changes in theta power from pre- to post-intervention were predictive of greater ADHD symptom reductions.

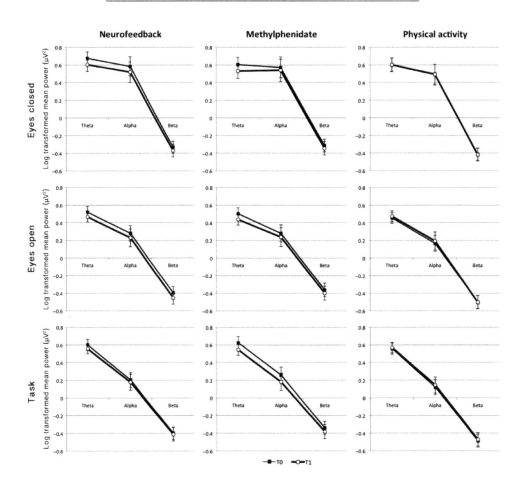

Figure 74. EEG power spectra at pre (T0)- and post (T1)-intervention for the mean of midline electrodes Fz, Cz and Pz (Janssen, 2016).

Lubar and Lubar (1999) suggested that training was completed if the theta/beta-1 ratio normalized or if the reward increased from 30% to 50% to 50% to 70% and the inhibit decreased from 70% to 50% to 50% to 30%. Over the course of training, tables and graphs were used to record the reward and inhibit percentages, average amplitude values of the trained frequency bands, and the alpha and beta-2 bands. In addition, the scores were recorded for each session. The standard deviations and the coefficient of variation were also useful. The coefficient of variation is the ratio of the standard deviation to the mean value and is thus a measure of the relative variability of the signal. The variability coefficients for theta, beta-1, and for the theta/beta-1 ratio often decline both within a session and over consecutive sessions. Changes in all of these variables are not a necessary condition for a successful course of treatment. Changes in any one will often suffice. A decreased variability coefficient, in Lubar's view, is a major indication that a more stable state is maintained during the session and that fluctuations between consecutive sessions are also more stable. This may reveal a better balance or homeostasis between dynamic brain systems, as reflected in EEG macrosystem dynamics. Lubar described some incidences of satisfactory treatment accompanied only by reduction in variability. In such cases, no decrease occurred in average theta or beta amplitude or in the theta/beta-1 ratio over the course of the treatment, but fluctuations around the average value certainly decreased over the final six sessions.

Concerning intra-individual variability, interestingly, a non-treated young adult ADHD group showed an increased central theta/beta ratio accompanied by a less inter-trial variability in power, particularly in alpha (the amplitude of which also decreased) (Woltering, 2012). These results are consistent with emerging notions in the field suggesting that low variability of metastable brain states is associated with less behavioral stability (with a high variability in task performance).

Moreover, Lubar (1995) noted that following successful training, EEG spectrum changes were not localized to one or two points on the scalp where the electrodes were placed during training but that small changes in frequency spectra were spread over the whole scalp. Lubar (1997) remarked that many neural pathways linked these different brain areas. Patients who showed no changes in the quantity of theta after neurofeedback also showed no indications of changes in other areas in the QEEG. Therefore, the EEG pattern in ADHD, with its similarities to the EEG of a normal person after sleep deprivation, normalizes. It is also known that after successful SMR/theta training, sleep quality improves, accompanied by a normalization of EEG spectra during sleep and an increase in stabilizing sleep spindles (Sterman, 1970, 1978; Hauri, 1983).

Although we cannot always measure changes in the statistical EEG in rest states after a rounded EEG neurofeedback treatment, there are frequent changes in cognitive electrophysiological activity. In comparison with the measurements prior to training, the P300 strengthens during an attention task (Egner, 2001), and the P3 potential strengthens during the 'no-go' condition in a response inhibition task (Kropotov, 2005). Following the treatment, the event related synchronization and desynchronization normalize in the EEG, even when no changes in rest EEG spectrum have been detected (Kropotov, 2007). There are indications that other EEG frequencies are modified often in a location different from the trained localization (Delorme, 2002). The coherence of certain EEG frequency bands between different brain areas has been found to be normalized (Coben, 2005).

6.3 Choice of Scalp Location and Training of EEG Frequency Bands

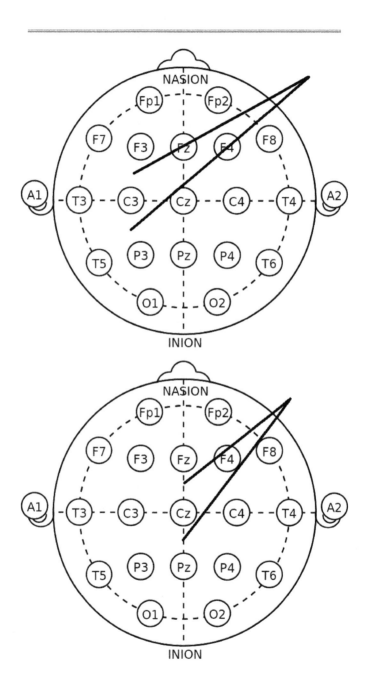

Figure 75. A comparison of montages used by Sterman and Lubar.

Sterman's original therapeutic studies, which focused on the control of epilepsy, used bipolar ('sequential') electrode montages in which one electrode is placed halfway between F3 and C3 and the other one is placed halfway between C3 and P3 because the sensorimotor rhythm (SMR, 12-15 Hz) is maximally measurable at these points. Initially, only the SMR was trained but afterwards, it was found that the global EEG pattern had normalized most notably with decreases in theta and fast beta activity. Tansey did not use a bipolar montage but an active electrode placed at Cz (with a reference electrode at the ear) to train the SMR and to target a decrease in theta waves.

Lubar was the first to apply neurofeedback to the treatment of ADHD using the identical training protocol employed by Sterman. Over time, Lubar came to favor the bipolar montage Cz-Pz as a training montage or a bipolar montage using a measuring point between Fz and Cz and another one between Cz and Pz (therefore on the midline). Placement along the midline was chosen partly because the deviant theta/beta-1 ratio was maximal along the midline in Monastra's QEEG studies (1999, 2001), and also because of LORETA studies. He assumed that the anterior cingulate, which plays a role in executive attention, conflict-monitoring during attention tasks, and response inhibition, would be trained in this manner. Since 1984, Lubar has trained the 16-20 Hz rhythm in ADD (subtype without hyperactivity or impulsivity), which is associated with weakening of theta waves and in his experience, it is more central to attentional control compared to the SMR. Lubar's followers also used this protocol (Linden, Monastra, and Thompson).

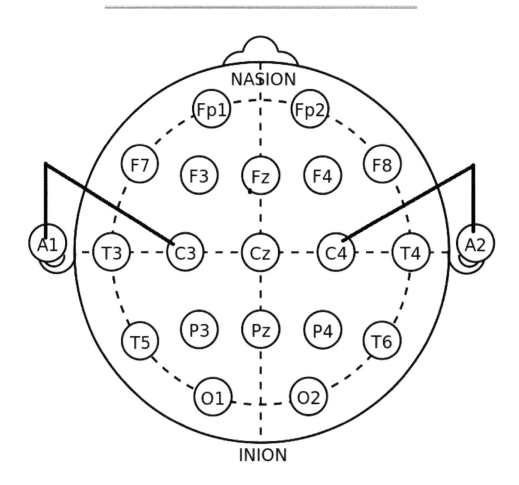

Figure 76. Othmer's C3/C4 protocol.

Othmer (1999) developed a training model on speculative grounds in which 15-18 Hz was trained at C3 (on the left) for the treatment of ADD and 12-15 Hz at C4 (right) was trained for the treatment of ADHD. It should be noted however that Sterman's (1980) original research indicated that the SMR band in the broadest sense includes 12-20 Hz and that SMR training automatically co-strengthens 15-18 Hz, and vice versa. For this reason, 13-21 Hz was chosen as the broad band, which was compared with the theta band to calculate Monastra's (1999, 2001) EEG distractibility index. Many researchers have followed Othmer's footsteps, choosing C3 (15-18 Hz) and/or C4 (12-15 Hz) (Fuchs, 2003; Kropotov, 2004; Rossiter, 2000). However, Rossiter (2002) showed that training the theta/SMR ratio at C4 and the theta/15-18 Hz ratio at C3 gave the same indications in the EEG, which was consistent with Sterman's results showing lowered theta, increased alpha, and lowered beta-2 activity.

The 'sequential' ('bipolar') electrode montage employed in the original studies used two positions close together on the scalp as active reference points. EEG activity can never be measured from one EEG point because the potential difference is the difference between two points, for example Cz-Pz. The development of QEEG allows for comparing individual measurements with averaged values obtained from a control group. This was often applied using the 'reference' electrode method (also known as a 'referential montage'), which finds the difference between a specific point on the skull and the averaged electrical activity measured at each ear, for example. Theoretically, it is assumed that no electrical brain activity is measurable around the ears and, consequently, that they offer a neutral measuring point. Thus, such reference montages are sometimes termed 'monopolar' montages. However, in practice, we know that EEG temporal cerebral cortex activity is measurable around the ears; therefore, this method of measurement, strictly speaking, also constitutes a bipolar montage. Notwithstanding this limitation, this method has practical utility in making QEEG measurements. Throughout the nineties, the referential montage was increasingly applied in neurofeedback.

In clinical practice, Lubar (1976) first trained the SMR in hyperactive children either along the midline or centrally on the left or right (choosing right central if impulsivity, aggressiveness, or emotional over-reactivity were prominent). He used either a sequential or a referential electrode montage but preferred that the greatest difference in signal intensity in theta and beta-1 activity determine the montage position. To avoid movement artifacts in the measured EEG, he did not use a referential montage with ear electrodes with the most hyperactive children. Kropotov and Clarke showed that in older children and adolescents, maximal theta was more often measured along the midline. To improve attention and motivation, Lubar trained 14-18 Hz along the centroparietal midline in children and along the frontoparietal midline in adults.

Summary

 Since 1984, Lubar and his followers (Linden, Thompson, and Monastra) trained primarily 16-20 Hz (together with decreasing theta waves) at Cz. They argued that the most consistent abnormality found in ADHD (theta/beta-1 ratio) was maximal at Cz, and that its source is located in the dorsal anterior cingulate. Othmer (1999) and his followers trained 12-15 Hz (SMR) at C4 (right) to treat hyperactivity and 15-18 Hz at C3 (left) to treat attentional difficulties on speculative grounds. No strong argument or research has been made to overwhelmingly differentiate between these two neurofeedback protocols, as of now, as 12-15 Hz is functionally similar to 12-20 Hz (and thus also 16-20 Hz), and this applies to C3, C4, and Cz. In the last 15 years, it has become common practice to use Cz while the theta/beta ratio is maximally deviant at this location and while it is assumed that the principal source of deviant activity at Cz in ADHD is the dorsal anterior cingulate.

6.4 Threshold Values for Neurofeedback

From the end of the 1960s until 1977, research has exclusively recognized 12-15 Hz training, which offered positive results in epilepsy and in ADHD (e.g., in many Sterman and Lubar studies in the 1970s and 1980s). In the 1970s, Sterman and Lubar had demonstrated that the SMR occurs in bursts lasting 0.5 to 2 seconds occurring about 10 to 20 times a minute in typical controls. Based on the previous research, frequently only five bursts per minute occur in ADHD and epilepsy. Originally, feedback in the form of a light flash and a tone was given when an SMR burst occurred. After a successful course of the treatment that consisted of at least 60 neurofeedback sessions, the quantity of SMR bursts normalized to 10 to 20 per minute. Thus, this original method provided feedback only when an SMR burst occurred, independent of the signal strength of the burst. Graphs from these early treatment studies clearly show that signal strength also increases. Since 1977, a decrease in 4-7 Hz was added to the treatment protocol because it was found that due to inherent problems with the analog filter method employed, 12-15 Hz rose at moments when 4-10 Hz was actually present. Afterwards, it appeared that decreasing the 4-7 Hz itself played an important functional role in bringing epilepsy and ADHD under control. Lubar (1976) was the first to produce a computer treatment protocol, as a DOS computer program ('Autogenics').

In 1991, Lubar wrote that he sometimes strayed from the principle of a fixed SMR threshold. Using the original method, he had found that while learning certainly occurred, it frequently required 60 sessions. In his new method, he set the SMR threshold for the first sessions at 2 µV, followed by some sessions at 3 µV, then by 3.8 µV, 4 µV, 4.3 µV, and finally 5 µV. Likewise, the theta thresholds systematically decreased five times. Generally, 30 sessions seemed sufficient. He argued that this method produced faster learning curves with less trouble; therefore, it offered a superior clinical approach. On the other hand, Lubar has elsewhere described that SMR demonstrates mostly amplitude of 5-6 µV, and that over the course of training, the number of bursts, but not their amplitude, increases. The original studies demonstrate that SMR amplitude is frequently higher in normal subjects than in people with epilepsy or ADHD. Considering that nowadays it is known that bursts of frequency bands have a 'power law' (1/f) distribution, we can expect that less bursts probably means that the mean amplitude of the bursts will also be lower.

Lubar (1995) adjusted his power or amplitude training protocol so that reward/feedback signals for children occurred during 15 to 25% of the training time and that during this feedback time, SMR (12-15 Hz) or beta (16-20 Hz) were maintained for at least 500 ms above the threshold. As soon as the feedback was consistent 25% of the time, the difficulty of threshold attainment increased. Lubar's golden rule was that the feedback should be established in the first session to deliver a reward 30 to 50% of the time, and the inhibitory threshold should be established so that inhibition occurs 50 to 70% of the time. Lubar reported that using this method, adults scored 7 to 15 points per minute and children younger than 12 scored between 10 to 25 points per minute. Overall, trainees received about 10 rewards per minute during the first session. If the thresholds were fixed in the first session and maintained over the following sessions, then a successful training can be described as finally achieving rewards 50 to 70% of the time and inhibition 30 to 50% of the time. Lubar (2000) set the reward threshold for children at 50%, for adolescents at 40%, and for adults at 30%. The inhibit thresholds for the three groups were 50%, 60%, and 70%, respectively. For children, it is less frustrating if the rewards follow each other quickly. However, a disadvantage is that lowered signal strength of 12-15 Hz activity is also awarded in addition to SMR bursts. With favorable training, the degree of difficulty may increase, bearing in mind the abovementioned advantages and disadvantages. Othmer decreased the degree of difficulty with a reward threshold set at 70%. In this manner, rewards are easily obtained (often in the form of a progressing game or video), although doubts may be raised about whether learning can take place when such frequent rewards are given from the start. Children do enjoy a wonderful game, but the question is whether it is still EEG training.

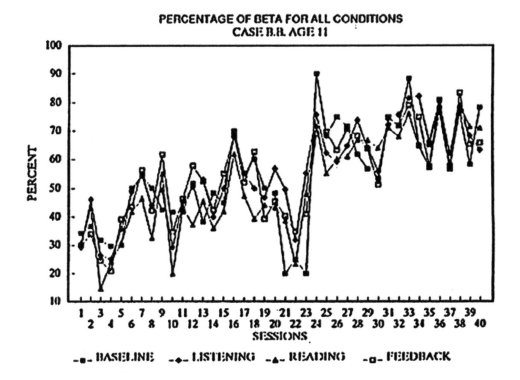

Figure 77. Case study of an 11-year-old boy in which the percentage of the time that beta-1-waves rose above the reward threshold increased from around 30% to 70% over 40 sessions. With kind permission from Springer Science+Business Media: Biofeedback and Self-Regulation, 16(3), 1991, 201–225, Lubar.

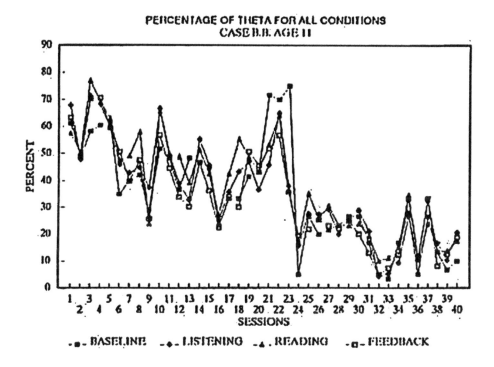

Figure 78. Case study of an 11-year-old boy with ADHD in which the percentage of the time in which theta waves rose above the inhibit threshold decreased from 70% to 20% over forty sessions. With kind permission from Springer Science+Business Media: Biofeedback and Self-Regulation, 16(3), 1991, 201-225, Lubar.

Thompson and Thompson (1998) used a minimum duration of 500 ms for power or amplitude to cross a threshold with a feedback at a rate of 15 to 20 points per minute. To combat boredom in children, a rate of 30 to 40 points a minute proved better. Sometimes, it helped to set a reward threshold 0.5 µV above the SMR average value or average beta-1 baseline and an inhibit threshold 1 µV under the average theta base line. In 2003, the prominent German/English research group (Fuchs, Birbaumer, Lutzenberger, Gruzelier, and Kaiser) set the reward threshold for SMR and beta at 60% of the time with the condition that the minimum duration of a rewarded 'burst' should be 500 ms. Similarly, theta activity had to stay below the threshold 70% of the time for a minimum duration of 500 ms. Thus, an ideal difficulty level of the training, as determined by the thresholds, lay between that set by Lubar and Othmer. The reward threshold increased if the reward threshold was exceeded 70% of the time for two consecutive sessions. The inhibit threshold decreased if theta amplitude stayed below the threshold 85 to 90 % of the time over two sessions, which is in line with Lubar's practice with over 40 years of experience. Another possibility exists to set an automatic reward threshold during the first two minutes of the initial training session at 40%, for instance, and an automatic inhibit threshold at 60%, both remaining fixed thereafter.

6.5 First Neurofeedback Studies

At the end of the sixties, Sterman studied SMR neurofeedback for the first time. He investigated the EEG characteristics of the transition from wakefulness to sleep in cats and apes. Sterman was inspired by Pavlov's model of 'internal inhibition', a process occurring during the extinction of learned behavior. Pavlov employed a classical conditioning experiment in which hearing a tone on provision of food led ultimately to the dogs salivating upon hearing the tone in the absence of food. A different tone signaled that an electric shock would follow on pulling their paw away from a handle. Whenever the two tones gradually became more and more similar to each other, the dogs no longer exhibited the conditioned behavior and eventually fell asleep. Pavlov called this process 'internal inhibition.' Sterman (Roth, 1967), who was initially interested in the EEG correlations during the transition from sleep to waking, saw Pavlov's 'internal inhibition' as a possible model. He used another method, that is, he trained hungry cats using operant rather than classical conditioning. In the first phase, the animals received 2 cc of milk and a chicken cube if they pushed a handle. In the second phase of the experiment, a food reward was given only if they learned not to push the handle upon hearing a tone. As long as the handle was pressed, the tone continued and stopped only when the handle was released. Whenever the cats learned to refrain from pressing the handle during the tone, an SMR was measurable in the EEG. After the reward was received, a parietal post reinforcement alpha rhythm appeared.

In the next phase of his experiment, Wyrwicka and Sterman (1968) trained the cats via operant conditioning to increase the SMR directly to obtain rewards. This was accomplished easily, and in the first session, the SMR occurred after 5 to 10 seconds. Inhibition of movement together with a lowered muscle tone was a necessary but not sufficient condition to generate SMR. After 150 to 200 conditioned SMR responses, satiety was reached and there was no need to continue further training in the same session.

Figure 79. One of Sterman's cats during an SMR experiment (Image appears with permission from Barry Sterman).

Immediately following the rewarding of SMR, the PRS rhythm (post reinforcement rhythm) also frequently occurred in these cats' parietal EEG (Howe and Sterman, 1972). This reflects brief moments of satiety and 'drive reduction' following a reward. If this learning process went well, the density of sleep spindles during sleep would increase, being accompanied by fewer moments of awakening in the course of sleep. The epilepsy threshold for these cats increased following injection of an epileptogenic GABA antagonist. This suggests that sensitivity of thalamocortical circuits decreased in these animals. Muscles relaxed, giving less sensory feedback from muscles to the thalamus, leading to consequent hyperpolarization of the ventroposterolateral nucleus. This led to an increase in SMRs and thus to stabilization of sleep and wake patterns. These results prompted Sterman to apply this training to people with epilepsy. He subsequently demonstrated concomitant improvements in frontal executive functions. In 1976, Lubar described an amelioration of hyperactivity and attention disorders in a hyperactive child with epilepsy. The training protocol was refined in subsequent studies to strengthen the 12-15 Hz (SMR) and weaken the 4-7 Hz (theta).

In the eighties, Tansey (1985) undertook multiple studies, demonstrating positive clinical effects of this treatment on children with various types of learning difficulties comorbid with attentional problems. A typical course of the treatment consisted of 20 to 40 weekly half hour sessions that boosted the quantity of SMR.

6.6 Controlled Studies

One of the legitimate criticisms of these early studies is that they did not control for confounding factors, that is, they did not include an untreated control group or comparison. This began to change in 1995 when Cartozzo examined the effects of 12-15 Hz training on eight children with ADHD in comparison with an untreated ADHD control group. He found significant improvement in the treated group but not in controls on WISC-R IQ subscales, which are arithmetic, digit span, and coding. This 'load' working memory is therefore sensitive to attentional difficulties. The treated group showed significant improvement on an attentional test (TOVA: Test of Variables of Attention). In the same year, Scheinbaum (1995) performed a controlled study providing neurofeedback training to eight children with ADHD. ADHD control group received training in a mathematical computer game. The treated group performed better on the TOVA and received better ratings on a behavioral scale.

Rossiter and La Vaque (1995) published a controlled study of a group of 46 children with ADHD. The subgroup that received neurofeedback training showed an improvement equivalent to a group treated with Ritalin or dextro-amphetamine. Nineteen of the twenty-three children who had received neurofeedback showed clear improvements. In 2004, the same author repeated this study, obtaining the same results for a group of 62 children with ADHD, half of whom received neurofeedback and the other half Ritalin or dextro-amphetamine.

Linden (1996) performed a controlled single blind study (in which the researcher did not know the participants' treatment group) of 18 children with ADHD. Nine children received 40 neurofeedback sessions and the other nine were placed on a treatment waiting list. A significant improvement in attention and in aggressive and hyperactive behaviors was measured in the treated group only.

Later in the nineties, a number of large-scale studies were conducted with more than 100 children and adult participants in the United States (Othmer, 1999; Thompson and Thompson, 1998). Neuropsychological attention tests and behavioral rating scales showed positive results, but there was no ADHD control group available for comparison. Despite this shortcoming, these results remain impressive because those children and adults who respond little to other treatments often resort to neurofeedback; thus, it is less probable that a placebo effect can wholly explain these results. Thompson's study included 100 child participants, 30 of whom took Ritalin from the start of the treatment. At the end of the treatment, only six of these children (20%) appeared to still need Ritalin.

Leins (2004) assessed a group of children with ADHD who had received neurofeedback training to lower the theta/beta-1 ratio at C3 and/or C4, finding a good response in 30% of the children.

Rossiter (2002) published an exhaustive case study of a 13-year-old boy with ADHD who also attained a lower theta/beta-1 ratio trained at C3 or C4. Rossiter remarked on the advantage of having only a single parameter displayed on the screen, in this case, the theta/ beta-1 ratio, as a measure of activation level; thus, making feedback clearer to the trainee. He set the threshold at 1.2 to 1.3 times the average ratio obtained during the first session. The very simple instruction asked to keep the column below threshold as much as possible and the screen next to the on screen column displayed the cumulative percentage success rate. A tone sounded if the column fell under the threshold. Rossiter strongly advised against experimenting with different goal reaching strategies. After 45 sessions, good clinical outcomes were attained, i.e., the theta/beta-1 ratio declined from 33.21 to 28.70 and theta amplitude decreased from 11.14 µV to 9.79 µV while SMR and beta (15-18 Hz) amplitude showed virtually no change. There was a slight increase in alpha amplitude from 6.44 µV to 6.92 µV and a slight decrease in beta-2 (22-39 Hz) amplitude from 4.82 µV to 4.54 µV. This discrete global stabilization of the EEG spectrum is comparable with Sterman and Tansey's findings. The standard deviation of the theta/beta-1 ratio and theta amplitude also decreased, as did the variation coefficient (the ratio of the standard deviation to the mean value). The last variable indicated that the trained parameters decreased not only in absolute terms, but also in relative terms, pointing to an increasingly stable, less labile signal. The standard deviation of the alpha amplitude and the variability coefficient increased (and therefore signal variability).

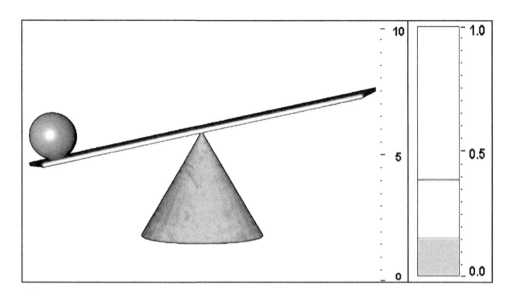

Figure 80. Screen display for training of theta/beta–1 or theta/ SMR ratio. The column indicates the value of this ratio at any given moment. The goal is to keep this column under the threshold as much as possible. Success is indicated whenever the animation shows the ball rolling to the left in accordance with the instruction to keep the ball to the left as much as possible.

Thompson, who scrupulously followed Lubar's training protocols in her published studies, wrote in her handbook (Thompson & Thompson, 2003) that in daily clinical practice, she used individualized training protocols, as Lubar did. She used a theta/SMR ratio and a theta/16-20 Hz ratio trainings protocol, similar to the protocol employed in Rossiter's case study.

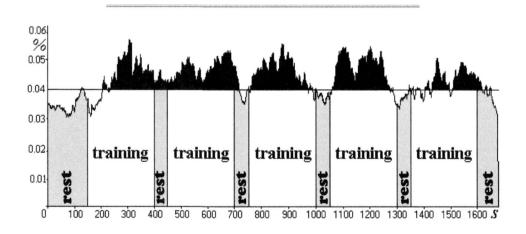

Figure 81. Progress of a boy with ADHD during the 15th neurofeedback session in which the ratio between beta-1 (15–18 Hz) and the rest of the frequency spectrum between 0.5 and 30 Hz was trained over 5 minute periods (300 seconds) with short rest pauses. During feedback, the ratio clearly increased, falling back again during rest. A smooth curve joins the points in the graph, creating false impression that there is no moment; that the ratio is above threshold during basic measurement and during rest periods; and that during neurofeedback segments, the ratio is practically never above the threshold. Reprinted from International Journal of Psychophysiology, 55(1), Kropotov, ERPs correlates of EEG relative beta training in ADHD children, Copyright (2005), with permission from Elsevier.

Kropotov (2005) published an analogous study in which the ratio of beta and SMR were trained at C3-Fz or C4-Pz in a group of 86 children. The threshold was set so that this ratio was above threshold 50% of the time during the first baseline measurement. The ratio increased in sessions 15 through 22, but this improvement was not maintained at the end of any session. Nevertheless, 82% of the children showed clinical improvement and an improvement in the go/no-go evoked P3 brain potential, which indicates a functional improvement in parietal stimulus evaluation and frontal response inhibition.

Monastra (2002) followed 101 children with ADHD who were treated with Ritalin and received parent counseling and educational support. A condition of participation in the study was an abnormally high EEG distractibility index (theta/beta-1) ratio. In addition, 51 of the children received neurofeedback training aimed at normalization of this index. Overall, participants completed 43 training sessions. Twelve months later, the trained group showed significant improvement on behavioral scale ratings, as assessed by parents and teachers. This improvement was seen even after the discontinuation of medication for a week! Lubar (1995) had previously shown that following neurofeedback, only 11 out of 17 children and young adults showed clear improvement and normalization of the theta/beta-1 ratio.

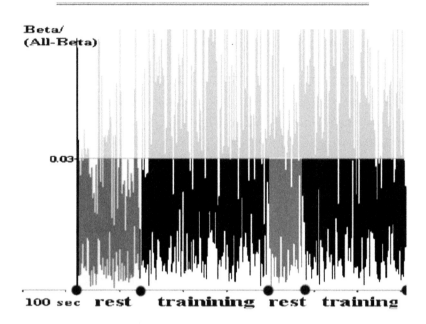

Figure 82. Fragment of neurofeedback session with the same training protocol as in Figure 81 showing an increase of beta-1 compared to the rest (all–beta) of the EEG spectrum. All measurement points are displayed without smoothing the curve (as in the previous figure). It is clear that during rest moments, values of the trained ratio frequently lay under the 0.03 reward threshold, but it is also true that it is above threshold from time to time. In the very first session, the threshold was set so that the measured values were above threshold 50% of the time. During training sessions measured values were frequently above the threshold, but also regularly below it. This is an early session, in contrast to the previous figure in which the reward threshold is higher. Reprinted from International Journal of Psychophysiology, 55(1), Kropotov et al., ERPs correlates of EEG relative beta training in ADHD children, Copyright (2004), with permission from Elsevier.

As far back as 1977, Lubar noticed that during SMR training for epilepsy, an increased quantity of SMR during early sessions, which was not maintained after the end of the sessions. During the final sessions of the treatment, the amount of SMR before and after the sessions increased, which he regarded as necessary, that is, if this transfer had not occurred, training would have been futile. He emphasized, as Sterman (1980) had in the infancy of neurofeedback, that the thinking behind the training is the attainment of a permanent reorganization of the nervous system. Undoubtedly, Sterman had demonstrated in 1980 that isolated training of the SMR rhythm could lead to global normalization of the EEG (with decreased theta and slowed beta activity).

Tansey (1985, 1991a), who also trained SMR at Cz (at the middle of the skull), found that decrease in theta activity accompanied this change. He visualized the brain as a functional network of reciprocal links, enabling the possibility that any pattern of neural activation may trigger a change in the entire matrix. Sterman (1980) had independently reached the same conclusion through his research. He considered SMR as a catalyst for a synergetic EEG normalization. Extending this line of thought, Monastra's (1999, 2001) distractibility index provides a measure of the functional integration of the unregulated subsystems in ADHD.

Lubar (1995) demonstrated that at least 20 to 40 sessions (1 to 2 times a week) are necessary to reach the desired goal, followed by several monthly sessions to consolidate the training. Lubar (1995a) obtained good results for 80% of treated children and adults, or 52 patients in total. Moreover, these gains appeared to be maintained after 10 years, as assessed by the Conners' Behavioral Rating Scale; general attitude; ability to complete tasks; better school results; and improved relationships with friends, family, and others. Fuchs (2003) studied a group of 34 children aged 8 to 12 years of whom 22 were treated with neurofeedback and 12 with Ritalin. Both groups showed similar improvement on the TOVA and behavioral scales, as rated by teachers and parents.

Since 2003, a number of methodologically stronger studies published the positive effects of neurofeedback for people with ADHD. The German research group of Birbaumer who studied slow cortical potential neurofeedback for years (see Chapter 8) published the first comparative study of slow cortical potentials neurofeedback and theta/beta neurofeedback for ADHD in 2004 (Leine, 2004). Both forms of neurofeedback appeared to deliver comparable clinical results. A later study (Strehl, 2006) in which the effects appeared to be maintained at 6 months (Leins, 2007) and at 2-year follow-up (Gani, 2008) confirmed this finding. Not only self-regulation of the EEG was maintained, but also the clinical results. After 2 years, half of the treated children no longer met the ADHD diagnostic criteria, with further improvements in the clinical situation immediately following the end of the course of the treatment.

Bakhshayesh (2011) compared the effectiveness of neurofeedback among 18 children with ADHD with the results of EMG biofeedback (with the same visual and auditory feedback) in 17 ADHD children and found that the effectiveness of the first treatment clearly surpassed the biofeedback. Two newer neurofeedback studies in 2009 provided comparison to computerized cognitive training (i.e., control group), which in itself was an important improvement in design. Moreover, both studies for the first time employed randomized trials, which finally addressed the shortcomings of earlier studies. Gevensleben (2009) studied 102 children with ADHD and the outcomes were clearly better for half of the children treated with neurofeedback. Neurofeedback consisted of a block of 18 sessions of theta/beta training and a block of 18 slow cortical potential training sessions. Both neurofeedback trainings yielded similar results. In a later publication (Gevensleben, 2010), the changes in the EEG of these two groups of children were examined. No significant differences in baseline activity were observed between the neurofeedback group and the cognitive training group, except, the former showed clear decrease in theta activity over central and theta midline (Cz, Pz). Moreover, higher theta baseline activity and a greater decline after theta/beta training were linked to clinical improvement. After six months, the positive clinical outcome was still maintained (Gevensleben, 2010b). Holtmann (2009) compared the outcome of theta/beta training among 20 ADHD children with the results of a computerized cognitive training among 14 ADHD children. In this study, the results of a neurophysiological response inhibition task were clearly better in the neurofeedback group. Two recent controlled studies also utilized cognitive training in a control group and compared the results with those of neurofeedback in ADHD children, also with clearly better outcome in the latter (Steiner, 2014; Studer, 2014). In a subsequent study, Steiner's positive outcome was also maintained after six months (Steiner, 2014b). Six recent randomized studies and one non-randomized study have utilized Ritalin in a control group, comparing it to neurofeedback in ADHD children, with similar outcome in both groups (Duric, 2012; 2014; Gonzalez-Castro, non-randomized, 2016; Janssen, 2016; Li, 2013; Meisel, 2013; Russell-Chapin, 2013). In Meisel and Li's study, positive clinical outcome was also maintained after six months. In Janssen and Gonzalez' study, both neurofeedback and Ritalin resulted in comparable reductions in theta power from pre- to post-intervention. For neurofeedback, greater reductions in theta were related to greater reductions in ADHD symptoms.

Four meta-analyses studies documented the therapeutic usefulness of EEG neurofeedback in ADHD. The first meta-analysis of Arns (2009) found an effect size (ES) that was more significant for the inattention dimension than for the hyperactivity dimension of ADHD. Arns computed the data from 12 studies and found a pooled within subjects ES of 1.02 for inattention, 0.71 for hyperactivity, and 0.94 for impulsivity. These results, however, may have been influenced by the placebo effect, because the ES for controlled studies was considerably lower, although still impressive. In the same meta-analysis, NF was superior to passive or semi-active control groups, with a pooled estimated ES of 0.81 for inattention, 0.4 for hyperactivity, and 0.69 for impulsivity. Arns' conclusion was that neurofeedback for ADHD is 'efficacious and specific'. Lofthouse (2012) conducted a systematic review and reported the findings of 14 randomized controlled trials, 11 of which were conducted between 2005 and 2010. These authors were able to identify 8 unpublished studies not included in Arns' review. Lofthouse was fairly more restrictive than the previous meta-analysis in regard to the minimal acceptable methodological quality of studies, although the results yielded comparable ES of 0.69 (95 % CI 0.34-1.66) for overall ADHD symptoms, 0.79 (95 % CI 0.41-1.62) for inattention, and 0.71

(95 % CI 0.35-1.55) for hyperactivity/ impulsivity. Five of the 14 studies showed neurophysiological changes that were specific to the neurofeedback treatment. Only four of the 14 studies utilized triple blind procedures (children, parents and/or teachers who rate children's behavior, and clinicians all blind) while in 6 of the studies, none of these 3 sources were blind. Lofthouse's conclusion was that neurofeedback for ADHD was 'probably efficacious.' One could also argue that requiring a triple blind trial with a credible sham condition is unreasonable because this is a higher standard than that employed in most psychotherapy outcome studies. To establish the efficacy of behavioral treatment for ADHD, for example, a triple blind trial is not possible because clinicians know what treatment they are providing and parents know what treatment their child is receiving. Despite this, behavior therapy is considered a strong evidence-based treatment for ADHD. In response to this objection, the authors argued that the highest standard of scientific rigor should be required for any treatment offered to the public for which triple blind studies are possible (they are not possible for behavior therapy), and which are not precluded by strong ethical considerations. They noted that this is especially true for neurofeedback, as such study is possible and the treatment requires substantial time, effort, and expense.

The third meta-analysis of Sonuga-Barke (2013) found a significantly higher ES than in the control group in randomized and open trials, but this effect became non-significant in randomized and blinded trials. The fourth meta-analysis of Micoulaud-Franchi (2014) included five published randomized controlled trials (RCT) with semi-active control and sham-neurofeedback groups: two from the previous meta-analysis of Sonuga-Barke, i.e., Gevensleben (2009b) and Bakhshayesh (2011), and three recently published RCTs (van Dongen-Boomsma, 2013; Maurizio, 2014; Steiner, 2014b). A significantly higher ES was found in randomized and blinded trials for the inattention dimension of ADHD compared to the control group. The major findings of this updated meta-analysis are that: (i) neurofeedback significantly improves the ADHD total score on a parent-assessment scale with a medium effect size of -0.49; (ii) neurofeedback significantly improves both the inattention and hyperactivity/impulsivity dimensions on a parent-assessment scale with medium effect sizes of -0.46 and -0.34, respectively; and (iii) neurofeedback significantly improves the inattention dimension on a teacher-assessment scale with a smaller effect size of -0.30. These results confirmed the findings of the meta-analysis of Sonuga-Barke (2013) on the overall ADHD score, showing a medium effect size of -0.59 for a probably blinded assessment and of -0.29 for a probably unblinded assessment. The methodological strength and novelty of the present updated meta-analysis was to combine stringent inclusion criteria similar to the meta-analysis of Sonuga-Barke (2013) with the additional consideration of the inattention and hyperactivity/impulsivity dimensions. These precautions allowed us to observe the effects of evidence-supporting neurofeedback on inattention symptoms in ADHD in both probably unblinded parents and probably blinded teacher assessments with similar effect sizes. It should be noted that efficacy concerning the inattention dimension was proportional to the number of neurofeedback sessions, and it seemed to be maintained over time.

6.7 Double Blind Studies

Until very recently, no double blind studies (in which neither the therapist nor the patient knows for sure who is in the group that receives neurofeedback or who is in a control group given pseudo-neurofeedback) had been undertaken. From a scientific viewpoint, this has been a major weakness for some years; fortunately, several double blind studies have been published lately. It should be noted that many authors have argued that the use of sham-neurofeedback as a control group is unnecessary (although individuals are not told in which treatment group they are, it is easy for them to guess whether they are in the effective treatment group or in the placebo group), unethical (ADHD is a debilitating disorder with known efficacious treatments) and even not feasible. However, all of these comments have been invalidated decisively.

DeBeus (2011) performed the first randomized triple blind (children, raters, trainers) study of the therapeutic efficacy of neurofeedback training for children in 2004. In the study, 53 children with ADHD (ages 7 to 11) completed 40 sessions with a cross over in treatment group after 20 sessions. During each session, every child had a metal electrode placed on the scalp (Fz) and watched a video game. For the first group, brain activity (neurofeedback) modulated the video game for 20 sessions, followed by 20 sessions in which brain activity (pseudo-neurofeedback) no longer modulated the game. The second group received the same treatment in reverse order. The real neurofeedback sessions improved attention, hyperactivity, aggressive behavior, adaptability to change, social interactions, and organizational skills. In addition, study habits and a better attitude toward school improved. The treated group scored better on computerized attention tests, and the results were more salient. Moreover, only this group showed a reduction in theta and an increase in beta-1 activity. About a third of the children were able to reduce their dosage of Ritalin after neurofeedback.

Orlandi and Greco (2004) described similar outcomes with two groups of 18 boys with the hyperactive subtype of ADHD. The children were assigned randomly to one of two groups. The experimental group received 40 sessions of neurofeedback in the form of a video game while the control group played a video game with the same complexity and duration as the neurofeedback group. For those in the control group, measurements were made with EEG electrodes without providing feedback. The therapists knew the assignment of children to groups, but the children's parents and the researchers who evaluated any behavioral changes in the children did not. Overall, 47% of the control group and only 6% of the neurofeedback group did not complete the course of 40 sessions. The treatment group showed clear improvement on behavioral scales.

A third triple blind study (Picard, 2006) ran in two phases. During the first phase, 31 children with an ADHD diagnosis and a theta/beta-1 ratio greater than 2.5 were assigned randomly to either a waiting list or a 40-session neurofeedback group (training to increase SMR and decrease theta). Only the children receiving neurofeedback improved on behavioral scale measurements. Neurofeedback measurements from the first phase were used to fake neurofeedback sessions in the second phase. In this second phase, 31 children were assigned randomly to one of the three groups, a wait list group, a neurofeedback group, or a pseudo-neurofeedback group. Once again, only the neurofeedback group showed improvement on behavioral scales while the ratings for the group that received pseudo-neurofeedback and the wait list group did not evidence statistically meaningful changes.

Li's study (2014) was a randomized controlled double blind study with 6 months follow up that demonstrated better results in the active neurofeedback group versus a sham neurofeedback group. Both groups were taking Ritalin at the same time as neurofeedback and sham neurofeedback.

On the other hand, a series of double blind studies of neurofeedback in ADHD were not able to demonstrate specific clinical improvements larger than placebo (Logemann, 2010; van Dongen-Boomsma, 2013; Arnold, 2013; Vollebregt, 2014). However, most of these studies failed by not respecting methodological neurofeedback requirements. For example, in some studies, a too high percentage (80%!) of rewards or an autothresholding method was offered, preventing real operant conditioning to take place (Arns, 2013). In Arnold's study, electrodes were placed on the forehead (and not Cz), a region known to be problematic for recording because of muscle artefacts.

6.8 Meta-Analysis of Non-Pharmacological Treatments in ADHD

All of the above-mentioned controlled neurofeedback studies were set up in a similar way as controlled studies to evaluate drug treatments. Some, however, considered neurofeedback as a psychological intervention (operant conditioning), which cannot be studied in a similar way as drug interventions. Psychological interventions employing behavioral and cognitive techniques have been shown to be effective in the treatment of ADHD in children in empirical studies. Hodgson (2014) presented a meta-analysis of seven controlled nonpharmacological treatments in ADHD: behavior modification, neurofeedback, multimodal psychosocial treatment, school-based programs, working memory training, parent training, and self-monitoring. This meta-analysis aimed to investigate, which psychologically based interventions were most efficacious in the treatment of ADHD in children aged between 5 and 10 years old. To determine the most efficacious ADHD intervention, their overall effect on outcome measures was examined. On that basis, neurofeedback treatment was the most efficacious, being associated with the largest positive average weighted effect size and thus greatest improvement in the treatment group for outcome measures combined, followed by the multimodal psychosocial intervention. According to the average weighted effect size across the outcome measures, the working memory training, behavior modification, school-based, parent training, and self-monitoring interventions did not result in greater improvement in the treatment group compared to the control group, and thus cannot be deemed to be efficacious. We can wonder why traditional nonpharmacological treatments are so well accepted ADHD treatments and why neurofeedback is still so difficult go be accepted.

Psychological intervention	Average weighted effect size	Ranking number
Neurofeedback	0.21	1
Multimodal psychosocial	0.09	2
Working memory training	−0.02	3
Behavior modification	−0.03	4
School based	−0.26	5
Parent training	−0.51	6
Self-monitoring	−5.91	7

Figure 83. Ranking of the psychologically based interventions for ADHD based on the average weighted Effect Size, across 20 outcome measures (Hodgson, 2014).

Summary

Neurofeedback can be understood as a learning process (specifically, operant conditioning) in which rewarding feedback signals are triggered every time the desired EEG pattern occurs. Another viewpoint argues that conscious self-regulation is involved to some degree. However, practitioners have come to think that in reality, this mechanism proceeds unconsciously. The most popular training programs aim to increase SMR rhythms or beta-1 rhythms and simultaneously decrease theta activity. This enables better behavioral self-regulation, which consists of, among other things, improvements in attention and executive functions.

In the 1980s, Lubar published the first neurofeedback research on children with ADHD. In the 1990s, a series of single blind studies were published in which outcomes were compared with either an untreated control group or a group treated with Ritalin. In the present decade, a number of double blind studies have also been published. Neurofeedback has been shown to be superior to a variety of control group conditions. It has been found to be equivalent to Ritalin in treating the core symptoms of ADHD in seven studies. Six of these controlled studies were randomized and were highly concordant with many of the more than fifty reports of open clinical trials since 1990. Regarding long term results, eight randomized controlled studies included two with 2-year follow-up assessments. In each of these studies, in one study, the gains were maintained after the treatment had ended and in the other one, they increased further in the 2-year follow-up assessment, such that 50% of the children no longer met the criteria for ADHD.

6.8 Changes in Cognitive Brain Potentials Following Neurofeedback

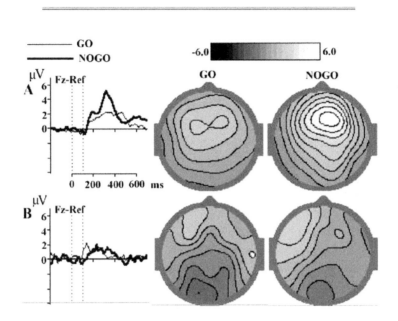

Figure 84. **Left.** *These images illustrate the average frontal potential values following neurofeedback training (uppermost trace) and preceding neurofeedback training (bottommost trace) among a group of 16 children with ADHD. Predominantly, the "no-go" P3 potential, and to a lesser degree the "go" P3 potential, is stronger after treatment.* **Right.** *These mappings illustrate the widely distribution of these potentials over the scalp. Reprinted from International Journal of Psychophysiology, 55(1), Kropotov et al., ERPs correlates of EEG relative beta training in ADHD children, Copyright (2004), with permission from Elsevier.*

Kropotov (2005) demonstrated that for people with ADHD, the evoked frontal no-go P3 brain potential measured in the go/no-go task (in which a response to the no-go stimulus must be suppressed) decreases following the no-go stimulus in good but not in bad performers. Source localization studies showed that this response-inhibition potential rises in the dorsal anterior cingulate. Following successful neurofeedback training, it has been found that with improvements in attentional functions and behavior, this potential is normalized, which reflects decreased impulsivity and improved action and conflict monitoring. Kropotov (2007) also found normalization of the weaker beta and theta synchronization during the go/no-go task, as well as normalization of the weaker alpha desynchronization. Kropotov emphasized that all neurofeedback-related changes were found only in EEG reactions (ERP and ERS/ERD), but not in the back-ground EEG spectrograms. There may be two reasons for that. First, spectrograms are more variable compared to ERPs/ERDs, i.e., inter-individual variations in spectrograms and consequently standard deviations are bigger compared to those for ERPs/ERDs. Thus, the power of the statistical criteria for assessment changes in spectrograms is infe-rior to those of ERPs/ERSs and, consequently, does not reveal any statistically significant change. Second, neurofeedback may indeed change only reactivity of the brain to certain stimuli in certain conditions. Holtmann (2009), comparing the effects of neurofeedback and attention skills training, found an improved frontal no-go N2 only after neurofeed-back in ADHD, which was accompanied by a reduction of impulsivity errors.

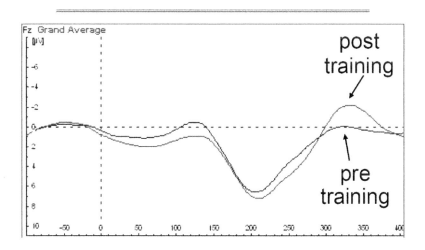

Figure 85. Improved frontal no-go N2 after neurofeedback in ADHD children (Holtmann, 2009).

In a recent study, clinical and neurophysiological differences were also found after 16 theta/beta neurofeedback sessions in a group of 18 boys when compared with a wait-ing list control group of 17 boys with ADHD (Bluschke, 2016).

After NFB ADHD boys committed significantly less false alarms on the go/no-go task, indicating less impulsivity in this group. In the waiting list control group, no such improvement was found. Also, all ADHD symptoms as measured by parent ratings were only reduced in the NFB group.

On no-go trials only, the P3 amplitude increased only in the NFB group, and its peak latency occurred approximately 100 ms earlier after training than before. sLORETA analysis showed that the differences in no-go P3 amplitudes after NFB were due to acti-vation differences in the anterior cingulate and superior frontal cortex.

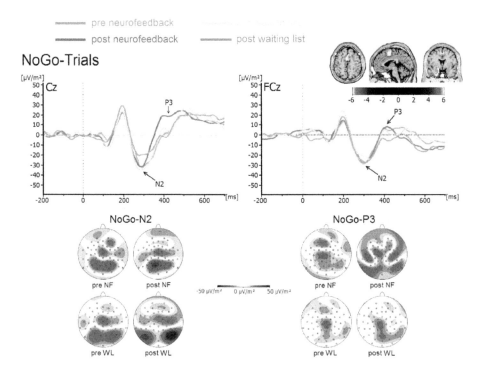

Figure 86. No-go N2 and P3 and their topographic maps for the neurofeedback (NF) and waiting list control (WL) groups. In the maps blue denotes negative deflections whereas red denotes positive ones. The sLORETA plot shows the pre–post difference in no-go P3 amplitudes within the ADHD group (Bluschke, 2016).

Egner and Gruzelier (2001) observed a strengthened P300 (P3b) potential following neurofeedback training in normal people. As previously described, this brain potential is a measure of effective response selection in attentional tasks. An ERP study in 48 ADHD combined type children before and after 30 neurofeedback sessions (Bakhtadze, 2011) confirmed the facts that in ADHD children younger than 12 years of age, the amplitude of P300 on target stimuli declined but latency increased compared to controls. However, the most important finding of this study was that neurofeedback training in these 48 children compared to a control group of 45 ADHD children, also combined type, causes significant increase of amplitude and decrease of latency of P300 without treatment. P300 amplitude reflects intensity of information processing (engagement operation, resource allocation) to select the appropriate behavior and accomplish decision making during the processing of the target stimulus, whereas P300 latency is taken as a reflection of the speed of information processing. This process, from a neurophysiological point of view, is associated with the activation of cortical and subcortical structures that are involved in execution of the selected action, which is disturbed in ADHD children.

Group N (%)	Age M (σ; min-max)	Latency N_1		Amplitude N_1		Latency P_3		Amplitude P_3		Omission errors		Commission errors	
		Before treatment	After treatment	Before treatment	After treatment	Before treatment	After treatment	Before treatment	After treatment	Before treatment	After treatment	Before treatment	After treatment
ADHD with treatment 16 (41 %)	10.63 (.81; 10-12)	115.19 (15.93; 83-133)	113.81 (16.19; 81-132)	5.31 (2.7; 1-10)	5.38 (2.68; 2-10)	465.94 (33.73; 401-523)	417.31 (22.51; 357-441)	6.87 (2.03; 3-10)	9.81 (1.87; 7-13)	5.13 (1.59; 2-8)	2.38 (.89; 1-4)	4.5 (2.31; 1-8)	.88 (.89; 0-3)
ADHD without treatment 23 (59 %)	10.57 (.73; 10-12)	116.78 (15.22; 85-135)	115.61 (16.68; 83-141)	3.61 (1.75; 1-7)	4.13 (1.82; 1-8)	445.26 (51.26; 354-501)	420.13 (45.4; 343-487)	6.39 (1.67; 3-9)	7.3 (1.69; 3-10)	5.39 (2.13; 1-9)	4.7 (1.79; 2-7)	4.3 (1.61; 2-8)	4.87 (2.91; 0-9)

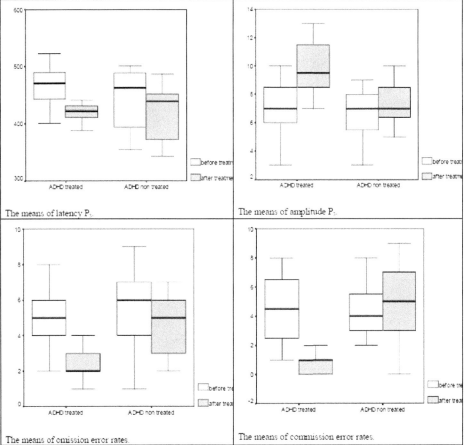

The means of latency P_3.

The means of amplitude P_3.

The means of omission error rates.

The means of commission error rates.

Figure 87. Decrease of P300 latency, increase of P300 amplitude, and decrease of omission and commission errors after active neurofeedback in ADHD (Bakhtadze, 2011).

Together with a positive behavioral outcome, Mayer (2011) found increased P300 amplitudes after 30 sessions of beta 1 and theta neurofeedback in 9 ADHD adults who completed 30 sessions where 15 started the training. No changes in P300 peak latency were found.

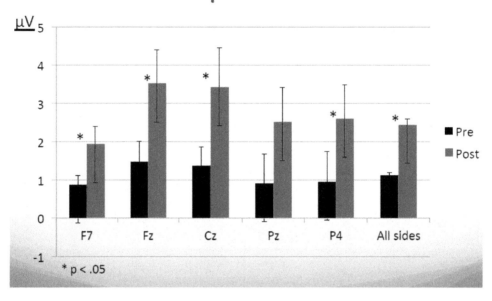

Figure 88. P300 amplitude increase after neurofeedback in ADHD adults (Mayer, 2011).

It is known that neurofeedback influences neural networks that support attention, executive functions, and motor regulation. The effectiveness of neurofeedback in the change of P300 parameters can be explained by the fact that structures, the functioning of which changes during neurofeedback treatment, participate in the electrogenesis of P300. The DLPFC, inferior parietal lobe, and auditory association areas at the junction of the temporoparietal lobes and their reciprocal connections play a significant role in the genesis of P300. Additionally, the amygdala and hippocampus are P300 generators.

6.9 Before and After fMRI Studies of Neurofeedback for People with ADHD

Beauregard (2006) found that a series of 40 EEG biofeedback sessions (SMR/theta Cz protocol) improved executive functions in a group of children with ADHD. He provided further evidence by comparing fMRI brain function images before and after a course of neurofeedback. He was inspired by two previous fMRI imaging studies of children with ADHD discussed in paragraph 2.3.1 in which Vaidya (1998) observed an underactive caudate nucleus in ADHD during the go/no-go task and its normalization after Ritalin administration. Remember that for the control group, the caudate nucleus was more active and became less active after the administration of Ritalin. Apparently, Ritalin had a different effect on children with ADHD in comparison to the children without ADHD.

The second study to influence Beauregard was undertaken by Bush (1999) who found the anterior cingulate to be underactive in adults with ADHD performing the Stroop task (in which the participant must name the color in which a color word is printed, the print color being different from the color indicated by the word).

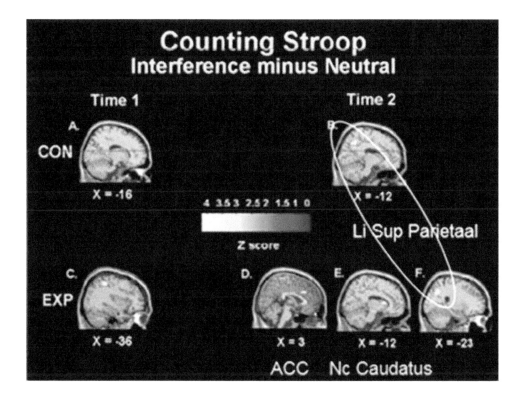

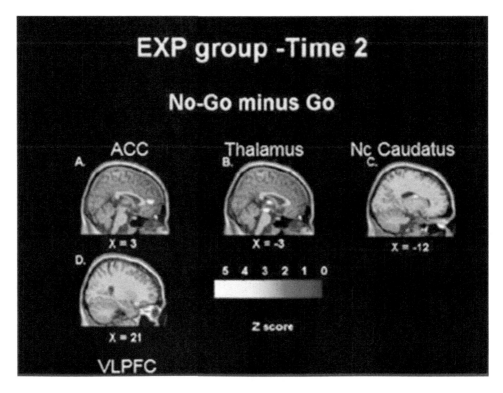

Figure 89. **PRIOR PAGE:** *Small picture on the left illustrates no activation of the anterior cingulate before neurofeedback in two groups of children with ADHD performing a Stroop task. Middle pictures show only the group who received neurofeedback training, showing activation of the dorsal anterior cingulate (D), caudate nucleus (E) and left lateral superior parietal cortex (F) during the Stroop task after training.* **ABOVE:** *Pictures show activation of the left caudate nucleus (C), the dorsal anterior cingulate (A), and bilateral ventrolateral prefrontal cortex (D) after training during a go-/no-go task. Reprinted from Neuroscience Letters, 394(3), Beauregard, Effect of neurofeedback training on the neural substrates of selective attention in children with attention-deficit/hyperactivity disorder: A functional magnetic resonance study, Copyright (2006), with permission from Elsevier.*

Beauregard (2006) investigated a group of 20 children with ADHD of which 15 followed a course of 40 neurofeedback sessions. Both groups of children took pre- and post-neuropsychological tests. Only the treated group showed clear improvements in hyperactivity and attention after the study. Both groups were imaged with pre- and post-fMRIs. Only the treated group showed increased activity in the left caudate nucleus, the dorsal anterior cingulate, and bilaterally in the ventrolateral prefrontal cerebral cortex during the go/no-go task as well as increased activity in the right dorsal anterior cingulate, the left lateral superior parietal cortex, and the caudate nucleus during a Stroop task. This corresponds with research by Kropotov (2005) and Bluschke (2016), who found that the no-go evoked P3 in the dorsal anterior cingulate normalized after the neurofeedback treatment.

Russell-Chapin (2013) investigated a group of 12 ADHD children who were randomly assigned to a neurofeedback group (40 sessions) and a control group. In addition to regulating and increasing SMR, neurofeedback consolidated the posterior default mode network when looked at with rest state fMRI, allowing for appropriate activation of the precuneus, posterior cingulate, the temporoparietal junction, and the cerebellar tonsils. Strengthening the DMN might enable the children to observe more openly without becoming swept-away in reactivity. It would make us understand that they become less error-prone, less volatile, and more adaptive.

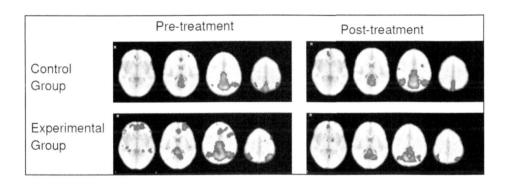

Figure 90. In the experimental group, we see a more consolidated default mode network in fMRI (Russell–Chapin, 2013).

Ros (2013) investigated the effects of one session of thirty minutes Pz alpha downtraining in 17 normal adults by comparing fMRI before and after the session. At the end of the session, he noticed a rebound of alpha at Pz and an improved functioning of the precuneus but also of the dorsal and middle anterior cingulate (salience network). Increased functioning of the precuneus correlated with increased alpha and increased mind wandering. Increased middle and dorsal anterior cingulate functioning facilitates internal or bottom-up attentional drive. It could be representative of enhanced tonic alertness/error monitoring demands in order to maintain task-set and attentional engagement.

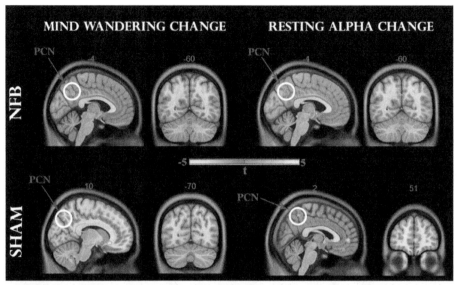

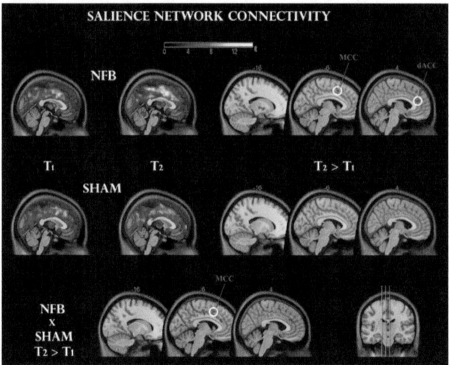

Figure 91. Increased functioning of precuneus, middle, and dorsal anterior cingulate after neurofeedback (Pz alpha downtraining) (Ros, 2013).

Beauregard and Russell-Chapin's discoveries are consistent with the view that a more stable EEG is associated with better functioning of frontal executive functions and with improved global self-regulation. Beauregard's study showed that SMR/theta neurofeedback in ADHD improves the functioning of the dACC while Russell-Chapin showed that it improved functioning of the default mode system. One could assume that improved salience network (dACC) functioning is stabilizing the default-mode network, where we can expect that it will result in more stable posterior alpha. On the other hand, Ros' Pz alpha-downtraining, resulting in alpha rebound, also stabilized the posterior default-mode network together with an improved functioning of the salience network. One could assume that both approaches – the one targeting the salience network (dACC), the other the default mode network (precuneus) - result in the same improvement of balance between the default mode network and the salience network.

Summary

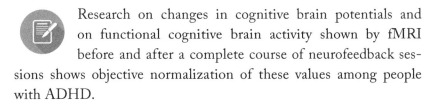 Research on changes in cognitive brain potentials and on functional cognitive brain activity shown by fMRI before and after a complete course of neurofeedback sessions shows objective normalization of these values among people with ADHD.

6.10 What are the Brain Processes During Neurofeedback?

6.10.1 What is Rewarding During a Neurofeedback Session?

Within behavioral therapy, operant conditioning was defined as an alteration in an 'operant,' which is a 'freely willed' behavior. An operant is a behavioral act that has an effect on the environment to produce an outcome, constituting an important component of voluntary behavior. Because the environment can be volatile, the same action may lead to different consequences. Thus, to obtain an optimal outcome, it is crucial to detect action–outcome relationships and adapt the behavior accordingly. Operant conditioning (reinforcement learning) is rewarding an operant, so a behavioral act has an effect on the environment to produce an outcome. The systematic association of a reward with the desired behavior brings about this change. In neurofeedback, a particular EEG pattern is the 'operant' or the 'freely willed' behavior. Feedback provided at specific instances rewards desired EEG patterns. It is sufficient to watch attentively and enjoy the reward that the mounting score offers. The question arises, is this acquisition of points in itself rewarding enough to become operant conditioning? Originally, Sterman studied the SMR rhythm in hungry cats and monkeys, rewarding them with milk and morsels of food. One can assume that the sensation of acquisition of control is part of the process of operant conditioning; after all, operant conditioning refers to a 'voluntary behavior.' The desired EEG pattern develops alongside greater vigilance, implying better functioning of the frontal executive functions. This discussion over voluntary control is an extension of the debate about whether executive functions are things that we do or things that happen to us. Chapter 4 described self-regulation and executive functions as assemblies built from basic elementary processes and not by the agency of a supervisory, guiding 'I.' This train of thought can be extended to argue that the framework of neurofeedback research provides a medium for further investigation into the nature of the executive functions. Neurofeedback can provide a powerful method with which to examine the limits of conscious control over a number of cognitive processes. This new learning process of neurofeedback allows us to access some network relations in the brain (Kotchoubey, 2002), showing that the ability to control a specific EEG parameter develops before the knowledge of how it is created is acquired.

Recent modeling has emphasized that reinforcement takes place not by presenting rewards, but by prediction of reward, but only when the rewarding values of the cues have been established (Schultz, 2007). Some have argued that in neurofeedback, the 'rewards' during sessions do not need to be necessarily intrinsically rewarding but that they should be considered as cues for later reward that can elicit phasic dopaminergic bursting when cues are presented (Thatcher, personal communication). However, such perspective seems incorrect, as for cues to be able to elicit phasic dopaminergic bursting, the relationship with the later rewards needs to have been established, unless one assumes that the rewarding points are associated with the later reward by hierarchical reinforcement learning. Another problem is that in ADHD, the phasic dopaminergic activity in the striatum related to cues is impaired, indicating that reinforcement may be impaired (Tripp and Wickens, 2008). This is precisely the reason why delay aversion is a problem in ADHD, implying that it is not easy to motivate ADHD subjects to perform a training, which is not immediately rewarding. Thus, hierarchical reinforcement learning in ADHD is poor. For this reason, certainly in ADHD, it is important to use immediately rewarding feedback in neurofeedback sessions to keep the subject motivated. As Sterman already emphasized in his early cat experiments, food rewards given to cats were only effective as long as the cats did not get satiated. If we can use effective feedback reward, immediate performance feedback may be beneficial for patients having problems with motivation or reinforcement anticipation, as is the case in ADHD. In these cases, reward feedback should be consistent, not intermittent. In that case, neurofeedback would be applicable particularly to such patients.

Interestingly, the EEG activity, which is trained in ADHD, is related to the dorsal anterior cingulate, which is a part of the loops that are involved in reinforcement learning that is deficient in ADHD. As such, neurofeedback intervention in ADHD is training brain activity associated with delayed reinforcement and with hierarchical reinforcement learning, and so it may also help acquire self-regulation skills useful for compensating motivational deficits and delay aversion in structured and potentially unattractive and boring situations.

6.10.2 Which Brain Systems are Involved in Neurofeedback?

Learning to modulate one's own brain activity is an essential part of neurofeedback applications. In addition to specific training of the neural networks directly involved in the generation and modulation of the neurophysiological parameter, general determinants of neurofeedback efficacy, such as self-referential processes and cognitive control, have been frequently disregarded. It is plausible that the subjective feeling emerging when one is engaged in a task that demands learning from feedback will be accompanied by the activation in brain areas involved in cognitive control.

Nonetheless, deeper insight into these cognitive control mechanisms and their neuronal underpinnings sheds light on various open neurofeedback related questions concerning individual differences, brain-computer interface (BCI) illiteracy, as well as a more general model of neurofeedback learning. In this context, Ninaus (2013) investigated the neuronal substrate of these more general regulatory mechanisms that are engaged when participants believe that they are receiving neurofeedback. Twenty healthy adults performed a sham neurofeedback paradigm during fMRI scanning. All participants were novices to neurofeedback experiments and were instructed to voluntarily modulate their own brain activity based on a visual display of moving color bars. However, the bar depicted a recording and not the actual brain activity of participants. The participants did not receive an explicit strategy on how to gain control over the feedback; therefore, the approach was comparable with conventional EEG neurofeedback instructions in which participants are instructed to relax and concentrate for a certain period of experimental blocks and to use the pauses between them to recover. Specific strategies about how participants were supposed to comply with the instructions were not provided. The visual display was a recording of different sessions of SMR neurofeedback training with EEG. Participants were not informed about the exact meaning of the different bars, only that it was important for them to succeed at keeping the central bar as high as possible and the two lateral bars as low as possible. The animation of the bars was updated 20 times per second and produced by sampling authentic EEG signal of persons undergoing neurofeedback training. Therefore, the movements were naturalistic and representative of a typical session in both 'watch moving bars' and 'get control' conditions. The reports collected at the end of the experiment indicated that participants were unaware of the sham feedback. In comparison to a passive watching condition, bilateral anterior insula, anterior cingulate cortex, supplementary motor, inferior parietal lobule, and dorsomedial and dorsolateral prefrontal areas were activated when participants actively tried to control the bar. In contrast, when merely watching moving bars, increased activation in other occipital, parietal, and temporal areas was observed. These results show that the intention to control a moving bar is sufficient to engage a broad frontoparietal and cingulo-opercular network involved in cognitive control. Especially interesting is that these networks are malfunctioning in ADHD and neurofeedback is trying to influence them positively! The results of the present study indicated that tasks, such as those generally employed in neurofeedback training, recruit the neuronal correlates of cognitive control even when only sham neurofeedback is presented.

In the present study, most participants reported moderate levels of perceived control over bar movements when in reality, they had absolutely no control over it. The results of double-blind studies (e.g., Witte, 2013) revealed that a similar pattern is observed when real neurofeedback is applied. In these studies, most participants receiving either real or sham neurofeedback were not able to guess to which group they were assigned even after many successful training sessions. This shows that even when neurofeedback is applied, the perception of control is not accurate in neurofeedback tasks. To the contrary, perception of control in neurofeedback tasks is inaccurate most of the time. The participation of the anterior insula in the present study may be understood as a central hub, which compares and integrates the external information provided by the feedback display with internal information regarding brain activity. The feedback, when effective, would enable participants to learn the mental representation of the interrelationship between oneself and the feedback bars in the immediate moment. Therefore, neurofeedback could be seen as an embodied tool, meaning that the users embody the provided feedback into their self in a way comparable to that in the BCI literature. Along with the importance of the insula in integrating information provided by the feedback into self-related processes, the participation of anterior cingulate and dorsolateral prefrontal cortex during the 'get control' (self-agency) shed further light onto the neural bases of the process of neurofeedback learning. Neurofeedback requires participants to compare the actual state with the desired state of the feedback to be able to learn how to get control over the neurofeedback paradigm. The anterior cingulate cortex is known to be associated with the detection of discrepancies between an actual and a desired state (Carter, 2000; Kerns, 2004), with self-reflection (Herwig, 2012), and with tuning attentional processes

(Bishop, 2004) connected directly to thalamus, insular cortex, amygdala, and parietal and prefrontal areas (Goldman-Rakic, 1988). Describing these functions of the anterior cingulate cortex highlights the importance of this region in neurofeedback, regardless of the content of specific training programs. Additionally, activation in the right pars opercularis of the inferior frontal gyrus and right middle frontal gyrus was observed. In several studies, those two regions were associated with stimulus-driven attention and the maintenance of attention (e.g., Corbetta and Shulman, 2002). Furthermore, the whole brain analysis revealed activation in several regions associated with cognitive control, such as dorsomedial and dorsolateral prefrontal areas. During the 'get control' condition, participants had to sustain their attention toward internal and external sources over a certain period.

Because of the use of sham feedback only, the activations observed in the present study were due to differences in perceived control and were not affected by specific neurofeedback learning processes. In a recent study, Kober (2013) showed that some strategies employed by neurofeedback participants might lead to a cognitive overload, which prevents neurofeedback learning. Due to the repeated attempts by those persons to gain control over the neurofeedback, they may impede themselves by trying too hard; therefore, they may not able to direct their attention to the quite subtle internal bodily cues, especially in the early stages of the training. Referring to voluntary control of circumscribed brain regions using real-time functional MRI, Birbaumer (2013) suggested that brain responses are learned, stored, and retained in a manner that is comparable to a motor skill, following the rules of implicit learning. In contrast to explicit learning, implicit learning and memory do not require conscious and effortful search.

6.10.3 Is the Trained EEG Activity an 'Operant' ('willed behavior')?

However, how should we understand a specific EEG activity as a behavioral action or an 'operant'? In contrast to some opinions, which assume that any EEG activity can be trained by operant conditioning (reinforcement learning), some basic research has shown that only EEG activity, which is related to motor activity, perceptual activity or, interestingly, executive functioning, can be trained. Although prefrontal neurons are known to change activity depending on expected reward, it remains unknown whether prefrontal activity contributes to obtaining reward. Kobayashi (2010) investigated this issue by establishing variable relationships between levels of single-neuron activity and rewarding outcomes in monkeys with intracerebral microelectrodes. Lateral prefrontal neurons changed their spiking activity according to the specific requirements for gaining reward, without the animals making a motor response. Thus, spiking activity constituted an operant response. The data from a control task suggested that these changes were unlikely to reflect simple reward predictions. These data demonstrated a remarkable capacity of prefrontal neurons to adapt to specific operant requirements at the single-neuron level. Several lines of evidence suggest that the primate lateral prefrontal cortex (LPFC) contributes to operant behavior at a level higher than the control of specific motor responses. Single-neuron activity in the LPFC changes by behavioral demand and correlates with performance rates in operant tasks. Patients with lesions in the LPFC lose intentional control of behavioral responses, making automatic responses that blindly follow given instructions. These observations led to the commonly held notion that the LPFC guides purposeful flexible behavior.

Kobayashi's operant schedule involved both the control of reward outcome and the prediction of reward. To dissociate between the two processes, he used the control schedule, which included simple reward prediction without involving operant control. He tested the effect of reward prediction by contrasting neuronal activity between rewarded and nonrewarded trials and found little effect of reward prediction on neuronal activity. This result suggests that presently tested prefrontal neurons were insensitive to the prediction of immediate reward outcomes in the absence of operant control. The control schedule was used to assess the potential role of reward prediction in increasing prefrontal activity. In this schedule, the bar stretched at a random pace, unlinked to neuronal activity. The animal obtained a reward if the bar stretched fast, acquired the goal within the cue period, and received no reward otherwise. The difference in activity between rewarded and nonrewarded trials (Pavlovian Index) would reflect the neuron's sensitivity to reward prediction in the absence of operant control. In this study, it was also demonstrated that only a major proportion (40 of 73) of prefrontal neurons in LPFC could be conditioned, probably only those that are involved in intentional control of behavioral responses. A recent study (Nigam, 2016) has shown that some neurons in a cell assembly transfer and receive much more information compared to others. Neurons with the highest outgoing and incoming information transfer were connected to each other more strongly than by chance, thus forming a 'rich club.' A rich-club structure has been found previously in large-scale human brain networks, and it is thought to facilitate communication among cortical regions. The discovery of a small, but information-rich, subset of neurons within cortical regions suggests that this population will play a vital role in communication, learning, and memory. It was found that ⊠70% of the information passed through only 20% of the neurons. Network models suggest that this highly concentrated pattern of information transfer would be both efficient and robust to damage.

Further investigation is required to clarify whether the LPFC constitutes a neural substrate for operant behavior. Testing operant behavior after lesions in the LPFC would provide important evidence. It would be also important to examine operant neuronal conditioning in other brain structures. For example, the orbitofrontal cortex and striatum, which are also suggested to be involved in goal-directed behavior, are interesting candidates for neuronal conditioning experiments. Indeed, recent imaging studies showed that hemodynamic responses in these structures change in parallel with operant contingency in behavioral tasks (Tanaka, 2008; Tricomi, 2004). Together with simultaneous recordings in downstream movement-related areas, neuronal conditioning experiments may be useful to clarify the top-down control mechanisms underlying voluntary, intentional behavior.

Another interesting aspect of Kobayashi's study is that it demonstrated that for operant conditioning of prefrontal neurons to be effective, the presentation of rewards had to be combined with a horizontal bar graph, which proceeded simultaneously with the neuronal bursting that was rewarded only when the bar graph proceeded long enough that its color changed from green to red. This means that a combination of information and reward is necessary for neurofeedback to be effective.

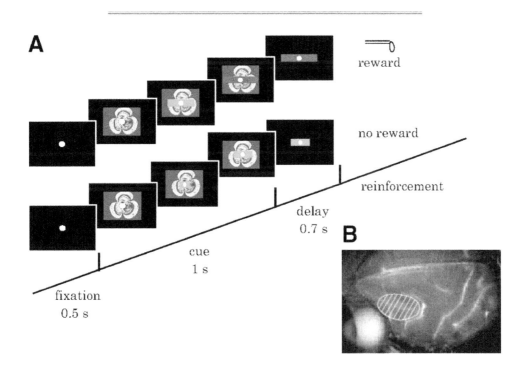

Figure 92. Reinforcement of lateral prefrontal neuron bursting is effective only when information (proceeding horizontal bar graph) is combined with the reward (Kobayashi, 2010).

Kobayashi's study demonstrated the feasibility of volitional control over neuronal activity. Sakurai (2014) discussed recent monkey studies on operant conditioning of synchrony and oscillation of neuronal activities. The main reason for emphasizing firing synchrony and oscillation in neuronal operant conditioning is that they reflect the activities of cell assemblies, which have been suggested to be basic neuronal codes representing information in the brain.

The fact that executive functioning (self-regulation) is trained in neurofeedback persuaded Barkley (Loo and Barkley, 2005) to challenge the utility of the principle application of neurofeedback. In his opinion, neurofeedback indeed improved attention, and frontal executive functions were able to be explained, by the fact that cognitive strategies were trained. Barkley concluded that the acquisition of conscious cognitive strategies triggered the changes in the EEG; therefore, it seemed simpler to him to train cognitive strategies directly with neurofeedback being superfluous. Several arguments can refute Barkley's opinion. First, research has repeatedly shown that teaching cognitive strategies and, above all, the transfer of such strategies to daily life is an ineffective approach to ADHD. Second, growing insights from practitioners of neurofeedback training suggest that for people with ADHD, cognitive strategies do not play a decisive role in the training process. One of the leading arguments that cognitive strategies do not play a key role in neurofeedback training of the SMR rhythm is the fact that following successful training, a lasting change can occur in the sleep EEG pattern (Rossiter, 2002; Sterman, 1980; Tansey, 1986) and in the dynamic EEG pattern, such as ERD /ERS and ERP (Kropotov, 2005, 2007). Eloquently, the quantity of sleep spindles during sleep also remains increased (Sterman, 1981; Hauri, 1981; Lubar, 1981) and associated with improved quality of sleep, which has a beneficial effect on daily functioning in and of itself. Sterman and a number of other scientists demonstrated in multiple studies that the susceptibility to epilepsy decreases permanently after the training, an effect that can be explained by the stabilizing influence of an increased number of sleep spindles. It is not just that one or another consciously experienced learned strategy is consciously applied in everyday circumstances. The well-known problems of inadequate transfer of trained cognitive skills (encountered with cognitive training programs, such as 'learning-learning' and Meichenbaum's 'stop-think-do' cognitive strategy learning) are not observed here. Moreover, in controlled studies of neurofeedback in ADHD where the control group was a group of children who got cognitive training, neurofeedback has been shown to be superior in clinical outcome.

6.10.4 Neurofeedback Takes Place Without the Participant's Knowledge, Awareness, and Intention

As will be discussed in Chapter 7, it has been demonstrated that fMRI-based neurofeedback is able to modulate localized neuronal activity and functional connectivity.

Recently, Ramot (2016) convincingly demonstrated that changes in functional connectivity could be introduced in the absence of participants' awareness that they are being trained. The participants received positive and negative rewards that were covertly coupled with activity in two category-selective visual cortex regions (the fusiform face area and the parahippocampal place area). Importantly, participants were not informed that the reward depended on their own brain activity. Rather, participants were told that the experiment was aimed at mapping reward networks, that they would receive monetary compensation for each positive sound, and that they would lose a similar amount for each negative sound. The sounds were chosen to be inherently associated with good/bad connotations (similar to computer game win or lose sounds). This created an implicit incentive for participants to wish for positive feedback while avoiding negative feedback without knowing that the sounds reflected the activity levels in their visual cortex. The button press task was designed to maintain alertness and attentiveness to the feedback. Participants were told that they must press the correct button after each positive/negative sound or else they would lose the monetary reward (in the case of the positive feedback) or would be further monetarily penalized (in the case of the negative feedback). In the post-experiment questionnaires, participants were found to have no knowledge of the origin of the feedback sounds to activity in two category-selective visual cortex regions. After the neurofeedback, not only activity in the trained area increased, but also changes took place in global connectivity well localized to the neurofeedback-related areas. The widespread nature of the connectivity changes is compatible with previous work, which has shown that neurofeedback training may affect entire networks. For example, targeted neurofeedback activation of the anterior cingulate cortex led to a long-term change in a widespread frontoparietal network (Harmelech, 2013).

The results indicated that brain networks could be modified even in the complete absence of intention and awareness of the learning situation and without any explicit strategy. According to Ramot, the true power of neurofeedback is that these induced connectivity changes without the participant's knowledge and awareness. This could potentially allow us to train and correct widespread network configurations in the brain that are associated with various pathologies, which might be difficult to control via an explicit task or strategy. One can of course assume that the same ideas apply for EEG-neurofeedback.

6.10.5 Practical Instructions for the Patient

We are left to answer the frequently asked question, 'Is there anything the individual can do to increase the number of feedback rewards?' The answer is that only to an extent, because for the individual, this directly relates not only to the quality of focused attention experienced, but mostly to the self-regulation mechanisms and indirect conscious experience of the flexible and global stability (metastability) of vigilance level, or in other words, the degree of flexible behavioral adaptability possessed by the individual. The term 'activation states' refers to the state of preparation for adaptive action, as described earlier. We recognize here the same twofold phenomenon encountered when examining changes in healthy participants' EEG following sleep deprivation. Specifically, wakefulness becomes less differentiated and subject to increased disturbances. Consequentially, specific attentional weaknesses are manifested. Section 3.4 examined the occurrence of a similar EEG pattern in people with ADHD after sleep deprivation (Brunner, 1993), a pattern that is most prominent at moments of weakened attention during attentional tests (Achim, 2004; Townsend, 1979).

Monastra explained the neurofeedback process to his patients by comparing it to the experience of learning to ride a bike. Indeed, we have no cognitive strategies to use in learning bike riding; instead, learning to ride involves the acquisition of coordination and balance skills enabled by pattern learning of concerned muscle groups and reflexive neural networks. However, motor skills are involved in learning to ride a bike so that these two processes are certainly not entirely comparable. As we master these skills, we have the feeling that we are guiding our learning and everything is under our control. However, in an individual without ADHD, the same can be said about regulation of attention and vigilance (in the sense of adaptive ability, level of wakefulness, and frontal executive functions), which are linked to a feeling of being independent and in control. Here lies the problem for people with ADHD. Monastra's analogy implies that at the neurophysiological level, acquired skills can subsequently be utilized as circumstances require. Once again, we should not assume that there is an 'I' that exercises direct cognitive control; instead, we speak more of 'bottom up' rather than 'top down' processes. In experimental participants without ADHD, we can surely speak of an 'I' because the underlying neurophysiology that supports adaptive skills makes the 'I' possible. It appears that effort towards cognitive control can negatively interfere with the learning process. This is consistent with the finding that during cognitive activation, frequently only an increase in theta or alpha waves is seen, particularly in people with ADD (Gurnee, 2000), or a more pronounced hyperactivity in frontal areas is identified using functional brain imaging methods. It has been observed that paying attention is often even more difficult than trying to make an extra effort, which sits well within the current conception of a lack of self-regulation in ADHD (see chapter 8). Kober (2013) has demonstrated that participants trying to control their SMR rhythm in neurofeedback by using a specific mental strategy were less effective, probably by overloading cognitive resources, which might be counterproductive in terms of increasing SMR power.

In the 1970s, research by Hardt at the Langley Porter Neuropsychiatric Institute showed that acquiring the desired EEG pattern during neurofeedback training demonstrates a learning curve. Throughout the early EEG sessions, improvements in the theta/beta-1 ratio are often rapid via habituation in the training session. This is often followed by a deceleration in the learning curve often associated with the patients feeling that they actively guide the learning process or that they must (counterproductively) work hard to relax. Only in the final sessions, when the patient is actively engaged, does the learning curve show an exponential upsurge, often accompanied by a feeling of passive will - a spontaneous, unforced, blooming of the will. It seems that the will in general becomes more smoothly self-directed, needing no extra effort to be exercised. In a way, the individual can be considered a captain of a team made up of all the mental and emotional systems of the brain (such as the anterior cingulate and the DLPFC). Neurofeedback training makes a better captain from the individual and makes the team players work and perform better together. When neurofeedback successfully trains the brain in the behavior that required much effort prior to the training, this behavior becomes less effortful, almost automatic. Neurofeedback trains the process of voluntary self-control, the foundation of conscious control. This training process takes place without explicit, conscious, voluntary control. Consequent improvements in self-control in people with ADHD occur without the patient knowing for sure what he has done to reach a homeostatic balance. There are many indications that in some or most cases, the attempt to exercise conscious control itself changes the EEG and therefore hinders the neurofeedback process. The effort to exercise voluntary control is thus not only trivial, but also counterproductive. Towards the end of the training process, a feeling of heightened self-control in daily life evolves with an improvement of executive functioning. Ultimately, the goal is to improve ADHD symptoms. Although the executive functions operate more fluently and the individual feels more in control of his life, one could argue that in reality, this adaptive process just happens to him or her. As an example, once the client manages the go/no-go task better after completing the training course, these gains are not attributable to something that he or she consciously does to improve previous performance. This is also true of the normalization of the go/no-go evoked brain potentials and of the event related synchronization and desynchronization of the EEG, all of which are associated with this task (Kropotov, 2005, 2007). This argument can be extended to improved organizational ability and increased robustness of goal motivation. The individual cannot verbalize what it is that he or she is doing that enables him/her to succeed better now than before the neurofeedback training. It may be best to instruct the patient explicitly not to try to influence the process consciously and to offer simply a brief comparison with the experience of learning to ride a bike, together with the instruction to relax, watch, and enjoy the rewards. This instruction is in reality aimed at avoiding movement artifacts during the training session. If indeed the instructions require paying attention, it quickly appears that the response is not proportional to the apparent degree of voluntary effort. Such instructions can surely impede the learning process at a neural level. The optimal direction should be limited to asking the participant to try to keep the mission on the game screen going without too much explanation of exactly what that entails and without offering mental 'tricks.' Some pragmatic instructions can however be useful for some patients (older children and adults) so that they know how to approach the training practically. It is integral to our culture to think of ourselves as active agents, as we get things done via our will and actions. Nevertheless, we discover more and more that the human mind and brain form a passive rather than active entity. Thoughts and mental development are things that we experience rather than things we initiate. Often, they occur despite our attempts to intervene without interventions. In mentally normal individuals, adaptive abilities usually run smoothly, undoubtedly accompanied by a subjective feeling of steering most of their affairs. This is certainly because of the well-balanced underlying neurophysiology. However, this is not the case for people with ADHD in whom self-guidance and optimal adaptive ability are inadequate. This is why neurofeedback aims to heighten the structure of self-regulation, as the employment of conscious strategies is more of an obstacle than a help.

The general instruction to someone following a course of neurofeedback might be to 'relax and let it happen,' 'let the computer tell your brain when you do the right thing,' and 'don't try, just let it happen.' When the trainee is asked what he/she did, he/she might say, 'I don't know how I am doing it, but I know when it happens.' Once progress begins to be made during the game, it often seems as if the patient becomes part of a circle. There is a viewpoint that the rewarding feedback provides the driving force in the first phase of training but during subsequent phases, the complete experience to get control, whether conscious or not, provides the greatest rewarding value.

6.10.6 Global EEG Reorganization

Neurofeedback training in ADHD produces a lasting, fundamental, and global EEG reorganization. Training a specific EEG frequency rather than the change of frequency alone thus sets in motion broader effects, reflecting reorganization of the global regulation state of the behavioral adaption system. SMR rhythms and sleep spindles both have a vigilance stabilizing function in this regard, protecting against system disruption (Pavlov's principle of internal inhibition). In fact, these modifications are frequently more clearly discernable in the form of an increase in the number of sleep spindles in the sleep EEG rather than in the form of the SMR rhythm in the waking EEG. Often, no distinct increase in the SMR rhythm is visible in the waking EEG. Sterman offered two reasons for this observation. First, the human waking EEG, in comparison with that observed in cats and macaques, often has no clearly detectable SMR rhythm, and second, during wakefulness, the SMR rhythm is often very variable during intervening cognitive activities.

6.11 What Kinds of Rewards are Effective in Neurofeedback?

An interesting study in cats, in which scalp lateral prefrontal EEG theta was down-trained together with beta up-training, has demonstrated ventral tegmental area dopamine neurons spiking (measured with intracranial electrodes) at moments of feedback (Fokina, 2010).

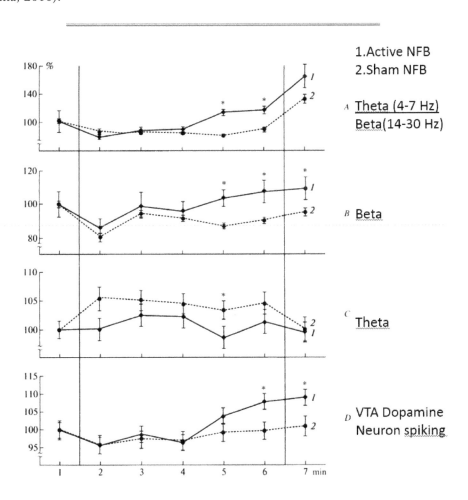

Figure 93. Ventral tegmentum area dopamine neurons spiking at moment of rewards in neurofeedback training of lateral prefrontal scalp theta/beta in cats. The data were averaged for 45 experimental sessions and 31 control sessions (Fokina, 2010).

Regardless of whether conscious cognitive strategies promote the learning process, the question remains as to what incentives are rewarding enough to promote the learning process. Currently, many therapists opt for an exciting video game to be played during more than 70% of the feedback session. This is assumed more motivating and rewarding, particularly when training hyperactive children. An alternative approach aims at the gradual constructive shaping of the SMR rhythm (shaping refers to successive approximations to the target pattern) by setting a progressively lower amplitude threshold. In their early studies from the 1970s, Sterman and Lubar stressed that the number of SMR bursts per minute increased in human subjects post-training but from their published EEG traces, it appears that the amplitude of SMR was higher in people without epilepsy or ADHD than in people with the disorders. In this light, Burner's (2006) investigation is interesting. He examined the effect of SMR neurofeedback training on learning of a paired associate word list, finding an improvement in list recall on the following day. Subjects studied the word pairs and subsequently received a session consisting of either four SMR neurofeedback periods or four pseudo neurofeedback periods. No increase in the number of sleep spindles during NREM was evident in the sleep EEG subsequent to training, possibly because the numbers of training sessions were limited. However, it was very clear that 12-15 Hz global activity increased in the frequency spectrum of the sleep EEG. Thus, in this single training session consisting of four 10-minute periods, there was initially an increase in 12-15 Hz amplitude. We can surmise that later in the training phase, this would have led to an increased quantity of sleep spindles. This research also identified a direct correlation between the number of sleep spindles and the quantity of remembered information from tasks studied the previous day. However, no link between the global quantity of 12-15 Hz activity and the amount of remembered information was found. Sterman (2006) has also described setting the reward threshold 20% above the average initial values, which can, if progressively increased after further sessions, lead to a greater feedback reward. According to Sterman, this threshold increase contributes to shaping of the SMR.

In contrast, the broader beta-1 band (12-20Hz) is more likely to be continuously present as well as some indications of a proportional relationship between amplitude and mental activation at this frequency (Townsend, 1979). Therefore, a more continuous type of feedback may work well at this particular frequency band. In the last years, the more common view has suggested that all EEG frequency bands are present as bursts in the EEG, where only the largest bursts are seen well with naked eye. A power law distribution exists for all EEG bursts, which implies that Sterman and Lubar's early viewpoint that SMR bursts have a minimum amplitude is incorrect.

A reward too easily obtained is no longer truly a reward. Sporadic rewards can be more motivating, especially for older children or adults who can develop an interest in their own learning curve and in the real time coaching during a session. Thus, it can be beneficial if the therapist explained the feedback process and explored, together with the trainee, any possible cognitive or competitive strategies that sometimes arise from the experience. The therapist who actively accompanies the patient through this process becomes part of the feedback cycle. In a sense, the strongest rewards are internal, namely the individual's recognition that he is master of his/her own self-regulation, since receiving an external reward evolves into an internal "aha!" feeling of reward.

Lubar described the establishment of a group protocol during carefully designed group studies in which operant conditioning was the critical factor while the intervention of the therapist was not. These studies achieved an 80% success rate over 40 to 60 sessions. However, in order to individualize the training, clinical practice can diverge from strict research protocol by adjusting various elements, including the precise training location on the scalp, the percentage of reward, the reward type, the active interventions of the therapist to make the reward more motivating, explanatory interventions that can make the reward experience more meaningful, and/or a training variant in which a short break is taken to examine and discuss the results with the patient after three minutes in the early sessions or after 10 minutes in the final sessions. Lubar found that this variant resulted in a training that was more effective, less boring, and required fewer (20 to 40) sessions with a greater success rate of 90%. In Lubar's footsteps, Thompson and Thompson (2003) also described the advantages of individualization of the training protocol in clinical practice.

Computer screen feedback can be sufficiently powerful motivator for adults and adolescents with ADHD because such feedback indicates progress towards personal goals, such as amelioration of symptoms and symptom control. As the novelty wanes, however, this feedback can be extremely dull, particularly for children who are moreover less likely to understand the nature of their ADHD, the negative effects of ADHD on their lives, or the possible long-term gains from neurofeedback. If feedback becomes boring, the feedback would likely not be rewarding enough for conditioning to happen.

It is clear that milk and food rewards can be sufficient to condition a hungry cat. For children, however, a therapist's stimulating approach offers an additional motivating aspect that can form part of the reward. Thompson and Thompson (2000, 2003), Rossiter and La Vaque (1995), and Leins (2004) have described how rewards can be enhanced using a supplementary reward system in the form of small prizes the children can earn by obtaining a certain number of points during a single session. Rossiter and La Vague's (1995) sessions consisted of two parts. During one section, the child received 100 points whenever he/she attained a theta/beta ratio lower than the median value of previous sessions. An additional 50 points were available if he/she attained this ratio in both sections of the segment and 100 points were available for a new minimum theta/

beta ratio. If the child accumulated 500 points, he/she received a certificate with a value of $5 that was exchangeable for a prize.

Thompson and Thompson (2000, 2003) asked the child to keep a record by writing down every 2 to 5 minutes the percentage of the time that the theta/beta ratio was below threshold. A certain number of points were awarded for this percentage and performance, with the therapist softly counting the passing seconds aloud. Another strategy sometimes employed uses neurofeedback exercises in a 'work-rest' protocol where the child must try to decrease theta activity as much as possible or increase beta activity as much as possible during a 45-second period or sometimes during 3-minute periods alternating with 15-second rest breaks. The use of five or more periods of repetitions encourages the child to compete with his or her own performance. Conscious control of theta or beta activity can be acquired in this manner. Short periods of two to five minutes are chosen because the percentage of time that the threshold is crossed is calculated from the average for several periods, making it harder to change the threshold over longer periods. Like Rossiter, Thompson and Thompson linked total points to small prizes, such as pens, bookmarks, action figures, or games. Thus, using the 'work-rest' protocol, Thompson consciously trained and subsequently rewarded skills with small prizes. This is very similar to the method used by Leins to train both theta/beta ratio and the slow cortical potential. Kropotov's method was also similar.

6.12 Homeostatic Plasticity, Metastability, and Criticality Involved in Neurofeedback?

Many studies described that after successful neurofeedback, changes in the trained amplitudes of theta and SMR rhythms may not always be found in the EEG. Kropotov (2005, 2007) described that often, there are no changes in EEG but that there are improvements in go/no-go ERP and in event-related EEG oscillations. Mayer (2011) and Bakhtadze (2011) described normalization of P300 amplitudes and latencies. Normalization of CNV has also been described. Lubar described that in some cases, no change in theta or SMR amplitude is seen but that the standard deviation decreases, which he considered a more stable EEG pattern. On the other hand, Woltering (2012) described a lower standard deviation of alpha activity in ADHD adults, what has been interpreted as a marker of lower metastability and criticality, which could explain behavioral variability that is not stabilized by a metastable system.

Ros (2014) demonstrated that posterior alpha downtraining in a group of healthy adults resulted in an increase of alpha amplitude at the end of one session. In such cases, changes in EEG synchronization occur in the opposite direction, as would be expected according to Hebbian plasticity. In neurofeedback studies of autism spectrum disorder, Pineda (2008) demonstrated that uptraining of the mu-rhythm results in a better mu-desynchronization during movement and social situations observation. Othmer (1999), in his speculative 'regulatory challenge model' or 'exercising model,' suggested that the inhibition of SMR and rewarding of SMR challenge the system equally.

A related phenomenon is the spectral over-synchronization frequently seen following sleep deprivation, which is understood to be a product of increases in local experience-dependent plasticity. Subsequently, following sleep, the EEG is restored to a less synchronized state the day after. It is fascinating that this latter process seems to be compromised in psychiatric disorder. This was in fact one of the cornerstones of Bente's EEG vigilance model for psychiatric disorders, with disordered vigilance being rigid or labile (Bente, 1969). Tying all this evidence together appears to lead to a beautifully parsimonious conclusion, which is that neither high nor low synchronization may be critical, but rather a balance between them, i.e., metastability. The brain, it seems, continuously oscillates between well-defined extremes of high and low synaptic strength. This appears to be the consequence of physiological and computational ceiling pressures that occur naturally in synapses, the molecular mechanism of which is still under investigation (Abraham, 2008). Many brain pathologies could thus be succinctly characterized as disorders of such homeostatic plasticity, considering the above evidence as well as the fundamental links between brain oscillations and synaptic potentiation. In other words, non-degenerative brain disorders may have a self-tuning impairment, having lost their dynamic repertoire by being 'trapped' in an abnormal resting-state oscillatory pattern (Ghosh, 2008). If this is correct, then one might expect measures of neural variability to be lower in brain disorders during task-free conditions. Several reports appear to support this hypothesis, as fluctuations of EEG synchronization are indeed diminished in brain disorders like ADHD (Woltering, 2012). Yet, given evidence of a common functional architecture between resting and task conditions, it is reasonable to posit that the more variable dynamic range of tonic (i.e., resting-state) EEG may underpin that of the phasic (i.e., task-related) EEG characterized by so called event-related oscillations (EROs), which have been strongly implicated in cognition (Klimesch, 2001; Neuper and Pfurtscheller, 2001). Hence, in light of the aforementioned physiological ceiling effects, it is plausible that resting-state hyper- and hypo-synchrony may dimensionally restrict the dynamic range of phasic event-related synchronization (ERS) and event-related desynchronization (ERD) patterns, respectively. To be exact, Ros (2014) speculated that the relative amount of ERS (ERD) represented by percent signal change from baseline (spontaneous) activity could be reduced in disorders presenting hyper- (hypo) synchronization.

Interestingly, it has been shown that lower tonic rest state theta predicts higher phasic frontal midline theta during working memory and during action monitoring. This explains the correlation of higher rest state theta in the anterior cingulate with a lower action monitoring theta in ADHD, which is related to lower dopaminergic activity. This homeostatic plasticity may aid in our understanding of why neurofeedback also produces variable intra- and inter-individual effects. Hence, changes in EEG synchronization frequently occur in the opposite direction that would be expected according to Hebbian plasticity. As a consequence of homeostatic plasticity, a key prediction of the proposed framework is that both unidirectional and rebound neurofeedback outcomes may be permissive toward normalizing pathological brain oscillation measures (e.g., power, phase-locking, peak frequency, 1/f) as well as the dynamical landscape that subserves them. From this perspective, neurofeedback training could 'tune' the brain's intrinsic mechanisms of homeostasis, which are used to self-organize to achieve an optimal (i.e., near-critical) set-point following a period of adaptive plasticity (Hsu and Beggs, 2006) but have become maladaptive in pathology.

The amplitude dynamics of neuronal oscillations, namely their scale-free, long-range temporal correlations (LRTCs), are considered to provide supporting evidence for criticality in the brain, a balanced state between order and disorder theoretically optimal for information processing. Scale-free relationships are frequently represented by the Hurst scaling exponent (H), as a measure of self-similarity within time-series, which indicates the degree of long-range temporal (auto)correlations (LRTCs) present between shorter and longer time scales (e.g., ranging from seconds to minutes). A larger H value generally reflects the presence of a long-range (yet transient) trend in the data, for example, when values alternate between high and low values but do so for a prolonged period at a time in each state. Given that H integrates a signal's temporal evolution, it may index its long-term dependence or memory. Thereby, H essentially estimates the extent of temporal memory in a signal, with random white noise and a smooth line taking on $H = 0.5$ and $H = 1$ values, respectively. Along with self-similarity, as in fractals, such memory is the hallmark of complexity in time series. The phenomenon is also referred to as 1/f noise.

Ros (2015) directly examined lasting changes in spontaneous LRTCs after a single neurofeedback training session consisting of a tonic suppression of alpha oscillation amplitude for 30 minutes. By applying detrended fluctuation analysis (DFA), he detected a post-neurofeedback enhancement of spontaneous alpha-amplitude LRTCs in a group of healthy young adults. Regarding the outcomes of feedback training, a significant interaction in H-exponent was revealed, demonstrating a dissociation in pre-to-post feedback resting state values between neurofeedback and sham groups. A significant increase of H-exponent values was observed in the neurofeedback group, while no reliable change was present in the sham group.

In a second experiment, Ros (2015) examined an equivalent mechanism in psychiatric patients with posttraumatic stress disorder (PTSD), replicating a comparable boost of alpha-amplitude LRTCs, which correlated with significant reductions in hyperarousal. Interestingly, neurofeedback rescued LRTCs in regions that were abnormally low in H-value (i.e., increased randomness of alpha bursts) compared to a healthy control sample. Additionally, the low alpha amplitude in the PTSD was normalized after neurofeedback. Lastly, he identified an inverted-U relationship between strength of LRTC and alpha amplitude, suggesting a gradual breakdown of long-range dependence at high/low synchronization extremes, consistent with theoretical predictions of criticality. Individual decreases in clinical arousal score correlated significantly with increases in Hurst exponent at the feedback channel Pz. A similar (marginally significant) trend was identified for mean alpha amplitude.

Combining the data from all experiments (n=123 subjects) into a single scatter-plot, Ros (2015) conducted a regression analysis to estimate the best curve-fit between LRTCs and oscillation amplitude. The statistical presence of an inverted-U relationship was striking, revealing a middle zone of maximal LRTCs and attenuated LRTCs at higher and lower alpha extremes. Considering the reports that alpha amplitude covaries positively with the synchrony of local neuronal populations, this seems to indicate that both hypo- and hyper-synchronization could be associated with a breakdown of long-range dependence, consistent with theoretical predictions of criticality. Neurofeedback thereby appears to have induced a plastic 're-tuning' of spontaneous neuronal dynamics, showing a tendency for alpha oscillations to remain alternatively high and low in amplitude for a longer duration of time and reflecting metastability and criticality. These results thus pave the way for future work investigating whether these effects can maintain themselves following multiple sessions of neurofeedback training, paralleling evidence of long-term changes in EEG amplitude (Gevensleben, 2009). The data appear consistent with the framework of Sporns (2002) who considered the LRTCs as a substitute measure of dynamical complexity, since once oscillations shift to excessively desynchronised (more disorderly) or synchronized (more orderly) levels, a parallel shift of LRTCs towards randomness occurs, reflecting a decrease in variability (shallower slope of critical exponent, i.e., dynamic range) and long-range dependence (i.e., memory). Hence, by means of a sustained modulation of oscillation amplitude, in line with conventional approaches (Heinrich, 2007; Lubar, 1997), neurofeedback might concurrently reinstate a self-tuning of temporal dynamics that are more complex (i.e., LRTCs, which are scale-free and intractable as a real-time parameter for feedback).

6.13 Neurofeedback Training's Effects on Intelligence and Learning Difficulties

Many people with ADHD have comorbid learning difficulties, such as dyslexia and dyscalculia, among others. Their scores on intelligence tests are frequently lower than expected. Attentional difficulties may partially explain these low scores. A number of researchers have investigated the effects of neurofeedback training on intelligence tests administered to children with ADHD.

Othmer (Othmer and Othmer, 1991) treated a group of 15 children with ADHD (between 6 to 16 years old), seven of whom had hyperactivity, four had dyslexia, six had oppositional behavioral disorders, two had a conduct disorder (a precursor for antisocial personality disorder), 13 suffered sleep disorders, five suffered chronic headaches, four had depression or dysthymia, three had chronic anxiety, and one had motor tics. The treatment consisted of 30 to 40 sessions delivered at the rate of two or three sessions per week (aimed at strengthening 15-18 Hz, weakening 4.7 Hz and 22-30 Hz) measured at C1-C5 (therefore, at the front and rear of C3) on the left or C2-C6 (front and rear of C4) on the right (depending on the side that showed the most abnormal EEG pattern).

Tansey (1990) treated a group of eight children (7 to 15 years) with attention disorders and dyslexia by administering 10 to 34 sessions (strengthening 12 -14 Hz, measured at C4). Notwithstanding that Tansey's group demonstrated more severe cognitive impairment, it appeared that both Tansey and Othmer's groups showed weaknesses on the subscales of calculation, substitution, information, and digit spans. These subscales are known to load on an attention factor (Kaufman, 1979) on the WISC-R intelligence tests. Following the neurofeedback, the mean IQ increased from 114 to 137 in Othmer's group and from 94 to 113 in Tansey's group.

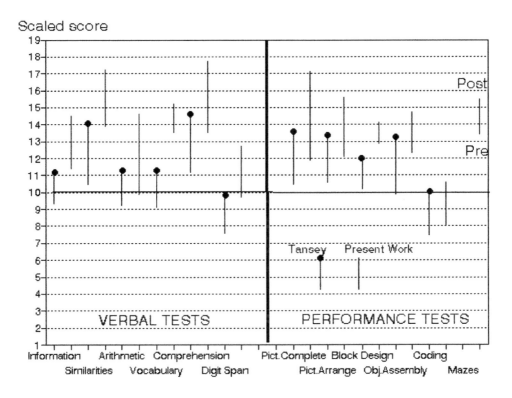

Figure 94. Mean WISC IQ measurements: For each of the 12 subscales, the values obtained by Tansey (1990) and Othmer and Othmer (1991) (labeled "present work") are displayed; both demonstrated lower pre-neurofeedback rather than post neurofeedback scores (Figure appears with kind permission from Othmer and Othmer).

Othmer and Othmer (1991) found the greatest improvement (an average increase of 33 points!) in the subgroup with an initial IQ lower than 100. The subscales with the greatest deficits showed the greatest improvements. The average increase per subscale was 5.1 points. The four subscales that contributed to the Kaufman attention factor were quite consistent in their growth (4 to 6 points). Two of the four children with ADHD and comorbid dyslexia showed significant amelioration of the dyslexia symptoms. In Othmer's group, the Kaufman attention factor was below the norm (= 10) in four children before training. These four children received average values on the information and arithmetic and digit span subscales and scores of 7 or 6 on the subscale substitution, suggesting a common underlying mechanism. In these four children, the first three subscales increased by 4 to 6 points and the substitution subscale by 3 points after the training. Othmer argued that this improvement in IQ score could not be attributed merely to the retest effect because there was an interval of nine months between the tests. In addition, these improvements cannot be attributed solely to the effects of better attention, decreased impulsivity, and decreased anxiety. Significant improvements were also noted on subscales measuring verbal understanding and perceptual organization, specifically memory (information, vocabulary), sequential processing (arithmetic, substitution), inferential thinking (similarities), verbal concept formation and expression (understanding), and visual perception (picture completion, arranging pictures). Both improvements in behavior and cognition seemed directly related to the EEG training rather than to the interactions between the new skill areas. Pronounced improvements on the arithmetic subscale (on average from 9.9 to 14.6 points) can probably be attributed to a combination of factors, such as improved attention span and enhanced sequential symbolic processing skills as well as to behavioral changes, such as decreased anxiety and impulsivity. Othmer himself attributed these effects to global cortical activation or stabilization regulated by the brain stem and the non-specific thalamic nuclei.

Follow up with the parents was maintained for more than a year after the treatment, with the improvements in self-esteem being most noticeable. Improvements in hyperactivity, concentration, and sleep disturbances (including bed-wetting) were maintained, and absence of headaches in children who had previously suffered headaches was noticeable. Social relationships with brothers, sisters, peers, as well as with authority figures, such as parents and teachers, improved.

Cartozzo (1995) evaluated the results from 30 neurofeedback sessions (weakening 4-7 Hz, strengthening 12-15 Hz, weakening 22-30 Hz) administered to eight children with ADHD. After the treatment, significant improvements were noted on the arithmetic, digit span, and substitution subscales of the WISC-R intelligence test.

The following case study illustrated these changes (Tansey, 1985*): A 12-year-old boy had hyperactivity and problems with sustained attention in class. His play skills were below the norm; he had a negative attitude towards learning in general and little success working either alone or in a group. Evaluation confirmed the hyperactivity and revealed deficits in verbal expression and word memory. In addition, he had difficulties with fine motor control, exhibiting by a very clumsy pencil grip. His WISC-R global IQ was 85 (low middle range), with a verbal IQ of 79 and a performance IQ of 93. SMR training was given with a base value of 5.6 µV. This value was 13 µV by the 19th session. Improvements in behavioral, educational, and intellectual functioning were already apparent. He was able to stay seated longer in class. At school, his pen grip improved by the fifteenth session, his vocabulary had expanded significantly, and he worked hard in class to complete written assignments. His achievements at school clearly improved, and he was calmer at home. The WISC-R was re-*

administered after the completion of training. Verbal IQ was found to have increased from 79 to 98, performance IQ increased from 93 to 109, and global IQ increased from 85 to 103.

It is worth to mention the studies of Giannitrapani (1988) and Patterson (1983) who found clear correlations between the quantity of 12-15 Hz measured in central brain areas (especially Cz) and global intelligence in children and in the elderly. Moreover, a decreased quantity of sleep spindles (the equivalent of SMR during sleep) has been demonstrated in elderly people with cognitive decline (Wauquier, 1991) and in children with mental retardation (Shibagaki, 1980).

In a later study, Tansey (1991) investigated the effects of SMR training (an average 28 weekly sessions) on a group of 24 children between 7 and 15 years old with learning difficulties (just two had a formal diagnosis of ADHD). In this case, he was especially interested in the effect of SMR training on the various subscales of IQ tests. Average global IQ rose from 98 to 118. In 22 of the 24 children, the increase in global IQ was at least one standard deviation (15 IQ points). The other two children showed an increase in IQ of 14 and 13 points. Prior to the treatment, the children with the lowest IQ (70 to 79) had a marked tendency to show the most theta activity in the EEG. These improvements are greater than might be predicted from a retest effect (the global IQ retest effect is about 7 points). Both the total and verbal performance IQ scores improved and the difference between verbal and performance IQ decreased.

The Bannatyne pattern of WISC-R sub-scales has been well documented in terms of inconsistency regarding a learning difficulty diagnosis. Four Bannatyne categories include Spatial, Verbal Conceptualization, Sequencing, and Acquired Knowledge. The score on each of these categories increased after the treatment. The Kaufman attention factor in the WISC-R clearly improved following the treatment. After the training, the learning difficulties significantly ameliorated.

Tansey cited Robinson's (1989) hypothesis suggesting a neurological base for variations in intelligence (for a long time, there has been no doubt about the decisive role of genetic predisposition). Robinson suggested that the relative balance within thalamocortical activities decides the natural frequencies of free spontaneous fluctuations in thalamocortical circuits, which themselves determine the EEG frequency spectrum. SMR neurofeedback activates increases in excitation and a positive shift in the peak frequency (and activity level in general) towards a more optimal level, which according to Robinson's theory will express itself with a higher IQ. The promotion of a positive balance of EEG frequencies above 10 Hz (neural excitation), with respect to EEG frequencies lower than 10 Hz (neural inhibition), is crucial for the acquisition of a higher order of learning and IQ.

Tansey thought that SMR training leads to a synergistic training of the EEG (accompanied by a decrease in theta activity) because no strong correlation between the strength of an EEG band and the global IQ or subscale scores is demonstrable. In this formulation, he viewed the brain as a matrix of interconnected functional networks within which any pattern of neural activation can trigger a change in the entire matrix. Localized functionally, specific areas can be considered sub networks within the larger matrix within which neuronal activity reflects only a part of the great symphony of brain rhythm, which itself echoes the global matrix's functional neuroanatomy. A shift in the whole EEG pattern reflects the neurological substrate of improved functioning and suggests the functional reorganization of brain activity. Improved SMR activity appears to catalyze the synergistic and efficient EEG normalization of the pre-treatment pathological balance of thalamocortical activation/inhibition. Sterman had already proposed in 1980 that SMR training leads to a normalization of the global EEG pattern. A recent study (Hanslmayr, 2005) demonstrated that cognitive skills improved in normal participants following the application of neurofeedback protocols to strengthen the fast alpha waves (10-12 Hz) and weaken theta. The experimental subjects were asked to mentally rotate complex three-dimensional block patterns before and after training to assess the changes in these mental rotation skills. Only those participants who had succeeded in strengthening fast alpha activity showed improvements in this test following the training. Moreover, there appeared to be a link between the two. During the time interval just before the task, fast alpha waves increased in those patients who had obtained good results from neurofeedback. This is consistent with studies demonstrating that a better cognitive performance follows fast alpha activity immediately preceding a stimulus.

Thatcher (2005) developed a practical application in which individual phase and coherence values can be calculated from the QEEG pattern. With this method, it is possible to predict the intelligence profile and eight verbal and performance subscale scores quite accurately. A high IQ is said to correspond with a frontal phase delay close to zero, long phase delays in the posterior cerebral cortex, lowered coherence, and global increases in EEG spectrum values. Shorter frontal phase-delays reflect faster frontal command processes and a more efficient control of information in posterior areas of the cerebral cortex. Longer phase-delays in these posterior areas mirror increased local processing time and integration of increased quantities of information. As described earlier, these values indicate greater neural efficiency and increased functional complexity. In high IQ, phase shift in short distances is longer (Thatcher, 2008), implying local differentiation and global integration while minimizing the energy costs of long-range connections (small world, which is the most efficient network). Longer phase shift duration increases the probability of identifying larger numbers of neurons capable of being phase locked, and this is why the relationship between shift duration and IQ is direct. These findings are consistent with the relationship between intelligence and coherence and the relationship between phase reset and coherence. That is, increased IQ scores correlate with shorter phase lock duration and longer phase shift duration, both of which correlate with lower coherence. This indicates that phase shift duration and phase lock duration are the elemental components of EEG coherence and these components represent the dynamics involved in information processing. Measures of phase shift duration and phase lock duration are important for understanding the underlying dynamics of coherence itself and provide a micro-view of the inhibitory and excitatory control mechanisms involved in entrainment and neural assembly selection. The combined values give a 'discriminant score' for each individual. Research has found a direct link between this score and IQ. These findings are in agreement with the network model of intelligence in which the frontal areas orchestrate the information sources processed in posterior and temporal areas. This can have useful practical applications, including monitoring of changes following the treatment. Now, in addition to psychological IQ tests, to assess the effects of neurofeedback, changes in the QEEG obtained after the neurofeedback can be directly analyzed to detect any changes in the EEG correlations of IQ.

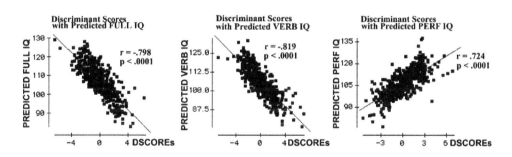

Figure 95. Direct relationship between the discriminant score of the QEEG and predicted IQ; **left:** *global IQ,* **middle:** *verbal IQ,* **right:** *performance IQ. Reprinted from Clinical Neurophysiology, 116(9), Thatcher, North, & Biver, EEG and intelligence: Relations between EEG coherence, Copyright (2005), with permission from Elsevier.*

Predicted Cognitive Performance

	Neuropsychological Tests	Scaled Score	Min SS	Max SS	Z Score	Min Z	Max Z
1	Information	10.75	5.18	16.33	-0.08	-1.78	1.62
2	Mathematics	10.50	4.73	16.26	-0.07	-1.90	1.76
3	Vocabulary	10.98	5.04	16.93	-0.15	-1.88	1.57
4	Digit Span	11.72	5.75	17.69	0.52	-1.40	2.45
5	Picture Completion	10.39	5.12	15.66	-0.24	-2.04	1.57
6	Block Design	9.31	3.15	15.48	-0.45	-2.24	1.34
7	Coding	7.41	1.57	13.25	-0.93	-2.77	0.90
8	Mazes	9.47	3.24	15.69	-0.60	-2.54	1.33
9	Full IQ	101.53	74.93	128.14	-0.33	-2.02	1.36
10	Verbal IQ	106.21	77.17	135.25	0.03	-1.70	1.75
11	Performance IQ	96.50	70.44	122.56	-0.67	-2.39	1.05

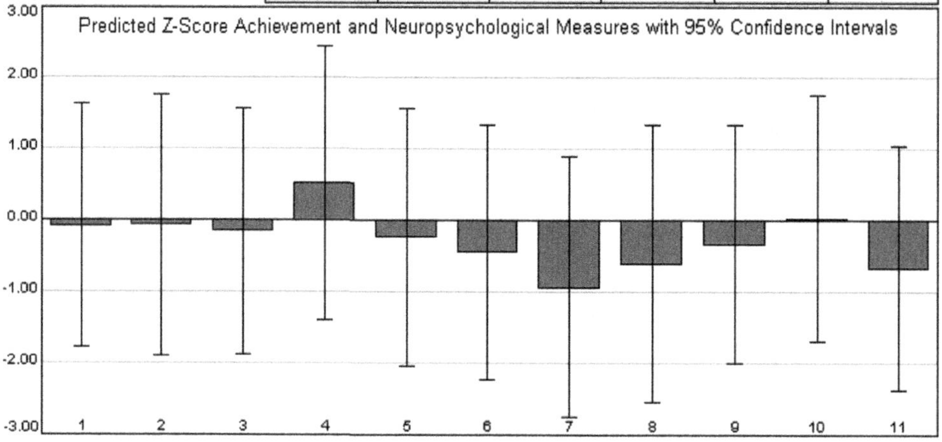

Figure 96. Graphed IQ profile of a 20-year-old woman calculated using QEEG (Neuroguide): total IQ 101.53. From Neuroguide, www.appliedneuroscience.com.

6.14 40 Hz (35-45Hz) Neurofeedback

Chapter 3 discusses the role of the 40 Hz (35-45 Hz) rhythm in attention and motor stillness in more detail. Sheer (1976) found no increase in electrical activity in children with ADHD during problem solving tasks in comparison to that observed in typically developing children (who moreover demonstrated better task performance). He showed the 40 Hz rhythm to be an expression of focused arousal, a process of some importance in consolidating information from short-term memory into long-term memory. Technically, it is extremely difficult to detect these small fast waves in the EEG (5-10 μV) and to distinguish them from electrical muscle activity (EMG). That is why neurofeedback research has developed little at this end of the spectrum. Concerns about muscle tension contamination have prevented the widespread use of the 40 Hertz rhythm for many years. The capability to reliably measure 40 Hz has become available only in recent years due to newer EEG amplifiers with less electrical noise and advances in neurofeedback software, which enables to decontaminate gamma EEG from EMG artefacts. Pearson correlation allows to differentiate genuine 40 Hz in the EEG from EMG artefacts.

In 1976, Bauer investigated the effects of approximately 40 Hz neurofeedback training in cats (using cortically implanted electrodes), which he clearly demonstrated to be a form of operant conditioning similar to that employed by Sterman in his original research, also on cats. The cats received milk as a reward whenever the targeted 40 Hz activity occurred in the EEG. This research indicated it was possible to strengthen 40 Hz activity in different brain areas. It was also observed that the cats were immobile during the training. If the 40 Hz activity were trained at the visual cortex, the cats would also visually fixate. This research is consistent with the research of Rougeul-Buser (1994) who investigated the link between 40 Hz activity and unmoving fixation of attention in cats described in Chapter 3.5.

In 1975, Sheer demonstrated that 40 Hz activity in the human visual cortex (O1-P3) increased with neurofeedback (with electrodes at the scalp) over the course of 8 daily sessions of 30 minutes in a group of just 5 human adults. He used ingenious methods to prevent the misreading of muscular electrical activity (EMG) as 40 Hz activity. At moments when 40 Hz activity was present in the EEG, the next slide in a series of slides was displayed and subsequently rewarded with money. The number of slides projected during the entire session (a form of operant conditioning) determined the exact monetary amount. During training, 40 Hz activity increased by 160% on average while EMG activity fell by 16% on average.

One to three weeks after the neurofeedback training, the experimental subjects were invited to voluntarily produce the 40 Hz activity (without feedback), and most of them succeeded. Eight weeks after the training, the subjects were once again asked to produce the 40 Hz activity and to solve some problems while in this voluntary brain state. The quantity of 40 Hz EEG activity was then compared with the quantity generated solving similar problems but with the command to voluntarily suppress 40 Hz activity.

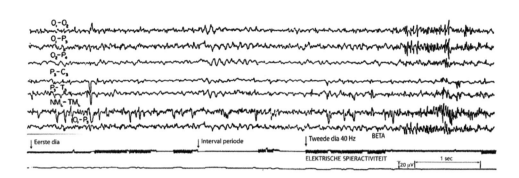

Figure 97. During administration of Sheer's test battery, EMG as well as EEG were measured. Slides were projected as feedback if a 40 Hz discharge occurred in the EEG (O1–P3). In this participant, following 40 Hz training, 40 Hz activity appeared at O1–P3 (Upper 2nd trace) during presentation of the first and second slides (indicated by small vertical arrows). At the end of the slide of the presentation, verbal answers were requested. They were associated with the EMG and most visible in the sixth trace NM-TM (neck muscles, temporal muscles). The 40 Hz activity is minuscule, and it can barely be discerned in the raw EEG, so that a computer analysis is best used to detect and quantify this activity. On the bottom right, the horizontal calibration line indicates a time unit of one second and the vertical line amplitude of 20 µV. Reprinted from Behavior and Brain Electrical Activity, Sheer, Copyright (1975), with permission from Plenum Press.

This command proved impossible to fulfill. During problem solution, 40 Hz activity was the same in both conditions. However, 40 Hz activity during both problem solution conditions was higher than it was prior to training. Moreover, these participants clearly showed better problem solving performance in psychological tests. To illustrate, thirty words were presented on slides in a word-learning test, one word per slide per second with a pause of 15 seconds between slides. After the training, subjects remembered on average 16.6 words compared to five words prior to the training. Furthermore, it was demonstrated that prior to the training, seventy-seven 40 Hz discharges occurred on average in the EEG during this task while after the training, this increased to an average of one hundred twenty-one 40 Hz discharges in the EEG.

Another test consisted of a series of five problem assignments, each displayed on a slide for 30 seconds. After a 15-second break, five slides each comprising a multiple-choice question were shown until the participant answered or until 60 seconds passed without an answer. Prior to the training, the participants solved on average 1.6 out of the 5 problems. After the training, and with a new series of problems, participants solved on average 4.4 problems. Prior to the training, on average forty-one 40 Hz discharges were noted during this task. After the training, the number of discharges increased to 158 discharges. We can conclude that the subject can generate this rhythm voluntarily, following indications of a successful 40 Hz training. Rather more to the point, 40 Hz activity at moments of task solution was involuntarily stronger compared to prior to training, and the performance in tasks also improved.

Bird (1978) trained two groups of 8 adults each (18 to 27 years old) with 40 Hz neurofeedback administered in six daily sessions of thirty minutes. One group was trained at O1-Cz (left) and the other at O2-Cz (right). This training appeared feasible and showed that the training 40 Hz activity on one side also increased the 40 Hz effect on the other side. Most subjects were able to voluntarily increase 40 Hz activity for several weeks following training.

Later, Ford assessed six adults (20 to 24 years old) from Bird's original group of 16 adults and found that the effects of 40 Hz neurofeedback training were maintained three years later. The six participants who participated in the 1978 study retrained best at O1-Cz. In the first phase of the assessment, they were trained again at 40 Hz. For five of the six participants it was possible to obtain an increase within the first five minutes of the first session. One participant required four sessions to achieve the same result. Thus, for five out of the six participants, the trained skills were maintained three years after the initial training. In the second phase on the day after, the participants had to demonstrate that they could voluntarily induce 40 Hz activity. These five participants were presented with four types of problem tasks on slides, each slide comprising 10 problems in multiple-choice format. While solving each of the first five tasks, the participants were asked to voluntarily increase 40 Hz activity. Subsequently the participants were asked to solve the remaining problems without generating 40 Hz activity. Both of these problem-solving conditions lasted five minutes. However, in five of the six participants, the task solution was associated with an increase in 40 Hz activities in both conditions. This confirms original research by Sheer (1975). The subjects' ability to voluntarily increase 40 Hz activity after training supports a conscious self-regulating mechanism, despite the apparent impossibility of consciously suppressing 40 Hz activity during problem solving.

Bearing in mind the involvement of evoked phase-locked early gamma synchrony in fundamental cognitive processes as well as the altered patterns in ADHD patients, Lenz (2009) raised the question of whether neurofeedback that incorporates the gamma frequency range might further enhance the effectiveness of a treatment using neurofeedback. However, one must keep in mind that phase-locked gamma activity has a different meaning compared to spontaneous rest-state gamma oscillations, which are often considered as 'neural noise' (Mathalon and Sohal, 2015).

Hillard (2013) demonstrated that only 12 weekly sessions of 25 minutes' gamma ('focus') EEG neurofeedback at Fpz in 18 ADHD children and adolescents improved behavior and attention as well as the central theta/beta ratio within and between sessions. Additionally, alpha amplitude correlated with beta-1 within and between sessions, which is in line with Bente's EEG vigilance model. Neurofeedback software, which allows one to decontaminate 40 Hz EEG from EMG artefacts, was used in this study.

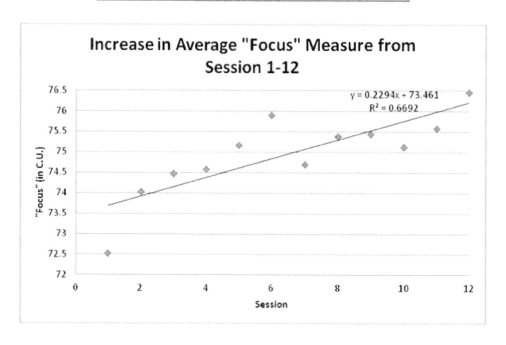

Figure 98. Plot of average 'Focus' (gamma) value for each session (session number 1–12), indicating an increase in the value of 'Focus' as session number increases (Hillard, 2012).

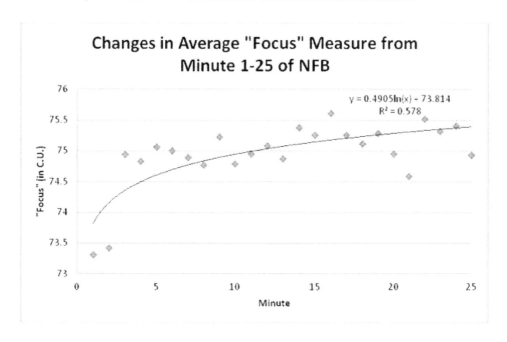

Figure 99. Plot of average 'Focus' (gamma) values (averaged across all sessions) for each minute of neurofeedback (1-25), indicating an increasing 'Focus' measure as minute of neurofeedback within a session increases (Hillard, 2012).

Summary

The 40 Hz neurofeedback training leads to improvements in attention and learning abilities. In practice, this training is technically not easy to implement because these fast EEG waves are very low voltage and therefore difficult to distinguish from technical noise and electrical muscle activity. However, new and more advanced software and hardware makes it possible to detect this signal more accurately. The effects of this training are abrupt and appear to be maintained three years later.

6.15 SMR-Neurofeedback in Insomnia

Sterman's early research (Sterman 1967, 1968) was inspired by his interest in wake-sleep transition, which awakened his interest in Pavlov's 'internal inhibition.' Sterman was able to pinpoint the SMR rhythm as a marker for this 'internal inhibition,' which stabilized sleep and wake patterns. Sterman noticed an increase in sleep spindles after the treatment (1970). Hauri (1981, 1982) applied SMR neurofeedback in primary insomnia, with good results.

Hoedlmoser (2008) replicated Hauri's experimental treatment of insomnia in a randomized controlled study in healthy participants, showing an increase in SMR amplitude during wakefulness and subsequent sleep spindle activity, a shortening of sleep latency, an increase of waking SMR amplitude, and an increase in retrieval score in a memory task.

Schabus (2014), after 10 SMR neurofeedback sessions compared with sham-neurofeedback, also demonstrated a significant increase of SMR activity and sleep spindles in 16 of 24 treated insomnia patients, with a decrease in the number of awakenings and an increase of slow-wave sleep and subjective sleep quality. Overnight memory consolidation also improved. Schabus (2006) also demonstrated a correlation between sleep spindles and intelligence. This could be related to Giannitrapani's (1988) findings indicating a correlation between intelligence and 12-14 Hz activity at Cz.

It is known that in ADHD, unstable sleep in very often one of the problems, so that one can assume that sleep improvement is also one of the results of the neurofeedback treatment in ADHD.

Interestingly, in insomnia studies, one can certainly not assume that any cognitive strategy would make sense, and the clinical results, which are sleep related, also cannot be explained by mental strategies. Thus, these findings provide a strong support for pure operant conditioning of SMR activity being a real mechanism, with lasting changes in sleep.

Moreover, it is interesting that although generated in the thalamic reticular nucleus, the cortical sources of sleep spindles, as they can be reconstructed with LORETA, can be found in areas of the default mode network, including the dorsal anterior cingulate (Anderer, 2013), where SMR is trained with neurofeedback.

6.16 Frontal midline (fm) Theta Neurofeedback

The identification of a particular oscillation reliably associated with cognition is of crucial importance for the development of effective neurocognitive training. For a putative modulation of executive functions, fm-theta might serve as an ideal parameter. In accordance with the nomenclature of Klimesch (1999), fm-theta represents a phasic oscillation in terms of a task-related modulation of the EEG, in contrast to tonic theta, which is not task-related and associated with a rather diffuse topography. Most often, enhanced cognitive processing is associated with an increase of fm-theta. More specifically, fm-theta oscillations have been associated with specific event-related brain potentials (ERPs), the so called fm-negativities in cognitive control (e.g., Cavanagh, 2014). Recent results support the view that the ERN and the N200 are generated by partial phase resetting and amplitude enhancement of theta activity. Cavanagh suggested fm-theta to be the universal source of fm-negativities, indicating a general biophysical processing mechanism for the coordination of performance-relevant information associated with dACC functioning.

Enriquez-Geppert (2014) reported a novel approach to an individualized, eight sessions, gap-spaced neurofeedback training conducted within two consecutive weeks in 16 healthy adults to enhance fm-theta amplitude. The individual fm-theta peak frequency was calculated from four executive functions (task-switching, memory updating, response inhibition, and conflict monitoring) known to be the important and independent representatives of executive functions. Each 30-min training session was further subdivided into six five-minutes training blocks with brief gaps. A pseudo-neurofeedback group (15 healthy adults) received a pseudo-feedback not related to the actual EEG activity, which was matched in its basic characteristics to those of the actual training group.

Fm-theta was strongly enhanced during training blocks with actual neurofeedback participants but not the pseudo training group. Similarly, high motivation to participate in the study, similarly high commitment to the study, but slight differences regarding the experienced training difficulty, were found in the neurofeedback and pseudo-neurofeedback group. Four out of the 16 participants belonging to the neurofeedback training group were identified as non-responders who were not able to modulate their fm-theta amplitude during the entire training time course. This does not seem to result from a lack of motivation or commitment, as responders and non-responders showed comparable results with respect to the subject self-reports.

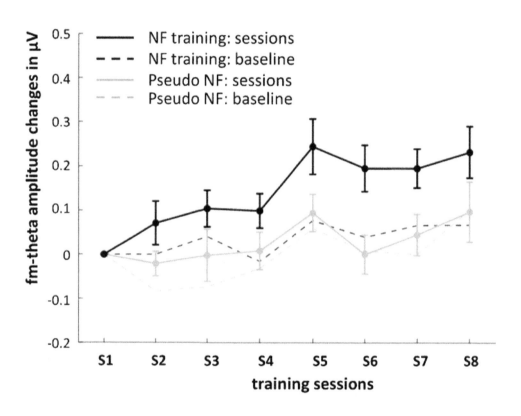

Neurofeedback gain: fm-theta enhancement during training

Training and baseline amplitudes

Figure 100. The fm–theta neurofeedback in healthy adults (Enriquez-Geppert, 2014).

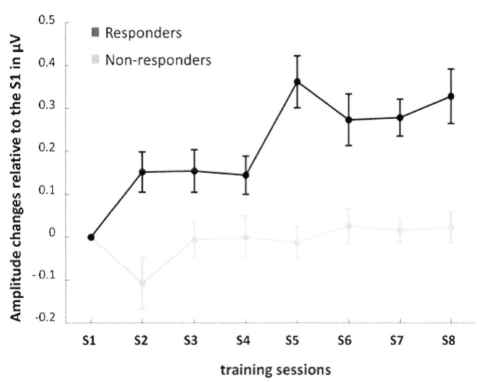

Figure 101. This figure depicts the training gain for responders vs. non-responders of the neurofeedback training group (Enriquez-Geppert, 2014).

The proportion of non-responders identified in the current study (25%) fits well with the observations made in earlier studies, e.g., Zoefel (2010) reported about 27%, Lubar (1995) about 37%. In another study (Enriquez-Geppert, 2013), it was found that initial training success, measured at the second training session, correlated with the final outcome measure. Volume of the dACC as well as volume and concentration of the underlying white matter structures, as measured by MRI, act as predictor variables of the general responsiveness to training. These findings suggest a neuroanatomical foundation for the ability to learn to control one's own brain activity.

The next crucial step was to investigate whether fm-theta neurofeedback trainings affect cognition, for instance, executive functions. Specifically, these higher cognitive functions are known to be involved in several aspects of everyday life, and they are associated with psychiatric disorders. The effects of fm-theta neurofeedback on the four most independent and representative executive functions, memory updating, set shifting, conflict monitoring, and motor inhibition, experimentally operationalized by a three-back, a number-letter task-switching, a Stroop-, and a stop-signal task, were investigated. Before beginning and after completing an individualized, eight-session gap-spaced neurofeedback intervention, the three-back, letter/number task switching, Stroop, and stop-signal tasks were tested while measuring the EEG. After neurofeedback, significantly enhanced behavioral performance was observed. The training group showed higher accuracy scores in the three-back task and reduced mixing and shifting costs in letter/number task switching. However, this specific protocol type did not affect performance in tasks probing conflict monitoring and motor inhibition.

For fm-theta neurofeedback training, positive effects on cognition have been shown for working memory and attention (Wang and Hsieh, 2013).

In ADHD, of course, the training protocol addresses theta down training because increased theta is often noted in a resting state. However, this deviation of theta measured at rest reflects a tonic condition that has to be dissociated from phasic theta responses, which in turn have been linked to specific cognitive functions. An important fact concerning the dissociation of tonic and phasic amplitude is the notion that successful behavior seems to be related to both of these EEG phenomena, as good performance is related to decreased tonic and increased phasic theta activity (see review, Klimesch, 1999).

In a second study (Enriquez-Geppert, 2014b) on neurofeedback up-regulating fm-theta, eight 30-minutes training sessions were conducted in 19 students, where pseudo neurofeedback was offered to 21 students. Each of the eight neurofeedback sessions furthermore consisted of six five-minute blocks of neurofeedback with self-paced breaks in-between. Before and after these blocks, a five-minute start/end-baseline was measured to assess resting state EEG activity.

To investigate transfer effects of neurofeedback training on cognitive performance, mean reaction time and mean accuracy of correct responses were calculated for all conditions of the four executive function tasks, namely for the three-back vs. zero-back conditions of the three-back task, the unmix vs. stay vs. switch conditions of the letter number task-switching task, the congruent vs. incongruent conditions of the Stroop-task, and the go vs. stop conditions of the stop-signal task. To investigate performance gains after neurofeedback training, performance differences between pre- and post-measurements were calculated for all the conditions of the four executive function tasks. A stronger performance gain was expected in conditions requiring executive functions. Nigbur

(2011) presented enhanced synchrony in the theta range between frontomedial and lateral frontal electrode sites, interpreted as cooperated work, to allocate control during conflict monitoring as well as between fronto-medial electrode sites with those over the contralateral motor area during conflict monitoring, possibly reflecting the renewed need of response selection during conflicts. Oehrn (2014) demonstrated by means of intracranial recordings that fm-theta originated from dACC as conflict detection signal, causally leading to entrained theta in the DLPFC and finally accomplishing a coupling between DLPFC-gamma power and dACC oscillations for conflict resolution.

Apart from the beneficial behavioral effects of proactive control, the current study revealed an overall alteration of fm-theta in executive function tasks after proper neurofeedback training, as compared to the active control intervention. This finding generally demonstrates that fm-theta neurofeedback affects the targeted executive function network.

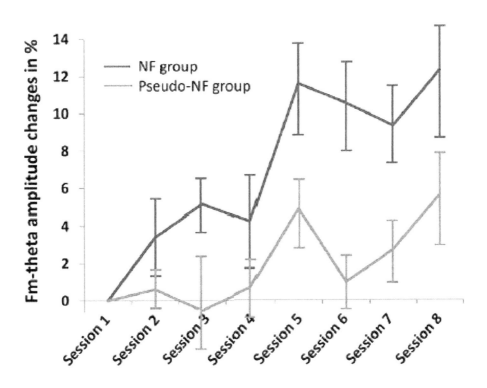

Figure 102. Fm-theta amplitude gain after neurofeedback (Enriquez-Geppert, 2014b).

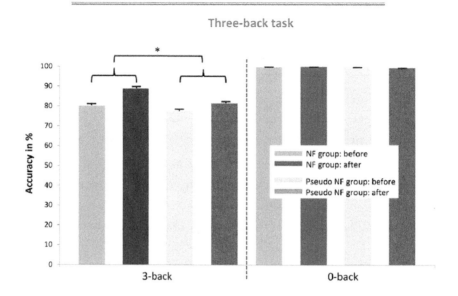

Figure 103. Improved accuracy in 3–back task, and not in 0–back task, after neurofeedback (Enriquez–Gerppert, 2014b).

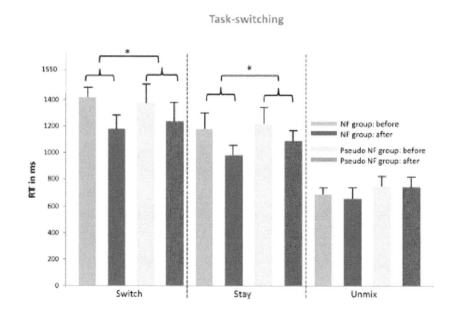

Figure 104. Improved reaction time in task switching after neurofeedback (Enriquez–Geppert, 2014b).

Improvements were found in the 3-back (and not the zero-back) task and in the switching task. No improvements were found in the Stroop task and the stop-signal task. As a result, it was shown that proper neurofeedback training facilitated memory updating and mental set shifting, two executive functions relying on proactive control, but not enhanced conflict monitoring and motor inhibition, two executive functions that built on reactive control.

Regarding the dual nature of the findings, the differential neurofeedback training effects of this fm-theta neurofeedback protocol on executive functions reflect the current qualitative distinction between proactive and reactive cognitive control mechanisms. Indeed, a dual mechanism framework (Braver, 2012) has been suggested that works by means of the abovementioned two distinct operating modes that probably differ in their temporal dynamics and relevant neural networks. As such, within this dual framework, proactive control is conceptualized as an anticipatory mechanism, actively maintaining task goals that serve as a source of top-down bias, thus supporting facilitated processing of expected events with a high cognitive demand before they actually occur. For instance, in the three-back task, subjects can process upcoming targets by subvocally repeating the sequence they have to keep in working memory and comparing it with their mental representation of the target stimulus. In contrast, reactive control is conceptualized as a reactive bottom-up mechanism that is recruited only when it is required, for instance, when interference is detected by a conflict monitoring system or when a stop-signal requires the inhibition of an initiated response, as is the case with the Stroop and the stop-signal tasks.

Interestingly, although all executive functions, regardless of whether they require proactive or reactive control mechanisms, recruit the superordinate cognitive control network (Niendam, 2012), the subtypes seem to rely on different sub-networks. Menon (2011) distinguished the central executive network, i.e., a frontoparietal system anchored in the dorsolateral prefrontal cortex (DLPFC) and lateral posterior parietal cortex crucially involved in actively maintaining task goals, from the salience network, i.e., a cingulate-frontal-opercular system reacting to detected task events. Similarly, Dosenbach (2008) proposed a dual-network architecture for executive functions based on graph analytic methods, differentiating the frontoparietal network from a cingulo-opercular network the implement proactive and reactive cognitive control, respectively.

From the lack of behavioral effects in the Stroop- and stop-signal tasks, one might be tempted to conclude that fm-theta is not necessarily crucial for the implementation of reactive control. Yet, the current fm-theta protocol of this study might have targeted primarily fm-theta used in the proactive control network while it might have addressed the network implementing reactive control less effectively, as fm-theta might affect primarily the detection signals generated in the dACC and less the resolution activity or the compensatory mechanisms processed in other brain regions of the executive function network (Botvinick, 2004). Indeed, fm-theta is thought to enable the transmission of information over different cortical brain areas by entraining activity in disparate neural systems (Cavanagh and Frank, 2014). More precisely, the properties of theta oscillations showing high-amplitude-low-frequency modulations denote an ideal neural parameter for neural organization over distal brain regions (Buzsáki and Draguhn, 2004). Theta phase synchrony between the dACC and distal brain regions has been observed in different studies on executive functions, such as the study of Cohen and Cavanagh (2011) who reported a single-trial phase synchrony between the dACC and lateral prefrontal brain areas that was modulated by reaction times during conflict monitoring.

Apart from the beneficial behavioral effects of proactive control, the current study revealed an overall alteration of fm-theta in executive function tasks after proper neurofeedback training compared to the active control intervention. Event-related spectral perturbations (ERSPs) were calculated for each task that represent log- transformed changes of power in dB relative to the baseline (Delorme and Makeig, 2004).

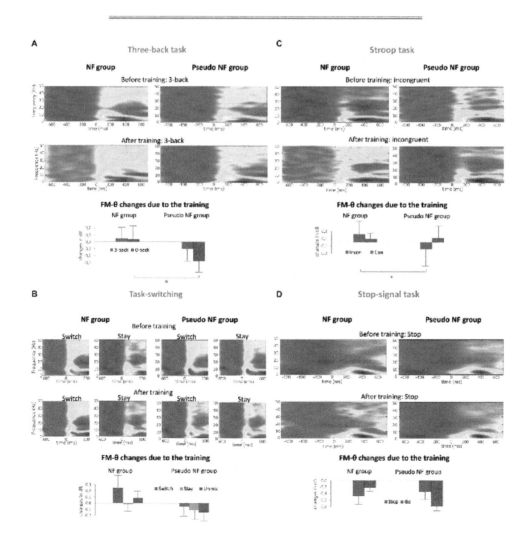

Figure 105. Event-related spectral perturbations before and after neurofeedback as well as extracted fm-theta changes as bar charts for the 3-back condition in the 3-back task (A), the switch and stay condition of the task-switching (B), the incongruent condition of the Stroop task (C), and the stop condition of the stop-signal task (D). Significant results are marked with a star (Enriquez-Geppert, 2014b).

Enriquez-Geppert herself emphasized the important fact concerning the dissociation of tonic and phasic amplitude, where successful behavior seems to be related to both of these EEG phenomena; good performance is related to decreased tonic activity and increased phasic theta activity. Good performance in cognitive and memory tasks is related to two types of EEG phenomena: a tonic increase in alpha but a decrease in theta power and a large phasic (event-related) decrease in alpha but increase in theta, depending on the type of memory demands (Klimesch, 1999). Event-related changes indicate that the extent of upper alpha desynchronization is positively related to (semantic) long-term memory performance, whereas theta synchronization is positively related to the ability to encode new information. Klimesch suggested that the encoding of new information is reflected by theta oscillations in hippocampo-cortical feedback loops, whereas search and retrieval processes in (semantic) long-term memory are reflected by upper alpha oscillations in thalamo-cortical feedback loops. Phasic or event-related changes in the EEG are more or less under volitional control and occur at a rapid rate, whereas tonic changes are less or not at all under volitional control and occur at a much slower rate. Phasic changes in the EEG are task and/or stimulus related. The extent of an event-related change in alpha and theta depends on absolute alpha and theta power. If theta power is low, theta synchronization is large and if alpha power is large, the extent of alpha power desynchronization suppression is large too. Large alpha power, which correlates with a pronounced decrease in event-related band power, and small theta power, which correlates with a pronounced increase in band power, indicate good cognitive performance. Studies on the hippocampal theta rhythm in animals have provided good evidence that theta power is related to the encoding of new information and to episodic memory in particular. Klimesch (1996) tested whether a task-related increase in theta power selectively reflects the successful encoding of new information. Because theta power increases in a large variety of different tasks, it seems plausible to assume that theta power reflects - at least in part - unspecific factors, such as attentional demands, task difficulty, and cognitive load.

In a pure logical sense, one would expect that the amount of desynchronization should depend on absolute power. A large extent of power suppression during task performance would be possible only if activity during a reference or resting interval is sufficient. The amount of alpha desynchronization is generally related to the relevance and/or difficulty of a task. More demanding or relevant a task is associated with stronger amount of alpha suppression or ERD. Most interestingly, the opposite holds true for the theta band. Here, small reference power is related to a large amount of synchronization or increase in power. With respect to the relationship between memory performance and absolute power, the reported findings allow us to make an important prediction. We would expect that good as compared to bad memory performers show significantly more power in the upper alpha but less power in the theta band. This result would be expected even when the EEG is measured during a resting phase.

Summary

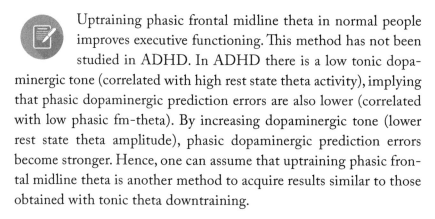 Uptraining phasic frontal midline theta in normal people improves executive functioning. This method has not been studied in ADHD. In ADHD there is a low tonic dopaminergic tone (correlated with high rest state theta activity), implying that phasic dopaminergic prediction errors are also lower (correlated with low phasic fm-theta). By increasing dopaminergic tone (lower rest state theta amplitude), phasic dopaminergic prediction errors become stronger. Hence, one can assume that uptraining phasic frontal midline theta is another method to acquire results similar to those obtained with tonic theta downtraining.

CHAPTER 7
Tomographic (LORETA) 3D Neurofeedback

7.1 3D Source Reconstruction of EEG

THE EEG IS a spatiotemporal sum of volume-conducted potentials originating from multiple cortical sources with electrical activity that is partially synchronized and suitably oriented to reach the scalp electrodes through volume conduction. The biophysical inverse problem of determining the physical source distribution of a given set of scalp maps is underdetermined. Therefore, additional information and hypotheses are derived from a mixture of exploratory and confirmatory approaches to fit a source model to EEG data.

Scalp EEG has several limitations, 1) blurring of the cortical signal by the skull and 2) volume conduction of cortical EEG activity, which means that sources that are more distant are also projected to the skull. Nunez and Lopes da Silva (2002) showed that about 50% of the scalp EEG amplitude arises from directly beneath each electrode and 95% arises from 6 centimeters around. Additionally, 3) at the scalp, there is no reference-free EEG signal, which means that electrical activity at the reference electrode influence the signal. Lastly, 4) in neurofeedback, it is not possible to target specifically EEG activity in a specific deep cortical source.

One of the limitations of modern neurofeedback methods is that they supply limited information, originating from just one or two electrode readings placed on the scalp. In theory, targeting feedback brain activity from specific areas deep in the cerebral cortex can lead to significant improvements in efficiency and precision. Classically, the EEG is measured at 19 points on the scalp, forming a somewhat geometrical shape of a hemisphere. Commonly, the source of measured activity lies deep in the cortex. By calculating an inverse mathematical solution involving three-dimensional distribution of each EEG activity measured at the scalp (such as certain EEG frequencies, epileptic discharges, or evoked potentials), it is possible to localize the source (or sources) and to measure its current density. These calculated three dimensional localizations can be linked to data from a brain atlas in order to obtain functional anatomic images similar to images obtained from other functional brain imaging research techniques, such as PET scans (positron emission tomography) or fMRI (functional magnetic resonance). The images are displayed in cross section, hence the origin of the term tomography.

LORETA (low resolution electromagnetic tomographic activity), developed in 1994 by Pascual-Marqui (Pascual-Marqui, Michel, & Lehmann, 1994; Pascual-Marqui, 2002), is one of the most well-known and used methods of source localization. This mathematical reconstruction is used only for imaging the cerebral cortical electrical activity and thus not for imaging the white matter, which consists of the neurons connecting different brain areas or for the grey nuclei deep in the brain (basal ganglia and thalamus) or the cerebellum. This restriction should be kept in mind because all EEG activity that is measurable at the scalp originates in the cortex (Nunez, 1995). Naturally, this does not simply imply that no electrical activity is processed in the grey nucleus. On the contrary, an important part of EEG activity measured at the scalp is processed in the thalamus and the reticular formation in the brain stem, playing an important role in the determination of states of consciousness and attention. These areas modulate electrical activity in the cerebral cortex, which is measured in EEG.

Compared to fMRI, spatial resolution is lower but temporal resolution is much higher in EEG and its source reconstruction. However, fMRI might not necessarily have higher spatial resolution compared to LORETA, since the BOLD signal depends on deoxygenated blood flow in veins that drain blood a distance from the active region and the area of blood deoxygenation can be quite large, i.e., several centimeters.

EEG reflects the macroscopic neuronal activity itself while fMRI reflects blood oxygenation level dependent activity and PET glucose consumption, which are indirect markers of neuronal activity. The 3-D source reconstruction (inverse solution) of superficial EEG is possible and offers a solution to some of these problems; however, it has its own limitations and pitfalls. 3-D source reconstruction is reference-free, without volume conduction and skull blurring, and it is more spatial and source specific. It is known that neurofeedback is more effective when specific cortical areas can be targeted, as in Sterman's original cat studies with implanted electrodes and in studies of operant conditioning of one neuron with intracranial microelectrodes. The pitfalls are that there is no single perfect inverse solution, the spatial resolution is still limited (LORETA's name implies low spatial resolution of 1-2 cm), and sensitivity to artefacts is high while the sources are reconstructed from 19 electrodes – even more when one is conducting neurofeedback sessions. On the other hand, it is interesting to note that more than 20 published studies using LORETA pinpointed correctly an increased theta activity, as an antidepressant response predicting biomarker, in the rostral anterior cingulate in depressed patients. The fact that even in fMRI studies, deviant areas in large-scale brain networks are often quite large, the spatial resolution does not need to be very high, as the brain operates by widely spatially distributed networks that include many Brodmann areas.

As several neurons activate synchronously through superposition, they generate a dipole moment that results in a measurable potential difference on the surface of the scalp. LORETA uses a powerful 3-dimensional spatial Laplacian operator that smooths the current density values over several centimeters. The Laplacian operator is a vector calculus method used in physics, and it is called an 'operator' because it is a general mathematical method that operates on vectors. In this case, the operator is a spatial smoothing process that maximally smooths the source space or the current generated by voxels. This is why neighboring voxels in LORETA correlate so highly and why the scientific literature uses the center voxels that are representative of a given node or Brodmann area when computing coherence and phase between Brodmann areas. The 3D Laplacian operator for a physiological constraint was selected in recognition that neurons discharge in large synchronous groups across space.

As we have discussed in previous chapters, it is assumed that the dorsal anterior cingulate is the typical target for neurofeedback in Cz SMR/theta neurofeedback for ADHD. However, as we know that only 50% of scalp EEG-activity has its source beneath the scalp electrode, the training will be at least for 50% not on target. The first LORETA neurofeedback studies for that reason have been targeting the dACC selectively, assuming that it would be more specific and hence more effective. Certainly, from a research perspective, these studies are very important also because they investigated changes in related networks in LORETA after neurofeedback.

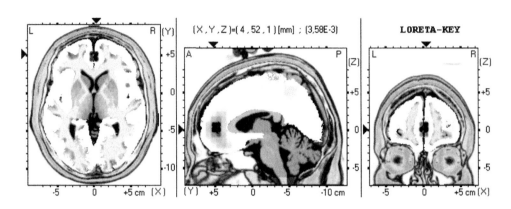

Figure 106. Three-dimensional cross sections of the brain from the Talairach Brain Atlas (Lancaster et al., 1997; Lancaster, et al., 2000) indicate areas of maximal distribution of certain electrical current densities; the reconstruction is based on the distribution of certain EEG activity over the surface of the scalp. In these images, current density is maximal in the anterior cingulate (colored black).

7.2 Lessons from fMRI Neurofeedback

The interest in LORETA neurofeedback has been boosted by the developments of fMRI neurofeedback. In the early stage of the development of this field, researchers were inspired by the traditional EEG biofeedback literature. fMRI neurofeedback has two applications; first, it offers the possibility to study the relation between behavior and localized brain activation. Unlike traditional fMRI studies in which brain activations are analyzed after they are elicited by a particular task, fMRI neurofeedback, as an independent variable, enables the manipulation of the brain activity to study its influence on behavior as the dependent variable. Second, the behavioral modification induced by the operant training of localized brain areas could represent a novel therapeutic approach to brain disorders. Most studies have focused on the volitional control of activity in circumscribed brain regions. A review (Ruiz, 2014) of published studies targeting circumscribed areas discussed amygdala, anterior insula, dorsal anterior cingulate, ventral anterior cingulate, rostral anterior cingulate, subgenual anterior cingulate, VLPFC, DLPFC, OFC, parahippocampal cortex, primary motor cortex, primary auditory cortex, visual cortex, and language areas. The post hoc analysis of these experiments suggested that modulations in the connectivity of brain networks accompany the successful modulation of a single region of interest.

These findings, together with the understanding that the brain functions by coordinated activity of spatially distributed regions, have recently began to incorporate real-time feedback of functional connectivity between different brain areas. Considering that normal brain functioning involves the concerted action of multiple brain networks, it is not surprising that abnormal brain states, as in several neuronal and psychiatric disorders, are thought to arise from the uncoordinated activation of distributed brain regions or from their impaired functional coupling. Ruiz (2011) performed the first study, demonstrating that it was possible to 'directly' train a group of healthy participants to achieve self-control of the functional connectivity between inferior frontal gyrus (IFG) and superior temporal gyrus (STG) in a few sessions. An enhanced automatic semantic priming was demonstrated, and it has been postulated that the neural bases of this phenomenon include the coupling of frontotemporal areas.

Even more intriguing are recent studies that have employed pattern classification approaches developed in the field of machine learning to train individuals to self-regulate the spatiotemporal patterns of the specific neurocircuitry involved in motor function, emotion, and perception (Moll, 2014; Sitaram, 2011). These studies have established that people can learn to regulate patterns in a specific manner that has behavioral consequences.

Knowing that the dorsal anterior cingulate (dACC) has an important role in ADHD and that it is assumed that SMR/theta EEG neurofeedback at Cz is targeting primarily this region, it is interesting to review an fMRI neurofeedback study, which uptrained BOLD activity in this area in only one session in a group of 20 healthy young adults (Harmelech, 2013). This protocol was chosen with the intent that a reorganization after such training may be potentially valuable if applied to patients suffering from volitional impairments. The neurofeedback session consisted of 3 runs, with each run constituting a 7.5 min scan that included blocks of 'dACC elevation' and rest. For the dACC-elevating condition, subjects were given a general cognitive strategy ('volitional prospection,' i.e., 'think about initiating a new project in your research') that is known to activate this region. Each block lasted 40 s followed by a 20 s rest period. During each run, subjects were provided with ongoing auditory feedback, specifically, a tone 2000 ms in length at every repetition time point, the pitch of which indicated the level of activity, from 1 to 7, in the target region of interest (ROI). All subjects were scanned during rest (6 min) at three time points of the experiment, before, immediately after, and 24 h after the session. During the session, there was a coactivation of several areas as well as a deactivation of other areas. High coactivation was seen in the inferior parietal lobule, superior frontal gyrus, middle frontal gyrus, and middle temporal gyrus, likely overlapping the default mode network.

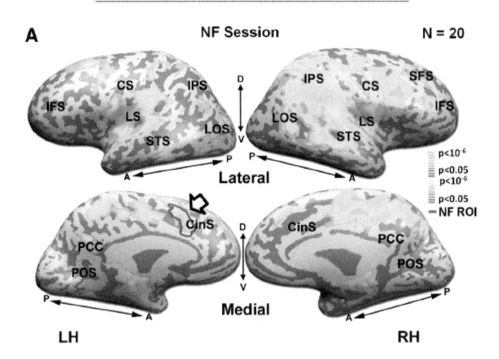

*Figure 107. Coactivation and deactivation of areas during dACC
activation neurofeedback session (Harmelech, 2013)*

To examine the quantitative relationship between the cortical activation during the session and the changes in resting-state FC, an analysis of the entire cortex was conducted as follows. For each subject and each cortical voxel, the level of its coactivation with the target ROI during the training was calculated. The relationship between this coactivation level and the increment in functional activity one day after the training was then plotted. The BOLD activation effect in the target dACC was robust and consistent across subjects during neurofeedback periods. The anatomical spread of rest-state functional activity of the dACC was reduced after the neurofeedback session, and this spread constricted further one day after the session. A decrease in functional connectivity was seen in regions that were inactivated during the training session, as opposed to an increase in the activated regions. The relationship between this coactivation level and the increment in functional connectivity one day after the training was plotted. A highly significant correlation was consistently evident in every subject who participated in the study. The relationship between neurofeedback coactivation and resting-state functional connectivity modulation was dependent on individual subjects' success in activating the neurofeedback target ROI during the training. The region that underwent the most prominent change in global connectivity after the training largely overlapped with the neurofeedback activation site (dACC).

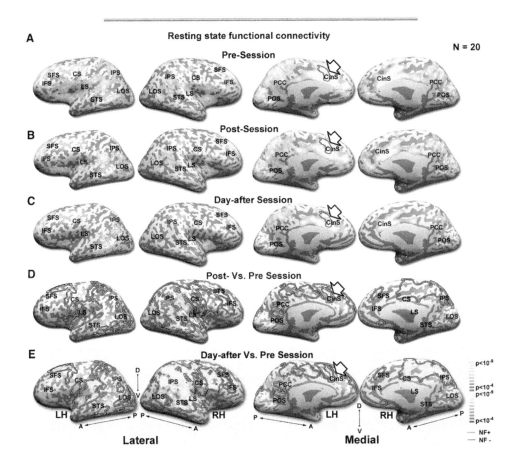

Figure 108. Decreased (blue) and increased (yellow-red) rest-state functional connectivity with dACC after one dACC activation neurofeedback session (Harmelech, 2013).

The study demonstrated that the pattern of resting-state activity can be reorganized after a single intense epoch of cortical activation. The reorganization process followed a remarkably consistent, unitary, 'Hebbian' rule ('what fires together, wires together'). Therefore, voxels that were coactivated during training increased their resting-state connectivity one day after training, whereas those that were decorrelated during training, decreased it. Furthermore, the effect appeared to be linearly related to the magnitude of the co-modulation. Therefore, cortical networks that showed antagonistic relationship during training (e.g., the right IPL and left dACC) showed a corresponding reduction in their resting-state FC after training. This would imply that the well-known anticorrelation between the dACC, which is part of the salience network, increases after dACC targeted neurofeedback. Interestingly, this study showed that the cortical restructuring was significantly accentuated when comparing long versus short delays. This unexpected finding raises the intriguing possibility that the enhancement reflects overnight consolidation effects.

Previous studies have shown that contingent feedback is the critical variable for learning BOLD control and that cognitive or emotional imagery instructions have no effect. Birbaumer (2013) emphasized that the brain responses in fMRI neurofeedback are learned, stored, and retained following the rules of implicit learning, which are comparable to a motor skill and a cognitive skill, such as category learning involving the dorsal striatum. No explicit instructions for the participants, such as imagery or other mental strategies, are needed; explicit instructions might even be counterproductive, as they could encourage unspecific brain activation that might interfere with the targeted brain responses. Reinforcement learning involves the ventral striatum by reward prediction errors, i.e., learning occurs through updating expectations of the outcome proportionally to prediction error in a way that across trials, the expected outcome converges to the actual outcome (Caria, 2012).

These studies are very exciting, but it is much too early to suggest that this method can already be applied to treat clinical disorders, as the long-terms effects have not been studied yet and no control studies have been realized. The region of interest or network targeted by fMRI neurofeedback should be accurately represented based on neuroscientific and clinical knowledge of the pathophysiology of the disorder at hand, which is a particular challenge in those psychiatric disorders where no clinically suitable imaging biomarkers have been identified. Looking forward, there is a clear need for cost-effective therapies. At this time, fMRI neurofeedback is costly. However, fMRI research can inform the development of more cost-effective and scalable clinical tools, such as LORETA neurofeedback.

7.3 LORETA Neurofeedback

Congedo published a dissertation under Lubar's supervision in 2003 in which he developed a method to train LORETA information about a specific EEG frequency band of a particular brain cortical area using real time neurofeedback. In theory, this method can designate the target with a greater precision compared to classical methods of neurofeedback. EEG activity measured at a specific point on the scalp is composed of activity originating from multiple brain areas, both at the surface and deep in the brain. Consequently, classical neurofeedback offers little precision concerning the anatomic localization of the trained function, such that it is almost impossible to target training of function in specific brain areas.

Congedo's experimental research employed three subjects without a psychiatric history and with normal QEEG and LORETA, as determined by the distribution of population norms. The ratio between beta (16-20 Hz) and slow alpha (8-10 Hz) current density was trained in the cognitive (dorsal) part of the anterior cingulate (dACC) to increase this ratio. Early studies of the anterior cingulate showed that different component areas each have a distinctive function so that a rough distinction can be made between areas dealing with cognitive and emotional processes (Bush, 1999). The cognitive area of the anterior cingulate plays a role in the initiation of actions, including goal directed actions, motivation, attention, and response selection.

The common pattern of increased slow alpha and decreased slow beta activity in people with ADHD motivated the choice of specific EEG frequency band relationships in LORETA neurofeedback training. In this experiment, the relationship between beta and alpha current density was targeted for improvement. Beta/alpha current density appeared to improve over six sessions. Further analysis of the data showed that this was a consequence of increased beta activity rather than increased muscle activity, which was taken into account. These results are encouraging but not wholly persuasive. It is not clear whether more training sessions would contribute to a further increase and whether these outcomes would last; any clinical applications to ADHD are also unknown.

Cannon together with Congedo, Lubar, and coworkers (2006, 2007) recently published two studies on LORETA neurofeedback training of eight normal students. Over thirty-three sessions, each consisting of four four-minute periods (three times a week over eleven weeks), were conducted to train the current density in the cognitive (dorsal) part of the anterior cingulate (dACC), which was reconstructed in real time from 14-18 Hz frequency bands, as measured on the 19 classic scalp measuring points. A sound feedback was given and received via a computer game. The EMG signal was suppressed during training at the temporal and occipital electrodes along with eye movement activity at the frontal electrodes. It was indeed possible to strengthen the activity in the anterior cingulate. Subsequently, the authors investigated which other cortical areas in the LORETA 14-18 activity correlated with this activity in the dACC. These were identified as the left and right dorsolateral prefrontal cortex (DLPFC) and the right post central gyrus. The dACC is known to monitor the need for executive function and signals the DLPFC to execute control. Before the DLPFC can be marshaled to modulate goal values based on long-term utility, conflict stimuli must be identified as such in the dACC. The DLPFC then plays a major role in solving the conflict. Executive functions are instrumental not only to cognitive processes, but also to effort and maintenance of attention. Furthermore, these studies demonstrated increased working memory and task processing speed, as measured by neuropsychological tests.

In his second study, Cannon investigated the changes in EEG at the scalp surface following the same LORETA neurofeedback training administered to the eight students in the first study. 14-18 Hz activity decreased in more posterior areas but the faster beta activity increased. There was reorganization of all frequencies in multiple brain areas. The absolute power of several EEG frequency bands increased in many areas known to have anatomical links with the anterior cingulate. In frontal and parietal areas, which are part of the executive function circuit, 14 -18 Hz activity increased. Coherence of delta, theta, alpha, and 14-18 Hz EEG bands increased while coherence of the fast beta (20-30 Hz) activity decreased. These studies support the idea that the anterior cingulate plays an important role in the initiation of mechanisms in different brain areas of the circuit responsible for executive functions. These findings affirm Lubar's earlier findings that theta/SMR neurofeedback at Cz leads to changes in the EEG frequency spectrum at most other measuring points on the scalp and that this training improves functioning of the anterior cingulate.

In a third study of 20 sessions LORETA neurofeedback training of 14-18 Hz in the dACC, the left DLPFC, and the right DLPFC in 14 normal adults Cannon (2008) demonstrated an increase of current density in dACC as well as in right and left DLPFC, and a strengthening of networks, which is in line with the increased coherence at the scalp, as demonstrated in his second study. While coherence among the dACC, both DLPFC areas, and parietal areas increased for some EEG frequency bands, for the left DLPFC, connectivity increased for all frequency bands (delta, theta, alpha-1 and alpha-2).

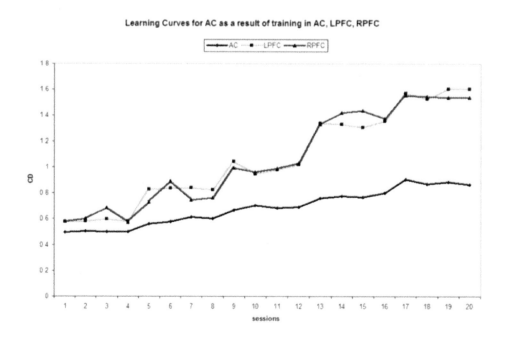

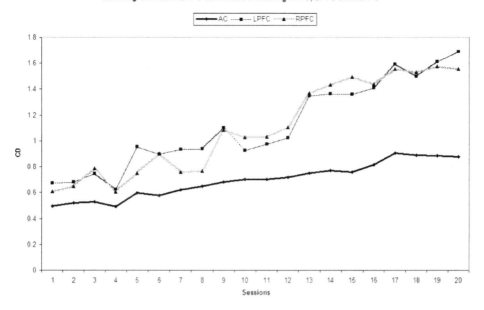

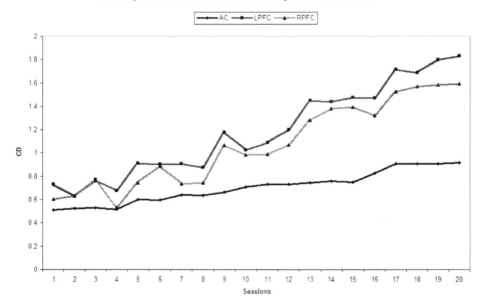

*Figure 109. Learning curves for dACC **(left figure)**, LDLPFC **(top figure)**,
and RDLPFC **(bottom figure)** after their training (Cannon, 2008)*

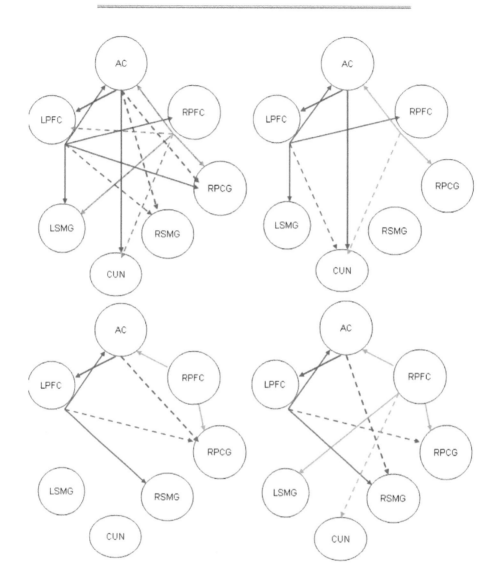

*Figure 110. Schematic of partial correlations after training: Coherence increase (solid lines) and decrease (dashed lines) for 8-10 Hz (**upper left**), 10-12 Hz (**upper right**), 3.5-8 Hz (**bottom left**), and 0.5-3.5 Hz (**bottom right**).*

*AC: dorsal anterior cingulate; **PFC**: dorsolateral prefrontal cortex; **SMG**: supramarginal gyrus; **PCG**: postcentral gyrus; **CUN**: cuneus (Cannon, 2009).*

*The **red** is for training in the AC. The **blue** is for training in the LPFC. The **green** is for training in the RPFC (Cannon, 2009).*

Cannon (2009) found an increased coherence with most other areas in a posterior zone of the precuneus (coherence increase with the left supramarginal gyrus, left superior parietal lobule, and the cuneus) after 14-18 Hz training in the dACC in monozygotic twins concordant with ADHD. For this reason, Cannon (2014), in a subsequent study, trained alpha in this area in 12 sessions in a mixed group of 5 nonclinical adults and 8 adults with AD/HD and other comorbidities, such as substance use disorder in remission, major depression, and anxiety. Significant improvements were noted in anxiety and depression symptom scales and in executive function scales. However, when we inspect what he called to be voxels in the precuneus, these are in fact posterior voxels in the ventral posterior cingulate, which are known to be connected with the anterior cingulate, the ventromedial prefrontal cortex (orbitofrontal cortex), the dorsolateral prefrontal cortex, and the inferior parietal lobule (Margulies, 2009).

In a follow-up analysis 13 months later (Cannon, 2014 presentation at annual conference of ISNR), he demonstrated an increased alpha current density in the trained area as well as in specific nodes shown to be associated with reward and addiction, e.g., right insula, medial prefrontal and parietal regions. The default and salience networks also showed significant increased alpha current density and coherence. Attention and executive function scales improved significantly or in the desired direction. There was also a notable sleep improvement.

In a follow-up study, Cannon (2014) trained alpha in the same area in a group of AD/HD children. Training alpha in the ventral posterior cingulate would be consistent with Leech and Sharp's ABBA model (Leech and Sharp, 2014) as well as with Ros' findings that training alpha at the scalp location Pz (the source of which is well known to be the precuneus/posterior cingulate) improves functioning of the dorsal anterior cingulate.

In two subsequent studies of sLORETA theta/beta neurofeedback in ADHD children, Liechti (2012) and Maurizio (2014) were not able to demonstrate significant specific electrophysiological or clinical improvements. Silberman (2014) performed a randomized controlled single-blind study using 16 sessions of sLORETA beta neurofeedback to up-regulate neural mechanisms underlying self-control and to improve self-control ability ('will power') in 8 dieting subjects. After two days of fastening, subjects had to choose between healthy and tasty food. Choosing the healthy food was an expression of self-control, and it correlated rudimentary with 16-18 Hz activity in the left DLPFC, in bilateral supplementary motor area, and in bilateral dACC. EEG during a subsequent go/no-go task (self-control) gave more precise voxel-by-frequency pairings. Beta activity was trained in the dACC in two subjects, in the left DLPFC in two subjects, and in the supplementary motor area in four subjects. Only in the active training group, all subjects were able to uptrain the beta activity and to demonstrate a better self-control in choosing the healthy food. These results are in line with fMRI neurofeedback studies in which the dACC was trained in people with addictions.

Summary

LORETA (low resolution brain electromagnetic tomographic activity) allows three-dimensional localization of the source deep in the brain of specific EEG activity measured at the scalp. Therefore, with neurofeedback, it is possible, in principle, to train specific source activity deep in the brain. This is, however, very problematic (requiring at least 19 measuring points at the surface of the scalp, with the possibility of a great deal of technical disturbance via muscle activity and eye movements) and not a realistic method in common clinical practice. Nevertheless, it has proved an extraordinarily useful method for investigating changes in brain circuits that play a role in attention and executive functions. Training of 14-18 Hz in the cognitive area of the anterior cingulate improves specific source activity not just in the trained area, but also in multiple brain areas that form a part of the cognitive circuits (especially frontal and right parietal areas). This new method is in the experimental stages.

CHAPTER 8
Slow Cortical Potential (SCP)
Neurofeedback

8.1 Slow Negative Cortical Potentials

SLOW CORTICAL POTENTIALS (SCP) have a frequency of less than 1-2 cycles per second and therefore a minimum duration of 0.5 seconds; however, they can last for up to 6 seconds. The EEG can measure these slow potentials by adjusting the filter width of the EEG band. To obtain these measurements, it is necessary to adjust the low-pass filter to 1.6 Hz and the high-pass filter to 10 Hz. Slow potentials are sometimes also called DC (direct current) potentials because they can be measured reliably only with DC amplifiers. They are a direct current in the brain on which faster AC (alternating current) waves ride.

The EEG shows a negative shift of the direct current base line for example during wakefulness and motor activity, indicating that it occurs at moments of increased cortical excitability. The occurrences of slow cortical potentials are associated with better response organization, perception, and problem solving.

A traditional way to excite slow brain potentials uses the so-called contingent negative variation (CNV) first described by the British neurologist Grey Walter in an article published in *Nature* in 1964. A second stimulus that requires a particular response (such as pushing a button), which triggers the appearance of a slow negative potential, follows a warning stimulus 1 to 6 seconds later. The first half of the SCP (occurring between 400 and 800 ms after the first stimulus) is an indicator of the expectation of the second stimulus. The second half reflects preparation to execute the required action.

Most events in everyday life are expected. The experiences gained earlier from the sequence of events in certain environments support anticipation and prediction of what will happen next. The event is described as contingent with the first warning stimulus. The first component of the contingent negative variation is maximally measurable at the front and center of the vertex of the scalp, the second component over the central cerebral cortex, and the active component in response preparation prior to the second stimulus. Usually, a button push is the required response to the second stimulus and is associated with a component that is maximally measurable over the left cerebral cortex, if the button is pushed with the right hand. The normal CNV amplitude lies between -12 and -20μV. In 12 year olds, the maximum is recorded over the posterior cerebral cortex, and in 12 to 15 years old, the maximum activity moves to the adult frontocentral position. In people with ADHD, the CNV amplitude is reduced. Aydin (1987) found that the average CNV is lower in children with ADHD than in other children. In 44% of the ADHD children, no CNV was measurable, which was never the case for the other children. CNV intensity correlated with school performance, and it was inversely proportional to the degree of hyperactivity. The administration of Ritalin normalized CNV.

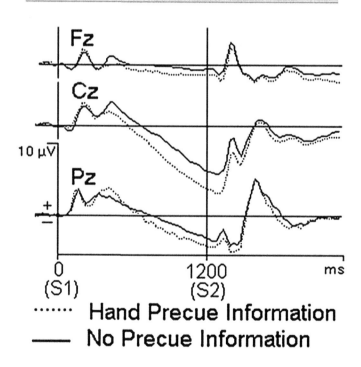

Figure 111. The CNV occurs between the warning stimulus S1 and the imperative stimulus S2 and is maximal at the crown of the scalp. If additional warning information (pre-cue) is given, the negative potential is more pronounced. Notice also the electrically positive P300 (following from S2) maximal at Pz.

Three research approaches have contributed to a better understanding of these poten-tials through the examination of: 1) self-regulation of SCP through neurofeedback, 2) weak external direct currents at the scalp, 3) fMRI research looking at the role of deeper brain structures in generating CNV as well as the role that deeper brain structures play in the strengthening of SCP shifts during neurofeedback. The application of weak direct current (DC stimulation 1 mA over 5 minutes) over the dorsolateral prefrontal cortex improves working memory (Lyer, 2005), but the effect is transient in nature. Ongo-ing studies are attempting to determine whether a lasting effect follows a series of such transcranial stimulations. An antidepressant effect was described following a course of five daily DC stimulations at the left frontal cerebral cortex (F3) of two mA, each lasting twenty minutes (Fregni, 2005).

Negative slow potentials happen if action potentials of the underlying neurons tran-spire for a longer period at higher frequencies. A normal EEG shows a few waves with a low amplitude and high frequency (beta, gamma). Simultaneous depolarization of neu-rons in the outermost layer of the cerebral cortex creates slow negative potentials, which are suspected to be initiated by the thalamocortical neurons.

8.2. A New Biological Approach to Cognitive Evoked Brain Potentials

The current explicative model of the evoked cognitive brain potentials described in earlier chapters of this book suggests that evoked potentials reflect successive stages of stimulus processing mechanisms that occur between the perception of a stimulus and the execution of an action. Theoretical models from cognitive psychology were used in its development based on the perspective that the brain's main task is to build a rep-resentation of reality named knowledge or cognition. Kotchoubey (2006) proposed an alternative model in which cortical behavioral control is considered as a repeating sensorimotor cycle that is built from two phases, a proactive anticipation phase and a cortical performance feedback phase. It has been described as a dynamic and interac-tive model. Kotchoubey himself chose the term a 'biological approach' to emphasize the contrast between the basic cognitive assumption and his basic assumption according to which behavior and linked brain processes are part of life and the chief function of the brain is to ensure survival of the organism through optimal adaptation of the behavior to the environment, rather than through processing information and gathering knowledge about the environment. Kotchoubey's approach is consistent with that taken by Free-man, who also described proactive anticipation as the primary drive behind behavior and contrasted it with the idea that mechanisms in the brain reflect reality (Freeman,

1999). These approaches are in line with Bente's description of the EEG as an expression of the degree of vigilance (in which vigilance is defined as the individual's ability to adapt to the environment) and with Van Orden's interaction dominant dynamic, which he contrasted with the component dominant dynamic when studying various aspects of neuropsychological cognitions. Cosmides (1994) summarized succinctly, 'Cognitive psychology has been conducted as if Darwin had never lived.' Koboutchey's biological approach is very close to the new perspectives on ADHD described at the beginning of this book. Attention is not itself the problem in ADHD; it is a weakened ability to adapt to the environment alongside decreased proactive anticipation of what will happen next. From the biological approach, each perceptive task or cognitive task is a specific moment in the adaptation of the organism to the environment. These moments may be the artificial requirements of an experimental laboratory task or a motivational state. This state facilitates the organism's ability to search for relevant stimuli in his/her environment. A particular tuning of receptors or preactivation of specific sensory neural pathways can express this state of preparation for perception. The manner in which the environment responds is the perceived event, and it plays a central role in cognitive brain potentials, such that 'event related potentials' (ERP) is a more fitting term. The different approaches to ERP components imply differing opinions about how the cerebral cortex controls behavior. In the cognitive model, only the beginning and end states of processing stages interact with the environment while in the biological model, all processing steps are in contact with the environment.

Slow cortical potentials (such as the CNV) usually occur prior to an 'event,' but classical ERPs are normally fast positive or negative potentials that follow an event. This distinction is relative, inasmuch as the fast ERPs, which follow in the first couple of hundred seconds after an event, often appear against a background of overlapping slow potentials (frequently not measured because slow potentials are often filtered from an EEG channel). In recent years, it has appeared that the traditional explanation of consecutive ERPs, as a sequence of cognitive processes during perception and reaction is inadequate. In Kotchoubey's alternative biological approach, perception and action are two aspects of the same entity simply described as control behavior or sensorimotor coordination. Both stimulus and response related ERP components (such as P300 and the readiness potential, respectively) express different aspects of the same entity, sensorimotor coordination.

Regarding the slow cortical potentials, we have very good insights into both the physiological cause and the functional significance. Whenever an area of the cerebral cortex prepares itself for a future activity, it is expressed neurophysiologically as an increase in the thalamocortical excitatory input in the outermost layer (I) of the cerebral cortex, which triggers a negative electrical potential measurable at the scalp. This in turn facilitates processing in this area of the cerebral cortex, a 'warming up' of neuronal groups to just under the firing threshold that is expressed in behavior. Such preparation of the cerebral cortex originates in the thalamus, with the reticular nucleus of the thalamus playing a leading role. This nucleus has the most important corticothalamic pathway under inhibitory control, and it is modified by the prefrontal cortex via a feedback ring that passes through the striatum. This cortico-subcortical ring allows the brain to preactivate both ascending and descending neurons.

Positive slow cortical potentials probably originated with a decrease in electrical negativity (through inhibitory processes) or through neuronal excitation (depolarization) in deeper layers of the cerebral cortex (layers III and IV). Negative slow cortical potentials reflect the provision of cortical energy for an expected activity and positive slow cortical potentials reflect the use of this energy in activity.

The same reasoning can be applied to the ERPs that occur following a stimulus. The same patterns of neuronal activation are seen whenever ascending pathways excite the cerebral cortex. This place of arrival of a specific excitation is always in cerebral cortex layer III or IV, and it is associated with a positive potential measurable at the scalp. This reflects a negative potential or depolarization in the upper cerebral cortex layer I, both for the pre-stimulus and post-stimulus potentials. In functional terms, both cases reflect a negative potential and preparation of energy resources to receive incoming information while the use of this energy reflects the positive wave, created by increased activity in deeper cortical layers, which follows.

Kotchoubey (2006) proposed a cyclic biphasic process instead of the classical description of the successive ERP components of consecutive processing stages occurring between stimulus and response. In the first preparatory phase, anticipatory states build up in some cortical networks cog that controls specifically sensorimotor coordination. The corresponding ascending and descending pathways are then open for excitation. In the subsequent consumption phase, information from the environment is processed in anticipation of the prepared activity. This information delivers feedback, which the cortical model of the immediate future either confirms or corrects and in this way optimizes the difference between the model and the external world. This cyclic process can repeat itself many times, depending on the nature of the task and the complexity of the stimuli. The negative ERP waves reflect the activation of anticipation while the positive ERP waves reflect the comparison with the expected input and updates.

From a cognitive perspective, the task of the brain after stimulus presentation is to build up a representation of the stimulus. In contrast, the biological approach assumes that following stimulus presentation, the brain must organize behavior interactively with the stimulus. From this standpoint, many things must be prepared or anticipated. In the first place, a response must be prepared. Second, another stimulus that would follow from the first must be prepared. Third, recognition of some relevant stimulus characteristics can evoke preparation for other behaviorally relevant event characteristics.

If we contrasted the anticipatory model with the conventional cognitive processing model, we could interpret classical cognitive potentials, or more aptly, event related potentials, in a different way.

1. Attention related negative potentials reflect feed forward anticipatory activity.

Termed 'processing negativity' by Näätänen (1982) and 'negativity difference' (Nd) by Hansen (1980), a slow negative potential occurs in classical selective attention tasks, the first peak being recorded at about 100 ms after the stimulus. 'Late frontal negativity' is a late component of this negative potential during which, according to Näätänen, a comparison is made between the actual input and an activated representation of a task relevant event. The biological model uses the same reasoning, but the interpretation thereafter is completely different. In the biological preparatory model, the organism creates the negative potentials, which reflect the feed forward anticipation of the next relevant stimulus characteristics following the recognition of previous indications of stimulus relevance. In the cognitive processing model, the negative potentials reflect information processing rather than the preparation of cortical energy for this processing. The stimulus creates them in association with the processing of characteristics that are perceived to be common to both real world stimulus and a relevant event.

The anticipatory model can also better explain the attention related negative potentials measurable in the very early stages of perception (such as in the cochlea, the hearing neuron, and the lower brain stem). In this model, the stimulus itself does not determine the negative potential. It arises from top down preparation in which instruction related modulation of early cortical, or even peripheral sensory processes, can be understood as a construction of active information-seeking hypotheses. The stimulus can certainly play a modulating or synchronizing role but not an instigating role.

2. Positive ERP components represent the uptake of information.

In this model, positive ERPs are associated with incoming feedback information from the environment, which can be used to confirm or actualize the preactivated sensorimotor networks. Thus, positivity marks the end of a specific cycle of information exchange between the organism and the environment. This is in agreement with the traditional view that the P300 reflects the comparison between the person's expectations and sensory input as well as the final processes in the course of processing the results of this comparison. The prior P200 component always occurs after the first negative (N100) component and if there are no more associated cognitive tasks. The P200 can be described as the last ERP component of the brain's response after the N100, which uses the energy prepared for the task.

8.3 Operant Conditioning of SCP (SCP neurofeedback)

The research group surrounding Birbaumer at the German university of Tübingen has meticulously studied SCP neurofeedback from 1979 to the present day, especially in its applications to the treatment of epilepsy. However, since 1980, research has focused on the role of attention, and especially the role of thalamocortical mechanisms in this area, and finally, over the last several years, on the therapeutic applications to ADHD.

A warning stimulus evokes a slow negative potential, thereupon the experimental participant must try to fulfill its instructions to increase the strength of this negativity. Then, the fun of the neurofeedback session, experienced as a game, rewards the participant. Birbaumer, Rockstroh, Lutzenberger, and Elbert showed that within two sessions, that is, within 80-160 feedback events, more than 200 participants (from eight different studies) succeeded in increasing or decreasing the negativity of the slow potentials (Lutzenberger, 1984). The EEG baseline was measured for one second prior to the presentation of the warning stimulus, with a 6-second interval between the two stimuli. Forty trials were administered within each session. The same stimulus was presented afterwards accompanied by the same instructions but without feedback. The changes in potentials happened to the same extent as with feedback, creating the appearance of transfer. Whenever self-regulation skills are acquired, they can be maintained over long periods even if no more feedback is given, just like a well learned skill, such as riding a bike.

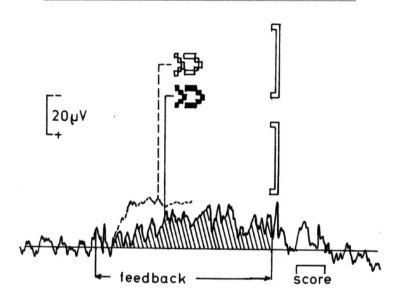

Figure 112. The slow electrical negative potentials with a 6-second interval for visual feedback are depicted. The bold line and rocket graphic indicate less negativity compared to the broken line, also with a rocket graphic at one end. During trials, the patient tried to dock the rocket in the uppermost port on the right, success being dependent on negativity strengthening (Rockstroh, 1984).

A pseudo-feedback control group in which the trajectory of the rocket depended on the brain potentials of another participant was also examined. The group that received neurofeedback gained control of the process, which was not the case for the pseudo-neurofeedback group.

Since only some brain areas are specifically prepared for an anticipated task during a CNV, this process reflects aspects of attention functions. Attention is responsible, among other things, for the selection of relevant stimuli from among the many other stimuli present. Inattentive behavior or a short attention span is frequently associated with a lowered CNV and a decreased ability to acquire self-regulation via feedback. The stimulus selection that is contingent upon the second stimulus in the CNV task is indeed of lower quality in people with attention disorders. Preactivation of the neuronal networks that is necessary for the execution of the expected task is of lower quality.

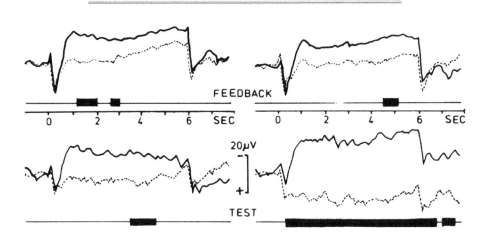

Figure 113. Slow cortical potentials measured at Cz in a normal adult during a second training session. The uppermost figure indicates the average values from the first series of feedback trials (1-40) on the left and the average values from the second series of feedback trials (51-90) on the right. The left graphic underneath shows the average values from the first course of transfer trials without feedback (41-50) that followed the first training trials and, on the right, the average values from the second series of transfer trials without feedback trials (trials 91-100) that followed the second training series. The bold line indicates those trials that targeted negativity for strengthening; the dotted lines indicate trials that targeted the negativity for weakening. The thick black band indicates the occurrence of significant differences between the two conditions (Rockstroh, 1984).

Lutzenberger (1980) found a lower early CNV component in patients with bilateral frontal brain injuries. Unlike healthy participants, while these patients succeeded in making this component stronger during neurofeedback, there was no transfer of skill to the situation where the same stimulus and instructions were offered without neurofeedback. Rockstroh (1990) replicated these findings with ADHD children. A lower early CNV indicates decreased anticipation of a task in these ADHD children, the late component that occurs prior to task execution is also lower. Furthermore, without prior warning stimulus, the negative potential following an imperative stimulus prior to a motor reaction is also lower in ADHD. Such negative potentials are known as 'Bereitschaftspotentials' or readiness potentials.

Two schools of thought may explain the slow negative brain potentials described in ADHD people. The first explanation uses the state regulation deficit model (Sonuga-Barke, 2002), which is related to the self-regulation deficit model (Douglas, 1972). According to the state regulation deficit model, children with ADHD have difficulties regulating their activation level. The cognitive energetic model of Sergeant (2000) argues that the activation level is not adapted to ADHD circumstances. Both models view the ability to regulate the level of activation as essential. A lowered CNV in ADHD indicates a diminished ability to regulate cortical activation using thalamocortical feedback loops. Neurofeedback training of the SCP aims to improve this cortical self-regulation.

Leins (2004) investigated a group of 19 children with ADHD, giving neurofeedback of the slow potentials over 30 sessions (once every school day), each consisting of four blocks of 38 trials lasting about 6 seconds. Six 12-second intervals between trials were given to avoid habituation. Half of the trials aimed to increase while the other half aimed to decrease the brain potentials. Earlier research had demonstrated that 40 trials were sufficient to strengthen the negativity, to obtain a clear improvement in symptoms, and to maintain these improvements after six months. An improvement occurred in social behavior at home and at school as well as on attention tests and IQ scale, as measured by the DSM-IV criteria. The improvements were more marked after six months than at the end of training. The skills appeared to have been acquired automatically.

A recent study of a group of 23 children with ADHD (Strehl, 2006) confirmed these results. Furthermore, it appeared that only those children who were able to evoke slow negative potentials outside the context of the thirty training sessions showed lasting behavioral improvement. Six months later, in comparison with the findings immediately after the treatment, additional significant improvements were demonstrated on all behavioral scales! Two years later, the improvement was still present (Gani, 2008).

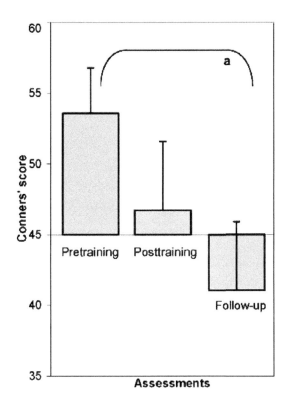

Figure 114. A clear improvement on the Connors parents rating scale following training and a more marked improvement six months after training are shown. The clinical cut off value bordering normal and abnormal is set at 45 (Strehl et al., 2000). Reproduced with permission from Pediatrics, Vol. 118(5), 1530-1540, Copyright (2006) by the AAP.

During Leins's study of SCP neurofeedback, a control group of 19 children with ADHD was treated with neurofeedback training of the theta/beta ratio. The children were not aware of the treatment protocol (thus a single blind study). Both groups of children showed the same degree of improvement on all the assessment scales. A recent follow up study also showed that the improvements were maintained and moreover increased six months and even two years (Gani, 2008) after the treatment (Leins, 2007).

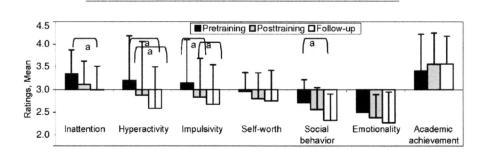

Figure 115. A clear improvement on teachers' assessment scales six months after treatment, with additional improvement at the six months follow up (Strehl et al., 2006). Reproduced with permission from Pediatrics, Vol. 118(5), 1530–1540, Copyright (2006) by the AAP.

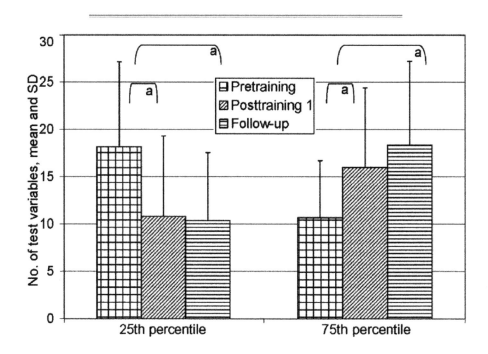

Figure 116. Prior to training, these values from an attention test lay below the 25th percentile for most of the ADHD children. Only a minority were above the 25th percentile. This ratio was reversed after the training and more so at the six months follow up (Strehl et al., 2006). Reproduced with permission from Pediatrics, Vol. 118(5), 1530–1540, Copyright (2006) by the AAP.

The results were maintained even 2 years after the end of neurofeedback training (for both the theta /beta group and the group of randomly assigned children in which the slow cortical potentials were trained). Both the ability to self-regulate the EEG and the results from clinical scales improved, and in each group, half of the children no longer met ADHD criteria (Gani, 2008).

Heinrich (2004) demonstrated that following a successful neurofeedback (25 sessions spread over three weeks), the CNV intensity increased in a group of 13 children (7 to 13 years) with ADHD. In this group, ADHD symptoms (assessed by behavioral scales) decreased on average about 25%, and the number of impulsive errors on attentional tasks declined. In seven children and in the control group of children with ADHD placed on a waiting list (no neurofeedback condition), no improvement in the CNV or in attention or behavior was noted.

Drechsler (2007) compared the treatment outcome for slow cortical potential neurofeedback in 17 children with ADHD with for the outcome of group cognitive behavioral therapy (social skill training, self-management, metacognitive skill training and enhancement of self-awareness) in 13 children with ADHD. There was significantly more improvement in the first group.

After 18 sessions of SCP NF training in ADHD children, an increase of the CNV in cue trials could be observed (Wangler, 2011). A larger pre-training CNV was associated with a larger reduction of ADHD symptomatology for SCP training.

Mayer (2012) treated 10 adult ADHD patients with 15 sessions SCP training at Cz. A significant improvement in self-ratings of ADHD symptoms was reported. In addition, a trend in increasing CNV mean amplitude was observed after the training.

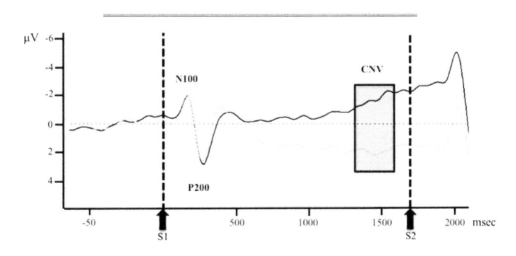

Figure 117. Grand average event–related potentials at Cz for the auditory contingent negative variation (CNV) task for the control group (black line) and the ADHD group at T1 (green line) (Mayer, 2012).

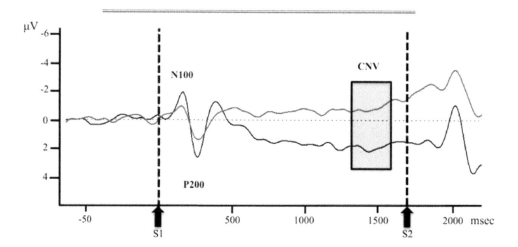

Figure 118. Grand average event-related potentials at Cz for the auditory contingent negative variation (CNV) task for the ADHD group at T1 (black line) and at T2 (red line) (Mayer, 2012).

Significant improvements on all symptom scales were observed with medium to large effect sizes in a group of 24 ADHD adults after SCP neurofeedback and at six months post treatment (Mayer, 2016). Reaction time and reaction time variability decreased significantly, and a trend for an increased CNV emerged. Half of the participants successfully learned to regulate their brain activity. In the long-term, the symptoms improved more in the group of learners compared to non-learners, and the improvements with large effect sizes were noted.

8.4 The Origins of CNV and SCP in the Brain

During SCP negativity, fMRI research has shown increased activity in prefrontal and parietal cerebral cortex and in all areas of the thalamus that play a role in the activation of selective attention (Hinterberger, 2003).

During the early phase (one second after the warning stimulus) of the CNV, an increased activity is observed in the thalamus, the cingulum, and the supplementary motor area (SMA) that borders the upper side of the cingulum, the insula, and the dorsolateral prefrontal and cerebral cortex (Nagai, 2004). The activity in both the cingulum and SMA is determined during the early and late phase of the CNV and correlates most strongly with activity in the thalamus. Rostral areas of the anterior cingulate are most strongly activated during the first phase, reflecting an orienteering reaction, while the dorsal anterior cingulate is more active in later, motor preparation phases of the CNV. The anterior cingulate plays an important role in tasks that involve working memory, selective attention, and response conflict monitoring. The reticular nucleus of the thalamus is inhibited during attentional tasks, which increases the flow of information in thalamocortical circuits, giving rise to the CNV. In addition to the role of the thalamic reticular nucleus in filtering sensory information, local inhibitory thalamic neurons in the mediodorsal nucleus play a critical role in thalamocortical information processing. Activity in the anterior cingulate is most pronounced in the first phase of the CNV, which gives ground for the suspicion that the CNV originates there. The thalamus, possibly together with the basal ganglia, acts as a secondary regulator of anticipatory cerebral activity. It is interesting that LORETA research has demonstrated the source of the early CNV to be in the anterior cingulate and the supplementary motor area (SMA) (Gomez, 2005).

8.5 Can People be Consciously Aware of their Brain State (SCP)?

While the brain enables us to perceive the interaction between the outside world and our body, it remains unclear whether one can perceive brain processes in and of themselves. Subjects succeed better at estimating the strength of the SCP shifts during training if they receive additional feedback. The question posed is whether the acquirement of EEG control (SCP neurofeedback) increases the awareness of conscious control strategies or direct awareness of the controlled SCP state.

This question was examined in a study comprising 20 daily sessions of 140 trials each lasting 8 seconds and additional 10 sessions after an 8-week break (Kotchoubey, 2002). Half of the 140 trials trained the SCP negativity and the other half the SCP positivity. Neurofeedback was given in the first 70 to 90 trials; however, no feedback was provided in the remaining 50 to 70 trials so that the researcher could assess whether the participants could increase the positivity or negativity without feedback. In this last phase, following the 70 to 90 feedback trials, the study investigated whether the participants could succeed in transferring the acquired ability without feedback. In the transfer condition, following each eight second trial, the participants were asked to give a digit between 1 and 3 as quickly as possible as an indication of how well they thought they had attained a good SCP negativity or SCP positivity. This request was repeated in the second, fifteenth, and thirtieth neurofeedback session. Only in the thirtieth session was there a reliable link between estimated perception of the SCP and the measured SCP, although by the fourteenth session, SCP control with neurofeedback was clearly demonstrable. Further, it was found that the participants who best succeeded in regulating SCP with neurofeedback also succeeded in correctly estimating the SCP. This indicates that estimation and control are linked to each other in some way.

Earlier theories on neurofeedback control suggested that the ability to be consciously aware of the control process is a necessary condition for the acquirement of control. This is in agreement with general cognitive models, which argue that perception plays a critical role in facilitating action. However, this perspective cannot explain why subjects were able to control SCP shifts several weeks before they developed the ability to evaluate these shifts. It appears that the ability to accurately judge the degree of shift develops as a result of efficient control over these shifts rather than vice versa. This could have major implications for the study of consciousness. This would mean that whenever we begin active learning of a completely new subject (in this case our own brain waves), the process of behavioral control (that is mainly or even fully unconscious) appears first, with conscious perception following in relatively late stages of learning. The question of what physiological mechanism is responsible for the learned perception and the changes in brain activity remains to be answered. One explanation assumes that the effective strategies are perceived before the effect. In contrast with previous models, to obtain the correct result, participant learning is not the result of the consequences of control actions but of the action itself. Accordingly, a very simple interpretation would be that people monitor their level of alertness and estimate the SCP shifts successfully when they think they had been attentive enough. However, this simple explanation is not consistent with the data. In his SCP neurofeedback study, Kotchoubey (2002) simultaneously measured visual potentials that gave an indication to the quality of attention and the EEG spectra. Neither the visual potentials nor EEG spectra differed or depended on subjective estimation of the SCP shifts. The alertness level in itself (which is a subjective estimation) therefore did not correlate with the strength of SCP shift.

The most plausible explanation is that when participants estimate their control strategies, these strategies are specifically linked to the control parameter (the slow cortical potential) rather than to some general state, such as the of level alertness. This visualization of perception as a function of control has been well recognized in control theory e.g., "when one is watching an aircraft fly overhead, neither the visual direction of the aircraft nor the aircraft's motion is represented on the retina. Rather, they are represented in oculomotor signals corresponding to the movements of the eyes. The position of the image on the retina is relatively fixed, reflecting simply the intent to watch the objects. The motion of the aircraft is registered in the brain a posteriori in terms of the oculomotor efference required to keep the aircraft's image on the fovea" (Hershberger, 1998).

These similarities suggest that the experimental subjects (at least those who succeeded in estimating SCP shifts accurately) were able to control the result of their activity (for example by holding it constant), consequently moving the slow brain potentials in the correct direction on the screen, just as the perceiver of the aircraft maintained its image centrally on the retina. The participants who after 15 training sessions succeeded in moving the SCP in the desired direction with neurofeedback appeared to be still able to evoke these shifts during the transfer sessions without neurofeedback. Since nonconscious strategies are conditioned via neurofeedback, the experimental subjects employed individual cognitive strategies that were not articulated. From this perspective, the perception arose from the strategies used to gain control of the SCP shifts. This implies that physiological information is perceivable when it is meaningful, for example, when the neurofeedback signal promotes operant conditioning.

Two possibilities remain at this point in the argument. The subject assesses the controlling strategies directly yet cannot separate these strategies from brain states that provided the medium for the creation of those strategies. However, one could argue that these strategies form through the agency of a 'supervisory executive system' and consolidate into a perception. We are not yet able to distinguish between these two possibilities. A decisive experiment would record the actual and the estimated SCP shifts in a state that is different from SCP neurofeedback. The CNV is a state of expectation for a relevant imperative stimulus to follow a warning signal. If the skill acquired (via neurofeedback) to correctly estimate the SCP shifts can transfer to a situation where these shifts are not directly occurring, it is possible that the participant's strategies that were strengthened during neurofeedback training will ultimately lead to two identifiable states of cortical negativity and positivity, the intensities of which can be correctly estimated. Another informative experiment would be to evoke a direct current in the frontal cerebral cortex using a transcranial stimulator, which is either positive or negative, depending on whether cathode or anode is used. It could then be investigated whether the participant can estimate the polarity and intensity of the slow cortical potential following successful neurofeedback training.

8.6 Activation by Transcranial DC Stimulation (tDCS), Micropolarization, and Neuroplasticity

In the introduction of this chapter, we compared slow cortical potentials with the negative potentials that can be evoked by direct current stimulation. The stimulating positive electrode (the anode) is placed over the area intended for stimulation while the negative electrode (the cathode) is placed at another point on the scalp. Anodal stimulation has been shown to trigger activation of underlying brain areas and thus decrease theta and alpha waves in the EEG and increase beta and gamma waves. This technique uses 5x5 cm wet sponge electrodes with a direct current of 1 mA over 15 to 20 minutes.

Since the beginning of the 19th century, the literature has been describing direct current treatments. However, these treatments were abandoned with the development of electroconvulsive therapy and psychotropic drugs. Since 2000, researchers (Nitsche, 2001; 2003; Priori, 2003) have begun to utilize this method again, primarily in order to study precisely the way stimulation activates the underlying brain areas in the form of membrane polarization of neurons.

It is common knowledge that neuronal activation increases electrical negative discharges on the outside of the cell membrane as well as electrically positive discharges on the inside of the cell membrane. This means that the excitability of these areas increases, which also means that less triggering factors are necessary to bring about an action potential in the affected areas. The information transfer system between neuron systems in the brain is electrical-chemical-electrical. Thus, any sensory stimulation initiates electrical activity in the sensory neurons (an action potential), which travels to the synapses that connect the neuron with the following circuit neurons. At the synapse, the electrical potential is converted through chemical release into the synaptic cleft between the two neurons, which briefly occupy the receptors on the next neuron in the chain. Depolarization is triggered with the discharge of an action potential in this neighboring neuron. In recent years, research has shown that tDCS can activate underlying brain areas accompanied by improved functioning of the concerned brain areas. Stimulation of the dorsolateral prefrontal cortex has been shown to lead to improved executive functions, such as working memory (Iyer, 2005; Kincses, 2003; Fregni, 2005) and improved symptoms of depression. Stimulation with direct current of 1 mA for 15 minutes improves functioning for a period of 90 minutes. A few recent studies demonstrated that when a dozen such sessions are given (for example three times a week), the outcomes are maintained for at least a couple of months. Fregni (2006) successfully applied this treatment to depression in a double blind study. This method has been successfully used to treat 57 children and adolescents with ADHD (Chutko, 2002) and a group of 12 children with ADHD (Saraev, 2002). The stimulating anode was placed over the right prefrontal cerebral cortex. Multiple researchers demonstrated that the obtained increased excitability in the stimulated areas was best used in conjunction with revalidation techniques. Accordingly, it has been shown that moderate paralysis after stroke rehabilitation techniques led to better clinical outcomes in the field of fine motor skills, if given over the affected motor cortex (Hummel, 2005). Kropotov (personal communication, 2005) found that the best results were obtained for ADHD if tDCS was combined with a course of neurofeedback (strengthening of beta waves and weakening of alpha waves).

These studies indicated that the active principle is not the direct current itself but the micropolarization field. This research has also elucidated the mechanism by which electrical stimulation can promote neuroplasticity in the form of permanently improved neural connectivity. Stimulation causes depolarization of the neuronal membrane, which then leads to an increased presynaptic electrical discharge. Together, both phenomena lead to the activation of the postsynaptic NMDA receptor. This triggers a greater influx of calcium ions into the postsynaptic neurons. The calcium influx triggers chemical reactions that strengthen synaptic connections. Short-lived excitation by the anode stimulator (which mimics natural sensory or internally invoked neuronal activation) leads to early Long Term Potentiation (LTP). LTP enables internal or external activation to trigger a higher postsynaptic action potential for a period lasting around an hour. The action of certain enzymes (protein kinases) initiates early LTP in response to increased calcium presence in the cell. These enzymes activate certain proteins, including specialized protein receptors on the postsynaptic membrane, allowing these neurons to demonstrate a stronger response to stimulation.

Late LTP, which is more permanent in nature, occurs following a long lasting or repeated external or internal stimulus. A long lasting memory is formed if LTP occurs in neural memory circuits. If LTP occurs in the prefrontal cortex, permanent improvements in attention, depression, and working memory, among others, may be obtained. In these cases, calcium activates many types of kinases that enter the nucleus and activate CREB proteins, which in turn activate specific genes. These proteins are synthesized at the synapses to strengthen synaptic connections and to forge new ones.

These new treatment methods are very promising, and extensive scientific research has been conducted over the mechanisms of neuroplasticity. These and other therapeutic techniques, such as transcranial magnetic stimulation, vagus nerve stimulation, and deep brain stimulation are gradually gaining acceptance in psychiatry. The growth of these techniques has contributed to the growing recognition that building an understanding of the brain should include its bioelectric functioning. Such insights will have major therapeutic consequences. These techniques reflect the continuing interventionist attitudes towards medicine and a growing interest in bioelectric regulation of the brain. This is just one small step towards gaining insight into the functioning systems of self-regulation of the brain. Neurofeedback can be seen as a dynamic control procedure that leads to reorganization of neuronal functions. A neuroplasticity model can provide a better explanation for the evidence that short-lived improvements appear in a number of patients in the first session of neurofeedback and remain after sufficient number of additional sessions. In tDCS, both a short-lived improvement in electrical activity and behavior can be observed; however, the effects are maintained only after following a course of repeated sessions. This same pattern has been recognized for a long time in electric shock therapy, which classically applies 6 to 10 sessions over a 2- to 3-week period. Recognizing that anode tDCS stimulation increases beta and gamma activity in the EEG (Antal, 2004), Kropotov applied tDCS over the dorsolateral prefrontal cortex alongside neurofeedback therapy to treat children with ADHD and obtained positive results. Anode tDCS also stimulates a negative DC potential and has been studied as a form of 'priming' or 'shaping' to facilitate training of the desired DC negativity during SCP neurofeedback.

Another interesting tDCS experiment of a single 20-minute session in 18 normal adults was published by Reinhart (2014), who put the anode between Cz and Fz, and the cathode on the cheek with an aim to stimulate the dorsal anterior cingulate, which is known as the source of the error related negativity that is often too weak in ADHD. Anode tDCS stimulation of the area between Cz and Fz enhanced performance-monitoring activity, increased behavior adjustment after an error, and sped learning. These beneficial effects fundamentally improved cognition for nearly 5 h after 20 min of non-invasive stimulation, with transfer to other tasks. Reversing the current flow (putting the cathode between Cz and Fz) eliminated performance-learning, reduced behavioral adjustment after an error, and slowed learning.

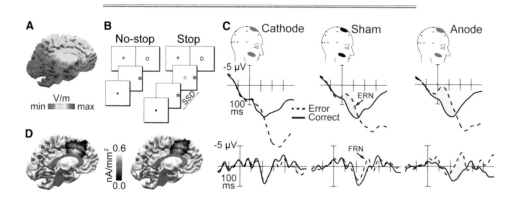

Figure 119. Strengthening of ERN/FRN after anodal stimulation and weakening after cathodal stimulation between Cz and Fz (Reinhart, 2014).

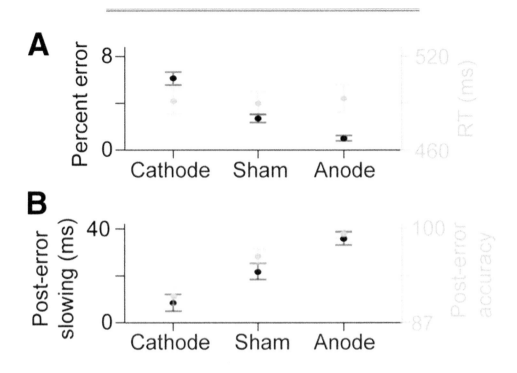

Figure 120. Decrease of percent error and increase of post-error slowing and of post-error accuracy after anodal stimulation between Cz and Fz and inverse effects after cathodal stimulation (Reinhart, 2014).

8.7 Explanatory Models of SCP Neurofeedback

A number of models have been proposed to explain the efficacy of SCP neurofeedback, which are not mutually exclusive.

1. *Activation of the underlying brain areas*

   The simplest and the earliest explanation assumes that the early CNV component occurred in the dorsolateral prefrontal cortex, which plays a role in attention and working memory. This sort of rather simplistic model is also found in neurofeedback literature in which quantitative EEG is used to detect brain areas that are the most statistically abnormal in certain EEG bands and, thereafter, to train that frequency using operant conditioning.

2. *Activation of neuronal networks*

If neurofeedback is applied at just one specific place on the scalp, it does not mean that EEG changes occur only at that place on the scalp. It is possible nowadays to identify functional correlations with other brain areas using quantitative EEG and LORETA. In SCP neurofeedback, the thalamocortical attention circuits, including the anterior cingulate, are trained. They form a part of a network and enhance the functions of different parts of the network. fMRI research has confirmed that a particular network is active in the CNV. This explanatory model is in agreement with Lubar's model in terms of theta/beta training. Recently, Cannon (2006, 2007) has further developed and documented this model in connection with LORETA neurofeedback. Using LORETA neurofeedback of the cognitive anterior cingulate has clearly demonstrated that EEG changes occur across extended circuits involved in attention and executive functions. The trained children are, for the most part, not aware of the conscious strategies that they applied and therefore it is likely that nonconscious learning processes play an important role in the integration of cortical self-control skills.

3. *Self-organizing complex systems*

In a study of the application of SCP neurofeedback to epilepsy, Kirlangic (2005) found that the breathing pattern changed along with the trained SCP shift. The results indicated an interaction between the cognitive processes that accompany SCP changes during the neurofeedback process and vegetative functions, such as breathing and heart rhythm patterns, and electrical skin conductance. Although these complex interactions are crucial to the neurofeedback process, it cannot be said that feedback about breathing patterns is crucial to the control of SCP changes. The importance of these complex interactions implies we can no longer simply consider neurofeedback as just another feedback loop to the brain. The analyses of a complex process that can bring about changes in a complex system, such as neurofeedback, and exceed the boundaries of conventional system approaches applied to closed systems. From a thermodynamic perspective, biological systems are open complex energy systems that exchange material and information with their surroundings while maintaining their structure and functions. Complex system approaches offer the possibility to model neural interactions of brain processes at a microscopic level and to raise cognitive structure at a macroscopic level. In the model developed by Kirlangic, the EEG is a parameter at an intermediate level ('microscopic level') between the psychological macro and the neurobiological micro level. In open systems, far from equilibrium, self-organization at the microscopic level has been demonstrated to be the fundamental mechanism of spontaneous pattern formation at a macroscopic level.

Self-regulation and self-organization are two strongly related phenomena that are both determined by nonlinear interactions at a microscopic level. The outcomes obtained from SCP neurofeedback in which the negativity and positivity are successfully acquired indicate nonlinear phase transitions between these two states. The synergetic approach taken by Haken (1996) offers a descriptive theoretical framework for self-organization that leads to the emergence of new properties on a macroscopic level. The phase transitions that occur in unstable states can be analyzed with the concepts of control and order parameters, in Haken's phraseology 'Versklavung' (literally: enslavement) and circular causality.

A *control parameter* controls the macroscopic behavior of a system. A control parameter arises at a critical value, and a bifurcation (breakdown) in the macroscopic system behavior occurs.

An *order parameter* describes the system at a macroscopic level. Whenever one or more control parameters are changed, the system becomes unstable. This leads to configurations set by the order parameters, which determine the behavior of the parts of the system via the slavery principle. The order parameters control the number of component systems by recruiting these component systems as slaves.

The principle of circular causality determines the causality between the order parameters and the behavior of part of the system. These parts of the system together determine the order parameters, which in turn determine the cooperation of individual parts of the system.

Synergetics offers a theoretical framework for analyzing neurofeedback as a complex learning process through examination of the effects of the learning process on the order parameters of a system. Numerous mechanisms can play a part in the learning process that produces changes in the EEG pattern described by the order parameters:

1. The dynamic of the order parameters can change if the potential landscape undergoes a transition.

2. New order parameters can arise because of interaction with old order parameters.

3. New order parameters can arise from microscopic component parts because of changes in control parameters at a microscopic level.

The pedalo experiment, which analyzed movement patterns produced during the learning process of learning to drive a pedalo, provides an ingenious example of a synergetic analysis of operant conditioning. As learning progressed, the learning pattern demonstrated fewer and fewer degrees of freedom. Finally, a single complex order parameter controlled the movement.

Analogies exist between the neurofeedback learning process and the pedalo experiment. In the pedalo experiment, motor units, such as parts of the four limbs under voluntary control, formed the subsystems. In the neurofeedback learning process, the subsystems are units of the brain's higher functions, including the cognitive functions and the autonomous nervous system, such as breathing, heart rate, and electrical skin conductance. The similarities can be summarized as follows: 1) the learning process results in attainment of a new specific coordination between subsystems and 2) this new coordination can be called upon and activated whenever a situation requires (for example a situation, which requires attention).

Different characteristics of changes in the DC level suggest that an order parameter can operate in the brain as a complex open system:

1. *Switching role of the order parameters and the DC level.* In the synergetic approach, the critical values of the control parameter can lead to a bifurcation (splitting) in which the order parameters have a conversion function between two of the multiple possible states. The results of SCP neurofeedback can be considered as a conversion from a more to a less responsive state and vice versa. The changes seen in the CNV potential can be interpreted in the same manner.

2. *Order parameters are long lasting.* DC level is maintained until the next stimulus in the CNV potential occurs and during the neurofeedback session. This determination argues for the long lasting property of the order parameters.

3. *Governing role of order parameters.* The perception of breathing patterns and electrical skin conductance may change during negativity and positivity training. This, together with the fact that voluntary DC regulation is not reached using breathing biofeedback, suggests that the DC level governs other subsystems such as functions of the autonomic nervous system.

4. *An order parameter describes the system at a macroscopic level.* The DC shift is an indication of changes in the cerebral cortex's sensitivity to stimuli. The shifts in DC potential can be defined as a functional reflection of the brain at a macroscopic level.

Whether the DC shifts observed in different states have the same source and mechanism of generation cannot be determined without investigating the correlations at the microscopic level (for example, the diverse control parameters: degree of acidity in the blood, CO_2 content in the blood, ions and hormones in the blood, but also external information, such as the warning stimulus in the CNV potential). No consensus exists about the generator(s) of the DC potential shifts (such as neurons, glial cells, the blood brain barrier, and cerebral blood circulation). However, the concept of order parameters provides a medium for describing DC shifts in different states at the macroscopic level because of the circular causal relationship between the DC level and the microscopic level. The DC level originates at the microscopic level, which in turn determines the sensitivity at the macroscopic level, where sensitivity is a measure of firing speed at the neuronal level.

Summary

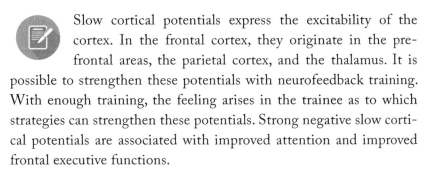 Slow cortical potentials express the excitability of the cortex. In the frontal cortex, they originate in the prefrontal areas, the parietal cortex, and the thalamus. It is possible to strengthen these potentials with neurofeedback training. With enough training, the feeling arises in the trainee as to which strategies can strengthen these potentials. Strong negative slow cortical potentials are associated with improved attention and improved frontal executive functions.

AFTERWORD

OVER THE LAST few years, the insights into neurological functioning of ADHD individuals have increased greatly, partly thanks to new functional imaging techniques, such as fMRI, and partly due to new electrophysiological research methods, such as QEEG, event related synchronization and desynchronization, cognitive brain potentials, and LORETA. In 2004, American Academy of Pediatrics announced, for the first time, that alongside the classical diagnoses, the QEEG provided a particularly interesting objective, biological, and noninvasive diagnostic tool for ADHD based on the rating scales of clinical characteristics. Recent research has shown that parents of children with ADHD who are better able to understand ADHD as a disorder of self-regulation with disturbance of executive functions and motivation adhere better to the treatment following this type of neurobiological assessment. This signifies that both psychoeducation and neuroeducation are important for those affected with ADHD. ADHD is a disorder of self-regulation with disordered executive functions. Newer theoretical models emphasize that these executive functions cannot be understood separately from motivational and emotional processes. ADHD can therefore be conceptualized as an expression of slight mental disintegration, which at both behavioral and executive functions levels demonstrates abnormalities similar to those observed in sleep deprived subjects through the EEG.

Practitioners need to be familiar not just with the behavioral symptoms, but also with the underlying system dynamic of inadequate behavioral regulation. In a similar way, it is best not to limit the investigation to EEG examination as a static, stationary phenomenon. In recent years, dynamic methods for analyzing the disturbed dynamic systems in ADHD, including the vigilance-stabilizing role of central beta rhythms as well as dynamic self-organization of the EEG and its various ongoing event related pattern changes in the EEG, have become increasingly more available.

Although neurofeedback was first applied in 1976 to the treatment of ADHD in form of training designed to strengthen SMR rhythm (12-15 Hz) and weaken theta rhythm (4-7 Hz) at the vertex of the scalp, it has been misapprehended for many years in the scientific world. A number of case studies were published in these early years, followed by some group studies. Single blind studies, using control groups treated by medication only, followed group studies. More recently, a whole series of randomized controlled studies and some double blind studies have also been published.

Over the years, insight into the electrophysiological changes that result from neurofeedback has grown. Localized training can trigger widespread changes in the EEG, which are carried over the entire cerebral cortex through neuronal circuits. Subsequently, the global EEG spectrum normalizes, despite the fact that only two frequency bands are trained. Moreover, we have learned from the studies discussed in this book that the SMR rhythm has a stabilizing function that supports self-regulation. Frequently, no clear changes in the statistical QEEG are measurable after neurofeedback training; however, clear improvements that are more dynamic and associated with attentional or response inhibition tasks are frequently measurable in the EEG.

Research using imaging methods, such as fMRI but also LORETA (three-dimensional reconstructions of the sources of EEG activity), has demonstrated that the dorsal anterior cingulate, as part of the salience network, functions suboptimally in people with ADHD, leading to secondary difficulties with inadequate executive functions in the frontal cerebral cortex. The same imaging methods have revealed normalization in these brain areas following theta/SMR neurofeedback, which is rather dramatic, especially since the scientific community commonly accepts these functional brain imaging research methods as a gold standard. Studies have shown that the experimental technique of LORETA neurofeedback therapy, which trains dorsal anterior cingulate activity, leads to favorable changes that are measurable in the EEG in untrained areas, such as the frontal and parietal cortex. The association of functional changes in the dorsal anterior cingulate with stabilization of the EEG can be understood in the light of research, which has demonstrated that frontal areas, and particularly the dorsal anterior cingulate, play a role in higher, more complex adaptive regulation of mental processes.

Since 2003, German researcher Birbaumer who studied slow cortical potentials for many decades and his research team have been demonstrating convincingly and consistently that neurofeedback training of the slow cortical potentials can also bring about improvements in people with ADHD and that these improvements are similar to those produced by theta/SMR neurofeedback. Imaging research has shown that these negative slow potentials have their origin in the anterior cingulate, the frontal cortex, right cerebral cortex, and the thalamus. These areas play a central role in attentional regulation and executive functions.

Neurofeedback therapy for people with ADHD causes a global reorganization of the neuronal circuits implicated in attention, motivation, emotions, and executive functions and, among other things, it improves measured IQ and decreases the (overly) elevated coherence between frontal hemispheres. We can interpret these changes as the outcome of operant conditioning. Reorganization of the EEG due to neurofeedback can be understood better at the dynamic level of the EEG, which explains why static measurements, such as the theta/beta-1 ratio, are not always altered following successful neurofeedback therapy. However, more dynamic neurofeedback measurements frequently evidence clear changes. Therefore, it is useful to understand both the static and the dynamic approaches to EEG measurement. The information from each method is useful, although each has its own particular limitations. Hence, the two approaches complement each other well.

The increased interest in bioelectrical regulation of brain functions (transcranial magnetic stimulation, deep brain stimulation, and transcranial direct current stimulation), the associated neuroplasticity, and new experimental fMRI neurofeedback methods have begun to melt the skepticism of scientists towards neurofeedback therapy. Historically, neurofeedback researchers have followed a separate path from the majority of EEG researchers, but over the recent years, neurofeedback has become more accepted in the mainstream for a number of reasons. Of course, new studies on the effectiveness of neurofeedback in ADHD that have been published over the last few years are contributing to the increased acceptance of this treatment.

Besides providing an efficient treatment method, neurofeedback opens the way to deep-seated effects of brain functioning on ADHD. Furthermore, it offers new perspectives on the true nature of ADHD and the mechanism that would allow us to better understand executive functions and its interactions with motivation and default mode functioning, among others. Since the 1980s, when cognitive psychology was dominant, the emphasis has been placed on attention deficit in the understanding of ADHD. The latest developments help us understand that ADHD is largely a disorder of self-regulation in which the ability to adapt to the environment whilst accounting for the long term consequences for the individual is inadequate. The attentional disorder is thus only one part of a wider disorder. Accordingly, it is misleading to emphasize 'attention' in the definition of the disorder. Convincing arguments have been made for a new name, such as self-regulation disorder or 'intention deficit disorder.' The published results from the investigations of neurofeedback therapy and neurophysiology reveal to us that the true nature of some functional disorders, such as ADHD, is *biological*, both static and dynamic in nature. This could explain why purely cognitive behavioral therapies adopt simplistic approaches. Newer models cross the borders between behavioral and cognitive psychological models by focusing on motivationally guided self-regulation. These models allow the acquisition of a deeper insight into the problems; thereby, they lead to a better and more frequent interaction of ADHD individuals with everyday problems, allowing for the optimization of the adaptive ability of ADHD children and adults.

REFERENCES

Aboitiz, F., Ossandón, T., Zamorano, F., Palma, B., & Carrasco, X. Irrelevant stimulus processing in ADHD: catecholamine dynamics and attentional networks, in *Frontiers in Psychology*, 5, 2014, p. 1-15.

Abraham, WC. Metaplasticity: tuning synapses and networks for plasticity, in *Nature Reviews Neuroscience*, 9, 2008, p. 387.

Achim, A., Michaud, K., & Robaey, P. EEG states before correct and incorrect trials in children with and without ADHD, 12th Annual Forum of the International Society for Neuronal Regulation, Fort Lauderdale, Florida, 2004.

Ahveninen, J., Kahkonen, S., Tiitinen, H., Pekkonen, E., Huttunen, J., Kaakkola, S., Ilmoniemi, RJ., & Jaaskelainen, IP. Suppression of transient 40-Hz auditory response by haloperidol suggests modulation of human selective attention by dopamine D2 receptors, in *Neuroscience Letters*, 292, 2000, p. 29-32.

Alper, K., Günther, W., Prichep, LS., John, ER., & Brodie, J. Correlation of qEEG with PET in schizophrenia, in *Neuropsychobiology*, 38, 1998, p. 50-56.

Amen, DG. *Change your Brain, Change your Life*. Times Books, New York, 1998.

American Academy of Pediatrics, *ADHD: A Complete and Authorative Guideline*, 2004.

American Psychiatric Association. *Diagnostic and statistical manual of mental disorders* (5th ed.). Washington, DC, 2013.

Anderer, P., Klösch, G., Gruber, G., Trenker, E., Pascual-Marqui, RD., Zeitlhofer, J., Barbanoj, MJ., Rappelsberger, P., & Saletu, B. Low-resolution brain electromagnetic tomography revealed simultaneously active frontal and parietal sleep spindle sources in the human cortex, in *Neuroscience*, 103, 2001, p. 581-592.

Anderer, P., & Saletu, B. Fundamentals of low-resolution electromagnetic tomography, in Nofzinger, E., Maquet, P., & Thorpy, MJ. (Eds.), *Neuroimaging of Sleep and Sleep Disorders*, Cambridge University Press, New York, 2013.

Andrews-Hanna, JR., Reidler, JS., Sepulcre, J., & Buckner, RL. Evidence for the default network's role in spontaneous cognition, in *The Journal of Neurophysiology*, 104, 2010, p. 322-335.

Antal, A., Varga, ET., Kincses, TZ., Nitsche, MA., & Paulus, W. Oscillatory brain activity and transcranial direct current stimulation in humans, in *Neuroreport*, 15, 2004, p. 1307-1310.

Arnold, LE., Lofthouse, N., Hersch, S., Pan, X., Hurt, E., Bates, B., Kassouf, K., Moone, S., & Grantier, C. EEG neurofeedback for ADHD: double-blind sham-controlled randomized pilot feasibility trial, in *Journal of Attention Disorders*, 17, 2013, p. 410-419.

Arns, M., de Ridder, S., Strehl, U., Breteler, M., & Coenen, M. Efficacy of neurofeedback treatment in ADHD: the effects on inattention, impulsivity and hyperactivity: a meta-analysis, in *Clinical EEG and Neuroscience*, 40, 2009, p. 180-189.

Arns, M., Drinkenburg, W., & Kenemans, LJ. The effects of QEEG-informed neurofeedback in ADHD: an open-label pilot study, in *Applied Psychophysiology and Biofeedback*, 37, 2012, p. 171-180.

Arns, M., Heinrich, H., & Strehl, U. Evaluation of neurofeedback in ADHD: the long and winding road, in *Biological Psychology*, 95, 2014, p. 108-115.

Aydin, G., Idiman, F., & Idiman, E. Contingent negative variation in normal children and children with attention deficit disorder, in *Advances in Biological Psychiatry*, 16, 1987, p. 178-195.

Baars, BJ. (1988). *A Cognitive Theory of Consciousness*. Cambridge University Press, New York, 2008.

Badre, D., & D'Esposito, M. Functional magnetic resonance imaging evidence for a hierarchical organization in the prefrontal cortex, in *Journal of Cognitive Neuroscience*, 19, 2007, p. 2082-2099.

Bak, P., Tang, C., & Wiesenfeld, K. Self-organized criticality, in *Physical Review A*, 38, 1988, p. 364 -374.

Bakhshayesh, AR. Neurofeedback in ADHD: a single-blind randomized controlled trial, in *European Child and Adolescent Psychiatry*, 20, 2011, p. 481-491.

Bakhtadze, SZ., Dzhanelidze, MT., & Khachapuridze, NS., Changes in cognitive evoked potentials during non pharmacological treatment in children with attention deficit/ hyperactivity disorder, in *Georgian Medical News*, 192, 2011, p. 47-57.

Banaschewski, T., Brandeis, D., Heinrich, H., Akbrecht, B., Brunner, E., & Rothenberger, A. Association of AD/HD and conduct disorder · brain electrical evidence for the existence of a distinct subtype, in *Journal of Child Psychology and Psychiatry*, 44, 2003, p. 356-376.

Banaschewski, T., Yordanova, J., Kolev, V., Heinrich, H., Albrecht, B., & Rothenberger, A. Stimulus context and motor preparation inattention-deficit/hyperactivity disorder, in *Biological Psychology*, 77, 2008, p. 53-62.

Bannatyne, A. *Language, Reading and Learning Disabilities.* Charles C. Thomas, Springfield, IL., 1971.

Bannatyne, A. Diagnosis: a note on recategorization of the WISC-R scaled scores, in *Journal of Learning Disabilities*, 7, 1974, p. 13-14.

Barkley, RA. *Attention Deficit Hyperactivity Disorder: A Handbook for Diagnosis and Treatment.* Guilford, New York, 2006.

Barkley, RA. *ADHD and the Nature of Self-Control.* Guilford, New York, 1997.

Barry, RJ., Clarke, AR., McCarthy, R., & Selikowitz, M. EEG coherence in attention deficit/hyperactivity disorder: a comparative study of two DSM-IV subtypes, in *Clinical Neurophysiology*, 113, 2002, p. 579-585.

Barry, RJ., Johnstone, SJ., & Clarke, AR. A review of electrophysiology in attention deficit/hyperactivity disorder: II. Event-related potentials, in *Clinical Neurophysiology*, 114, 2003, p. 184-198.

Barry, RJ., Clarke, AR., McCarthy, R., Selikowitz, M., Brown, CR., & Heaven, PCL. Event-related potentials in adults with attention-deficit/hyperactivity disorder: an investigation using an inter-modal auditory/visual oddball task, in *International Journal of Psychophysiology*, 71, 2009, p. 124-131.

Barry, RJ., Clarke, AR., Johnstone, SJ., McCarthy, R., & Selikowitz, M. Electroencephalogram theta/beta ratio and arousal in attention-deficit/hyperactivity disorder: evidence of independent processes, in *Biological Psychiatry*, 66, 2009b, p. 398-401.

Barry, RJ., Clarke, AR., Hajos, M., Dupuy, FE., McCarthy, R., & Selikowitz, M. EEG coherence and symptom profiles of children with attention-deficit/hyperactivity disorder, in *Clinical Neurophysiology*, 122, 2011, p. 1327-1332.

Bartlett M, Makeig S, Bell AJ, Jung TP., & Sejnowski TJ. Independent Component Analysis of EEG Data, in *Society for Neuroscience Abstracts*, 21(437), 1995.

Başar, E., Başar-Eroglu,C., Rosen, B., & Schutt, A. A new approach to endogenous event related potentials in man: relation between EEG and P300 wave, in *International Journal of Neuroscience*, 26, 1984, p. 161-180.

Başar, E., Demiralp, T., & Schürmann, M. P300-response: possible psychophysiological correlates in delta and theta frequency channels: a review, in *International Journal of Psychophysiology*, 13, 1992, p. 161-179.

Bassett, DS., & Bullmore, E. Small-world brain networks, in *Neuroscientist*, 12, 2006, p. 512-523.

Bates, JA. Electrical activity of the cortex accompanying movement, in *Journal of Physiology (London)*, 113, 1951, p. 240-257.

Bauer, RH., & Jones, CN. Feedback training of 36-44 Hz EEG activity in the visual cortex and hippocampus of cats: evidence for sensory and motor involvement, in *Physiology of Behavior*, 17, 1976, p. 885-890.

Beauregard, M. Effect of neurofeedback training on the neural substrates of selective attention in children with attention-deficit/hyperactivity disorder: a functional magnetic resonance study, in *Neuroscience Letters*, 394, 2006, p. 216-221.

Beek, P., & Daffertshofer, A. Zelforganisatie in het brein, in *Neuropraxis*, 2, 1998, p. 37-41.

Benikos, N., & Johnstone, SJ. Arousal-state modulation in children with AD/HD, in *Clinical Neurophysiology*, 120, 2009, p. 30-40.

Bente, D. Vigilanz, dissoziative Vigilanzverschiebung und Insuffizienz des Vigilitätstonus, in Kranz H. & Heinrich, K. (Ed.), *Begleitwirkungen und Misserfolge der psychiatrischen Pharmakotherapie*, Thieme, Stuttgart, 1964, p. 13-28.

Bente, D. Veränderungen der Vigilanzregulierung bei Schlafentzug, in Jovanonic, VJ. (Ed.), *Der Schlaf – Neurophysiologische Aspekte*. Barth, München, 1969, p. 185-189.

Berner, I., Schabus, M., Wienroither, T., & Klimesch, W. The significance of sigma neurofeedback training on sleep spindles and aspects of declarative memory, in *Applied Psychophysiology and Biofeedback*, 31, 2006, p. 97-114.

Birbaumer, N., Ruiz, S., & Sitaram, R. Learned regulation of brain metabolism, in *Trends in Cognitive Sciences*, 17, 2013, p. 295-302.

Bird, BL., Newton, FA., Sheer, DE., & Ford, M. Behavioral and electroencephalographic correlates of 40-Hz EEG biofeedback training in humans, in *Biofeedback and Self-Regulation*, 3, 1978, p. 13-28.

Bishop, S., Duncan, J., Brett, M., & Lawrence, AD. Prefrontal cortical function and anxiety: controlling attention to threat-related stimuli, in *Nature Neuroscience*, 7, 2004, p. 184-188.

Blanco, S., D'Attellis, CE., Isaacson, SI, Rosso, OA., & Sirne, RO. Time-frequency analysis of electroencephalogram series. II. Gabor and wavelet transforms, in *Physical Review E*, 54, 1996, p. 6661–6672.

Block, V. Facts and hypotheses concerning memory consolidation processes, in *Brain Research*, 24, 1970, p. 561.

Bluschke, A., Roessner, V., & Beste, C. Specific cognitive–neurophysiological processes predict impulsivity in the childhood attention-deficit/ hyperactivity disorder combined subtype, in *Psychological Medicine*, in press.

Boes, AD., Bechara, A., Tranel, D., Anderson, SW., Richman, L., & Nopoulos, P. Right ventromedial prefrontal cortex: a neuroanatomical correlate of impulse control in boys, in *Scan*, 4, 2009, p. 1-9.

Bollimunta, A., Chen, Y., Schroeder, CE., & Ding, M. Neuronal mechanisms of cortical alpha oscillations in awake-behaving macaques, in *The Journal of Neuroscience*, 28, 2008, p. 9976-9988.

Bollimunta, A., Mo, J., Schroeder, CE., & Ding, M. Neuronal mechanisms and attentional modulation of corticothalamic alpha oscillations, in *The Journal of Neuroscience*, 31, 2011, p. 4935-4943.

Booth, JR., Burman, DD., Meyer, JR., Lei, Z., Trommer, BL., Davenport, ND., Li, W., Parrisch, TB., Gitelman, DR. & Mesulam, MM. Neural development of selective attention and response inhibition, in *NeuroImage*, 20, 2003, p. 737-751.

Botvinick, MM., Cohen, JD., & Carter, CS. Conflict monitoring and anterior cingulate cortex: an update, in *Trends of Cognitive Science*, 8, 2004, p. 539-546.

Bouyer, JJ., Montaron, MF., & Rougeul, A. Fast fronto-parietal rhythms during combined focused attentive behaviour and immobility in cat: cortical and thalamic oscillations, in *Electroencephalography and Clinical Neurophysiology*, 51, 1981, p. 244-252.

Bouyer, JJ., Tilquin, C. & Rougeul-Buser, A. Thalamic rhythms in cat during quiet wakefulness and immobility, in *Electroencephalography and Clinical Neurophysiology*, 55, 1983, p. 180-187.

Braver, TS. The variable nature of cognitive control: a dual mechanisms framework, in *Trends in Cognitive Sciences*, 16, 2012, p. 106-113.

Bresnahan, SM., & Barry, RJ. Specificity of quantitative EEG analysis in adults with attention deficit hyperactivity disorder, in *Psychiatry Research*, 112, 2002, p. 133-144.

Broyd, SJ., Johnstone, SJ., Barry, RJ., Clarke, AR., McCarthy, R., Selikowitz, M., & Lawrence, CA. The effect of methylphenidate on response inhibition and the event-related potential of children with attention deficit/hyperactivity disorder, in *International Journal of Psychophysiology*, 58, 2005, p. 47-58.

Broyd, SJ., Demanuele, C., Debener, S., Helps, SK., James,CJ., & Sonuga-Barke,EJ. Default-mode brain dysfunction in mental disorders: a systematic review, in *Neuroscience & Biobehavioral Reviews*, 33, 2009, p. 279-296.

Brunner, DP., Dijk, DJ., & Borbély, AA. Repeated partial sleep deprivation progressively changes the EEG during sleep and wakefulness, in *Sleep*, 16, 1993, p. 100-113.

Bullmore, E., & Sporns, O. Complex brain networks: graph theoretical analysis of structural and functional systems, in *Nature Reviews Neuroscience*, 10, 2009, p. 186-198.

Buschman, TJ., & Miller, EK. Top-down versus bottom-up control of attention in the prefrontal and posterior parietal cortices, in *Science*, 315, 2007, p. 1860-1862.

Bush, G., Frazier, JA., Rauch SL., Seidman LJ., Whalen, PJ., Jenike, MA., Rosen, BR., & Biederman, J. Anterior cingulate cortex dysfunction in attention-deficit/hyperactivity disorder revealed by fMRI and the Counting Stroop, in *Biological Psychiatry*, 45, 1999, p. 1542-1552.

Buzsaki, G. *Rhythms of the Brain*, Oxford University Press, New York, 2006. Buzsaki, G., & Draguhn, A. Neuronal oscillations in cortical networks, in *Science*, 304, 2004, p. 1926-1929.

Cabral, JRB. *Brain activity during rest: A signature of the underlying network dynamics.* Thesis, Universitat Pompeu Fabra, Barcelona, 2012.

Cai, W., Chen, T., Szegletes, L., Supekar, K., & Menon, V. Aberrant cross-brain network interaction in children with attention-deficit/hyperactivity disorder and its relation to attention deficits: a multi- and cross-site replication study, in *Biological Psychiatry*, in press.

Camille, N., Tsuchida, A., & Fellows, LK. Double dissociation of stimulus-value and action-value learning in humans with orbitofrontal or anterior cingulate cortex damage, in *The Journal of Neuroscience*, 31, 2011, p. 15048-15052.

Cannon, R., Lubar, J., Gerke, A., Thornton, K., Hutchens, T., & McCammon, T. EEG spectral-power and coherence: LORETA neurofeedback training in the anterior cingulate gyrus, in *Journal of Neurotherapy*, 10, 2006, p. 5-31.

Cannon, R., Lubar, J., Congedo, M., Thornton, K., Towler, K., & Hutchens, T. The effects of neurofeedback training in the cognitive division of the anterior cingulate gyrus, in *International Journal of Neuroscience*, 117, 2007, p. 337-357.

Cannon, R., & Lubar, J. EEG spectral power and coherence: differentiating effects of spatial–specific neuro-operant learning (SSNOL) utilizing LORETA neurofeedback training in the anterior cingulate and bilateral dorsolateral prefrontal cortices, in *Journal of Neurotherapy*, 11, 2008, p. 25-44.

Cannon, R., Congedo, M., Lubar, J., & Hutchens, T. Differentiating a network of executive attention: LORETA neurofeedback in anterior cingulate and dorsolateral prefrontal cortices, in *International Journal of Neuroscience*,119, 2009, p. 404-441.

Cannon, R., Baldwin, DR., Diloreto, DJ., Phillips, ST., Shaw, TL., & Levy, JJ. LORETA neurofeedback in the precuneus: operant conditioning in basic mechanisms of self-regulation, in *Clinical EEG and Neuroscience*, 2014.

Cannu, MH., & Rougeul, A. Nucleus reticularis thalami participates in sleep spindles, not in beta rhythms concomitant with attention in cat, in *Comptes Rendus de l'Académie des Sciences, Série III*, 315, 1992, p. 513-520.

Canon, WB. *Bodily changes in pain, hunger, fear, and rage*. Appleton, New York, 1915.

Cao, Q., Shu, N., An, L., Wang, P., Sun, L., Xia, MR., Wang, JH., Gong, GL., Zang, YF., Wang, YF., & He, Y. Probabilistic diffusion tractography and graph theory analysis reveal abnormal white matter structural connectivity networks in drug-naive boys with attention deficit/hyperactivity disorder, in *The Journal of Neuroscience*, 33, 2013, p. 10676-87.

Capotosto, P., Babiloni, C., Romani, G.L., & Corbetta, M. Frontoparietal cortex controls spatial attention through modulation of anticipatory alpha rhythms, in *The Journal of Neuroscience*, 29, 2009, p. 5863-5872.

Caria, A., Sitaram, R., & Birbaumer, N. Real-time fMRI: a tool for local brain regulation, in *Neuroscientist*, 18, 2012, p. 487-501.

Carmichael, ST., & Price, JL. Limbic connections of the orbital and medial prefrontal cortex in macaque monkeys, in *Journal of Comparative Neurology*, 363, 1995, p. 615-641.

Carter, CS., Braver, TS., Barch, DM., Botvinick, MM., Noll, D., & Cohen, JD. Anterior cingulate cortex, error detection, and the online monitoring of performance, in *Science*, 280, 1998, p. 747-749.

Carter, CS., Macdonald, AM., Botvinick, M., Ross, LL., Stenger, VA., Noll, D., & Cohen, JD. Parsing executive processes: strategic vs. evaluative functions of the anterior cingulate cortex, in *Proceedings of the National Academy of Sciences USA*, 97, 2000, p. 1944-1948.

Cartozzo, HA., Jacobs, D., & Gevirtz, RN. EEG biofeedback and the remediation of ADHD symptomatology: a controlled treatment outcome study, in *Proceedings of the Association of Applied Psychophysiology and Biofeedback*, 1995, p. 21-25.

Caspers, H. DC potentials of the brain, in Haschke, W., Speckman EJ., & Roitbak, AI. (Eds.), *Slow Potentials in the Brain, Chapter 1*. Birkhauser, Boston, 1993, p. 9-20.

Castellanos, FX., Margulies, DS., Kelly, C., Uddin, LQ., Ghaffari, M., Kirsch, A., Shaw, D., Shehzad, Z., Di Martino, A., Biswal, B., Sonuga-Barke, EJ., Rotrosen, J., Adler, LA., & Milham, MP. Cingulate-precuneus interactions: a new locus of dysfunction in adult attention deficit/hyperactivity disorder, in *Biological Psychiatry*, 63, 2008, p. 332-337.

Castellanos, FX, & Proal, E. Large-scale brain systems in ADHD: beyond the prefrontal-striatal model, in *Trends in Cognitive Sciences*, 16, 2012, p. 17-26.

Cavanagh JF., Zambrano-Vazquez, L., & Allen, JJB. Theta lingua franca: a common mid-frontal substrate for action monitoring processes, in *Psychophysiology*, 49, 2012, p. 220-38.

Cavanagh, JF. & Frank, MJ. Frontal theta as a mechanism for cognitive control, in *Trends in Cognitive Sciences,* 18, 2014, p. 414-421.

Cavanagh, JF. & Shackman, AJ. Frontal midline theta reflects anxiety and cognitive control: meta-analytic evidence, in *Journal of Physiology Paris*, 109, 2015, p. 3-15.

Chabot RJ., & Serfontein,G. Quantitative electroencephalographic profiles of children with attention deficit disorder, in *Biological Psychiatry*, 40, 1996, p. 951-963.

Chang, C., Liu, Z., Chen, MC., Liu, X., & Duyn, JH. EEG correlates of time-varying BOLD functional connectivity, in *NeuroImage*, 72, 2013, p. 227-236.

Chatham, CH., Claus, ED., Kim, A., Curran, T., Banich, MT., & Munakata, Y. Cognitive control reflects context monitoring, not motoric stopping, in response inhibition, in *PloS One*, 7, 2012, e31546.

Chen, AC., Oathes, DJ., Chang, C., Bradley, T., Zhouf, ZW., Williams, LM., Glover, GH., Deisseroth, K., & Etkina, A. Causal interactions between fronto-parietal central executive and default-mode networks in humans, in *Proceedings of the National Academy of Sciences USA*, 110, 2013, p. 19944-19949.

Cherkes-Julkowski, M., Sharp, S., & Stolzenberg, J. *Rethinking Attention Deficit Disorders.* Brookline Books, Cambridge, MA, 1997.

Choi, J., Jeong, B., Lee, SW., & Go, H.-J. Aberrant development of functional connectivity among resting state-related functional networks in medication-naïve ADHD children, in *PloS One*, 8, 2013, p. 1-11.

Chutko, LDS., Kropotov, YD., Yakovenko, EA., & Surushkina, SY. Transcranial micropolarization in the treatment of children with attention deficit hyperactivity disorder in children and adolescents, in *Ros Vestn Perinatol Pediat*, 4, 2002, p. 35-38.

Clements, SD. The child with minimal brain dysfunction. A multidisciplinary catalyst, in *Lancet*, 86, 1966, p. 121-123.

Cinciripini, PM. Discrimination of sensorimotor EEG (12-15 Hz) activity: a comparison of response, production, and no-feedback training sessions, in *Psychophysiology*, 21, 1984, p. 54-62.

Clarke, AR., Barry, RJ., McCarthy, R., & Selikowitz, M. Electroencephalogram differences in two subtypes of attention-deficit/hyperactivity disorder, in *Psychophysiology*, 38, 2001, p. 212-221.

Clarke, AR., Barry, RJ., McCarthy, R., & Selikowitz, M. Excess beta activity in children with attention-deficit/hyperactivity disorder: an atypical electrophysiological group, in *Psychiatry Research*, 103, 2001, p. 205-218.

Clarke, AR., Barry, RJ., McCarthy, R., & Selikowitz, M. EEG-defined subtypes of children with attention-deficit/hyperactivity disorder, in *Clinical Neurophysiology*, 112, 2001, p. 2098-2105.

Clarke, AR., Barry RJ., McCarthy, R., & Selikowitz, M. EEG differences between good and poor responders to methylphenidate and dexamphetamine in children with attention-deficit/hyperactivity disorder, in *Clinical Neurophysiology*, 113, 2002, p. 194-205.

Clarke, AR., Barry, RJ., McCarthy, R., Selikowitz, M., Clarke, D. & Croft, RJ. Effects of stimulant medications on children with attention-deficit/hyperactivity disorder and excessive beta activity in their EEG, in *Clinical Neurophysiology*, 114, 2003, p. 1729-1737.

Coben, R. Assessment-guided neurofeedback for autism spectrum disorder, 13th Annual Forum of the International Society for Neuronal Regulation, Denver, 2005.

Cohen, JR., Berkman, ET. & Lieberman, MD. Intentional and incidental self-control in ventrolateral PFC, in Stuss, D., & Knight, R. (Eds.), *Principles of Frontal Lobe Functions*. Oxford University Press, New York, 2013.

Cohen, MX., & Cavanagh, JF. Single-trial regression elucidates the role of prefrontal theta oscillations in response conflict, in *Frontiers in Psychology*, 2, 2011, p. 30.

Cohen, RA., Kaplan, RF., Zuffante, P., Moser, DJ., Jenkins, MA., Salloway, S., & Wilkinson, H. Alteration of intention and self-initiated action associated with bilateral anterior cingulotomy, in *Journal of Neuropsychiatry and Clinical Neuroscience*, 11, 1999, p. 444-453.

Colditz, PB., Burke, CJ., & Celka P. Digital processing of EEG signals, in *IEEE Engineering in Medicine and Biology*, September/October 2001, p. 21-22.

Congedo, M. *Tomographic Neurofeedback: A New Technique for the Self-Regulation of Brain Activity*. Doctoral Dissertation, 2003, University of Tennessee, Knoxville.

Corbetta, M., Kincade, JM., Ollinger, JM., McAvoy, MP., & Shulman, GL. (2000) Voluntary orienting is dissociated from target detection in human posterior parietal cortex. *Nature Neuroscience*, 3, 2000, p. 292-297.

Corbetta M., & Shulman, GL. Control of goal-directed and stimulus-driven attention in the brain, in *Nature Reviews Neuroscience*, 3, 2002, p. 201-215.

Corbetta, M., Patel, G., & Shulman, GL. The reorienting system of the human brain: from environment to theory of mind, in *Neuron*, 58, 2008, p. 306-324.

Cosmides, L., & Tooby, J. Beyond intuition and instinct blindness: toward an evolutionary rigorous cognitive science, in *Cognition*, 50, 1994, p. 41-77.

Crick, F. *The Astonishing Hypothesis*. Simon & Schuster, London, 1994.

Cumyn, L., French, L., & Hechtman, L. Comorbidity in adults with Attention-Deficit Hyperactivity Disorder, in *Canadian Journal of Psychiatry*, 54(10), October 2009, p. 673-680.

Dahl, RE., The regulation of sleep and arousal: development and psychopathology, in *Developmental Psychopathology*, 8, 1996, p. 3-27.

DeBeus, R., Ball, JD., & DeBeus, M.E. Attention training with ADHD children: preliminary findings in a double-blind placebo-controlled study, in *Journal of Neurotherapy*, 8, 2004, p.145-147.

DeBeus, RJ. & Kaiser, DA. Neurofeedback with children with attention deficit hyperactivity disorder: A randomized double-blind placebo-controlled study. In R. Coben & J.R. Evans (Eds.), *Neurofeedback and neuromodulation: Technique and applications,* 2011, pp. 127-152. Elsevier, San Diego.

Decety, J., & Lamm, C. The role of the right temporoparietal junction in social interaction: how low-level computational processes contribute to meta-cognition, in *Neuroscientist*,13, 2007, p. 580-593.

De Havas, JA., Parimal, S., Soon, CS., & Chee, MW. Sleep deprivation reduces default mode network connectivity and anti-correlation during rest and task performance, in *NeuroImage*, 59, 2012, p. 1745-51.

Delignières, D., Fortes, M., & Ninot, G. The fractal dynamics of self-esteem and physical self, in *Nonlinear Dynamics in Psychology and Life Sciences*, 8, 2004, p. 479-510.

Delorme, A., & Makeig, S. EEG changes accompanying learned regulation of 12-Hz EEG activity. *IEEE Transactions on Neural Systems and Rehabilitation Engineering*, 11, 2002, p. 133-136.

Delorme, A., & Makeig, S. EEGLAB: an open source toolbox for analysis of single-trial EEG dynamics including independent component analysis, in Journal of Neuroscience Methods, 134, 2004, p. 9-21.

Demiralp, T., Ademoglu, A., Comerchero, M., & Polich, J. Wavelet analysis of P3a and P3b, in *Brain Topography*, 13, 2001, p. 251-267.

Desmedt, JE, & Tomberg, C. Transient phase-locking of 40 Hz electrical oscillations in prefrontal and parietal human cortex reflects the process of conscious somatic perception, in *Neuroscience Letters*, 168, 1994, p. 126-129.

Deuker, L, Bullmore, ET., Smith, M., Christensen, S., Nathan, PJ., Rockstroh, B., & Bassett, DS. Reproducibility of graph metrics of human brain functional networks, in *NeuroImage*, 47, 2009, p. 1460-1466.

Diener, C., Kuehner, C., & Flor, H. Loss of control during instrumental learning: a source localization study, in *NeuroImage*, 50, 2010, p. 717-726.

Ding, YC., Chi, HC., Geady, DL., Morishima, A., Kidd, JR., Kidd, KK., Flodman, P., Spence, MA., Schuck, S., Swanson, JM., Zhang, YP., & Moyzis, RK. Evidence of positive selection acting at the human dopamine receptor d4 gene locus, in *Proceedings of the National Academy of Sciences USA,* 99, 2002, p. 309-14.

Dippel, G., Chmielewski, W., Mückschel, M., & Beste, C. Response mode-dependent differences in neurofunctional networks during response inhibition: an EEG-beamforming study, in *Brain Structure and Function*, 2015.

Doehnert, M., Brandeis, D., Straub, M., Steinhausen, HC., & Drechsler, R. Slow cortical potential neurofeedback in attention deficit hyperactivity disorder: Is there neurophysiological evidence for specific effects? in *Journal of Neural Transmission*, 115, 2008, p. 1445-1456.

Doehnert, M., Brandeis, D., Imhof, K., Drechsler, R., & Steinhausen, H.C. Mapping attention-deficit/hyperactivity disorder from childhood to adolescence—no neurophysiologic evidence for a developmental lag of attention but some for inhibition, in *Biological Psychiatry*, 67, 2010, p. 608-616.

Donchin E. Surprise!…. Surprise?, in *Psychophysiology*, 18, 1981, p. 493-513.

Donchin E., & Coles, MGH. Is the P300 component a manifestation of context updating?, in *Behavioral and Brain Sciences*, 11, 1988, p. 357-374.

Donkers, F. & van Boxtel, G. The N2 in go/no-go tasks reflect conflict monitoring. Not response inhibition, in *Brain and Cognition*, 56, 2004, p. 165-176.

Doppelmayr, M., Weber, E., Hoedlmoser, K. & Klimesch, W. Effects of SMR feedback on the EEG amplitude, in *Human Cognitive Neurophysiology*, 2, 2009, p. 21-32.

Doppelmayr, M., & Weber, E. Effects of SMR and theta/beta neurofeedback on reaction times, spatial abilities, and creativity, in *Journal of Neurotherapy*, 15, 2011, p. 115-129.

Dosenbach, NU., Visscher, KM., Palmer, ED., Miezin, FM., Wenger, KK., Kang, HC., Burgund, ED., Grimes, AL., Schlaggar, BL., & Petersen, SE. A core system for the implementation of task sets, in *Neuron*, 50, 2006, p.799-812.

Dosenbach, NU., Fair, DA., Miezin, FM., Cohen, AL., Wenger, KK., Dosenbach, RA., Fox, MD., Snyder, AZ., Vincent, JL., Raichle, ME., Schlaggar, BL., & Petersen, SE. Distinct brain networks for adaptive and stable task control in humans, in *Proceedings of the National Academy of Sciences USA*, 104, 2007, p. 11073-11078.

Dosenbach, NUF., Fair, DA., Cohen, AL., Schlaggar, BL., & Petersen, SE. A dual-networks architecture of top-down control, in *Trends in Cognitive Sciences*, 12, 2008, p. 99-105.

Dosenbach, NU., Nardos, B., Cohen, AL., Fair, DA., Power, JD., Church, JA., Nelson, SM., Wig, GS., Vogel, AC., Lessov-Schlaggar, CN., Barnes, KA., Dubis, JW., Feczko, E., Coalson, RS., Pruett, JR. Jr., Barch, DM., Petersen, SE., & Schlaggar, BL. Prediction of individual brain maturity using fMRI, in *Science*, 329, 2010, p. 1358-1361.

Doucette, MR., Kurth, S., Chevalier, N., Munakata, Y., & LeBourgeois, MK. Topography of slow sigma power during sleep is associated with processing speed in preschool children, in *Brain Sciences*, 5, 2015, p. 494-508.

Douglas, VI. Stop, look, and listen: the problem of sustained attention and impulse control in hyperactive and normal children, in *Canadian Journal of Behavioural Science*, 4, 1972, p. 259-282.

Douglas,VI. Can Skinnerian theory explain attention deficit disorder? A reply to Barkley, in *Attention Deficit Disorder. Current Concepts and Emerging Trends in Attentional and Behavioral Disorders of Childhood*, 4, 1989, p. 235-254.

Douglas, VI. *"Core Deficits" and Contingency Management in Attention Deficit Hyperactivity Disorder.* University at Buffalo Center for Children and Families Speaker Series, Buffalo, New York, 2008.

Drechsler, R., Straub, M., Doehnert, M., Heinrich, H., Steinhausen, HC., & Brandeis, D. Controlled evaluation of neurofeedback training of slow cortical potentials in children with attention deficit/hyperactivity disorder (ADHD), in *Behavioral Brain Functions*, 3, 2007, p. 35-47.

Dresler, T., Ehlis, A.-C., Heinzel, S., Renner, TJ., Reif, A., Baehne, CG., Heine, M., Boreatti-Hümmer, A., Jacob, CP., Lesch, K.-P. & Fallgatter, AJ. Dopamine transporter (SLC6A3) genotype impacts neurophysiological correlates of cognitive response control in an adult sample of patients with ADHD, in *Neuropsychopharmacology*, 35, 2010, p. 2193-2202.

Dumenko, VN. Changes in the electroencephalogram of the dog during formation of a motor conditioned reflex stereotype, in *Pavlov Journal of Higher Nervous Activity*, 11, 1961, p. 64. Edelman, GM. *Bright Air, Brilliant Fire: on the Matter of the Mind*. Basic Books, New York, 1992.

Duric, NS., Assmus, J., Gundersen, D., & Elgen, IB. Neurofeedback for the treatment of children and adolescents with ADHD: a randomized and controlled clinical trial using parental reports, in *BMC Psychiatry*, 12, 2012, p. 1-8.

Duric, NS., Assmus, J., & Elgen, IB. Self-reported efficacy of neurofeedback treatment in a clinical randomized controlled study of ADHD children and adolescents, in *Neuropsychiatric Disease and Treatment*, p. 1645-1654.

Egner, T., & Gruzelier, JH. Learned self-regulation of EEG frequency components affects attention and event-related brain potentials in humans, in *Neuroreport*, 12, 2001, p. 4155- 4159.

Egner, T., Zech, TF., & Gruzelier, JH. The effects of neurofeedback training on the spectral topography of the electroencephalogram, in *Clinical Neurophysiology*, 115, 2004, p. 2452-2460.

Elbert, T., Rockstroh, B., Lutzenberger, W., & Birbaumer, N. Slow brain potentials after withdrawal of contro, in *Archiv für Psychiatrie und Nervenkrankheiten*, 232, 1982, p. 201-214.

Elliott, R., Dolan, RJ., & Frith, CD. Dissociable functions in the medial and lateral orbitofrontal cortex: evidence from human neuroimaging studies, in *Cerebral Cortex*, 10, 2000, p. 308–317.

Enriquez-Geppert, S., Konrad, C., Pantev, C., & Huster, RJ. Conflict and inhibition differentially affect the N200/P300 complex in a combined go/nogo and stop-signal task, in *NeuroImage*, 51, 2010, p. 877-887.

Enriquez-Geppert, S., Huster, RJ., Scharfenort, R., Mokom, ZN., Vosskuhl, J., Figge, C., Zimmermann, J., & Herrmann, CS. The morphology of midcingulate cortex predicts frontal-midline theta neurofeedback success, in *Frontiers in Human Neuroscience*, 7, 2013, p. 1-10.

Enriquez-Geppert, S., Huster, RJ., Scharfenort, R., Mokoma, ZN., Zimmermann,J., & Herrmann, CS. Modulation of frontal-midline theta by neurofeedback, in *Biological Psychology*, 95, 2014, p. 59-69.

Enriquez-Geppert, S., Huster, RJ., Figge, C. & Herrmann, CS. Self-regulation of frontal-midline theta facilitates memory updating and mental set shifting, in *Frontiers in Behavioral Neuroscience*, 8, 2014b, p. 1-13.

Erika-Florence, M., Leech, R., & Hampshire, A. A functional network perspective on response inhibition and attentional control, in *Nature Communications*, 5, 2014, p. 1-12.

Evans, BM. Periodic activity in cerebral arousal mechanisms - the relationship to sleep and brain damage, in *Electroencephalography and Clinical Neurophysiology*, 83, 1992, p. 130-137.

Evans, BM. Cyclical activity in non-rapid eye movement sleep: a proposed arousal inhibitory mechanism, in *Electroencephalography and Clinical Neurophysiology*, 86, 1993, p. 123-131.

Ey, H., & Rouart, J. *Des idées de Jackson à un modèle organo-dynamique en psychiatrie*. Doin, G. (Ed.), Paris, 1938

Fagerholm, ED., Lorenz, R., Scott, G., Dinov, M., Hellyer, PJ., Mirzaei, N., Leeson, C., Carmichael, DW., Sharp, DJ., Shew, WL. & Leech, R. Cascades and cognitive state: focused attention incurs subcritical dynamics, in *The Journal of Neuroscience*, 35, 2015, p. 4626-4634.

Fair, DA., Cohen, AL., Power, JD., Dosenbach, NU., Church, JA., Miezin, FM., Schlaggar, BL., & Petersen, SE. Functional brain networks develop from a "local to distributed" organization, in *PLoS Computational Biology*, 5, 2009, p. 1-14.

Falgätter, AJ., Ehlis, AC., Rösler, M., Strik, WK., Blocher, D., & Herrmann, MJ. Electrophysiological dysfunction in the anterior cingulate cortex in attention deficit hyperactivity disorder (ADHD), in *Brain Topography*, 16, 2003, p. 125.

Fallgätter AJ., Ehlis, AC., Seifert, J., Strik, WK., Scheuerpflug, P., Zillessen, KE., Herrmann, MJ., & Warnke, A. Altered response control and anterior cingulate function in attention-deficit/hyperactivity disorder boys, in *Clinical Neurophysiology*, 115, 2004, p. 973-981.

Fallgätter, AJ., Ehlis, AC., Rösler, M., Strik, WK., Blocher, D., & Herrmann, MJ. Diminished prefrontal brain function in adults with psychopathology in childhood related to attention deficit hyperactivity disorder, in *Psychiatry Research*, 138, 2005, p. 157-69.

Falkenstein, M., Hohnsbein, J., Hoormann, J., Blanke, L. Effects of crossmodal divided attention on late ERP components. II. Error processing in choice reaction tasks, in *Electroencephalography and Clinical Neurophysiology*,78, 1991, p. 447-455.

Falkenstein, M., Hoormann, J., & Hohnsbein, J. ERP components in Go/Nogo tasks and their relation to inhibition, in *Acta Psychologica*, 101, 1999, p. 267-291.

Fallon, SJ., Williams-Gray, CH., Barker, RA., Owen, AM., & Hampshire, A. Prefrontal dopamine levels determine the balance between cognitive stability and flexibility, in *Cerebral Cortex*, 23, 2013, p. 361-369.

Fan, J., Byrne, J., Worden, MS., Guise, KG., McCandliss, BD., Fossella, J., & Posner, MI. The relation of brain oscillations to attentional networks, in *The Journal of Neuroscience*, 27, 2007, p. 6197-6206.

Fan, J., Kolster, R., Ghajar, J., Suh, M., Knight, RT., Sarkar, R. & McCandliss, BD. Response anticipation and response conflict: an event-related potential and functional magnetic resonance imaging study, in *The Journal of Neuroscience*, 27, 2007, p. 2272-2282.

Fassbender, C., Zhang, H., Buzy, WM., Cortes, CC., Mizuin, D., Becket, L., & Schweitzer, J. A lack of default network suppression is linked to increased distractibility in ADHD, in *Brain Research*, 1273, 2009, p. 114-128.

Fearing, F. (1970). Reflex action: A study in the history of physiological psychology, MIT Press, Massachusetts, (Original work published 1930).

Fernandez, T., Harmony, T., Rodriguez, M., Bernal, J., Silva, J., Reyes, A., & Marosi, E. EEG activation patterns during the performance of tasks involving different components of mental calculation, in *Electroencephalography and Clinical Neurophysiology*, 94, 1995, p. 175-182.

Ferri, R., Bruni, O., Miano, S., & Terzano, MG. Topographic mapping of the spectral components of the cyclic alternating pattern (CAP), in *Sleep Medicine*, 6, 2005, p. 29-36.

Ferrier, D. *The Functions of the Brain*. Elder, London, 1876.

Fischer, S., Hallschmid, M., Elsner, AL. & Born, J. Sleep forms memory for finger skills, in *Proceedings of the National Academy of Sciences USA*, 99, 2002, p.11987-11991.

Fitzgerald, KD., Welsh, RC., Gehring, WJ., Abelson, JJ., Himle, JA., Liberzon, I., & Taylor, SF. Error-related hyperactivity of the anterior cingulate cortex in obsessive compulsive disorder, in *Biological Psychiatry*, 57, 2005, p. 287-294.

FitzGerald, TH., Friston, KJ., & Dolan, RJ. Action-specific value signals in reward-related regions of the human brain, in *The Journal of Neuroscience*, 32, 2012, p. 16417-16423.

Flores, AB., Digiacomo, MR., Meneres, S., Trigo, E., & Gomez, CM., Development of preparatory activity indexed by the contingent negative variation in children, in *Brain and Cognition*, 71, 2009, p. 129-140.

Fluck, E., File, SE., Springett, J., Kopelman, MD., Rees, J., & Orgill, J. Does the sedation resulting from sleep deprivation and Lorazepam cause similar cognitive deficits? *Pharmacology and Biochemistry of Behavior*, 59, 1998, p. 909-915.

Ford, M., Bird, BL., Newton, FA., & Sheer D. Maintenance and generalization of 40-Hz EEG biofeedback effects, in *Biofeedback and Self-Regulation*, 5, 1980, p. 193-205.

Fokina, YO., Kulichenko, AM. & Pavlenko, VB. Changes in the power levels of cortical

EEG rhythms in cats during training using acoustic feedback signals, in *Neuroscience and Behavioral Physiology*, 40, 2010, p. 951-953.

Franzen, JD., Heinrichs-Graham, E., White, ML., Wetzel, MW., Knott, NL. & Wilson, TW. Atypical coupling between posterior regions of the default mode network in attention-deficit/hyperactivity disorder: A pharmaco-magnetoencephalography study, in *Journal of Psychiatry & Neuroscience*, 38, 2013, p. 333-340.

Freeman, WJ. *How Brains Make up their Minds*. Phoenix, London, 2000.

Freeman, WJ. A proposed name for aperiodic brain activity: stochastic chaos, in *Neural Networks*, 13, 2000, p. 11-13.

Freeman, WJ. Origin, structure, and role of the background EEG activity, Part 1. Analytic amplitude, in *Clinical Neurophysiology*, 115, 2004, p. 2077-2088.

Freeman, WJ. Origin, structure, and role of the background EEG activity, Part 2. Analytic phase, in *Clinical Neurophysiology*, 115, 2004, p. 2089-2107.

Fregni, F., Boggio, PS, Nitsche, M., Bermpohl, F., Antal, A., Feredoes, E., Rigonatti, SP., Silva, MT., Paulus, W., & Pascual-Leone, A. Anodal transcranial direct current stimulation of prefrontal cortex enhances working memory, in *Experimental Brain Research*, 166.1, 2005, p. 23-30.

Fregni, F., Boggio, PS., Nitsche, M., Marcolin, MA., Rigonatti, SP., & Pascual-Leone, A. Treatment of major depression with transcranial direct current stimulation, in *Bipolar Disorders*, 8, 2006, p. 203-204.

Friston, KJ. The labile brain.I. Neuronal transients and nonlinear coupling, in *Philosophical Transactions of the Royal Society of London*, 355, 2000, p. 215-236.

Fuchs, T., Birbaumer, N., Lutzenberger, W., Gruzelier, JH., & Kaiser, J. Neurofeedback treatment for attention-deficit/hyperactivity disorder in children: a comparison with methylphenidate, in *Applied Psychophysiology and Biofeedback*, 28, 2003, p. 1-12.

Galambos, R. Electrical correlates of conditioned learning, in Brazier, M. (Ed.), *The Central Nervous System and Behaviour*, Josiah Macy, Jr. Foundation, New York, 1958, p. 375.

Gallinat, J., & Hegerl, U. Elektroenzephalographie, in Hegerl, U. (Ed.), *Neurophysiologische Untersuchungen in der Psychiatrie*, Springer, Wenen, 1988, p. 7-94.

Gani, C., Birbaumer, N., & Strehl, U. Long term effects after feedback of slow cortical potentials and of theta-beta-amplitudes in children with attention-deficit/hyperactivity disorder (ADHD), in *International Journal of Bioelectromagnetism*, 10, 2008, p. 209-232.

Gehring, WJ., Himle, J., & Nisenson, LG. Action monitoring dysfunction in obsessive-compulsive disorder, in *Psychological Science*, 11, 2000, p. 1-6.

Gevensleben, H., Holl, B., Albrecht, B., Vogel C., Schlamp, D., Kratz O., Studer, P., Rothenberger, A., Moll, G., & Heinrich, H. Is neurofeedback an efficacious treatment for ADHD? A randomised controlled clinical trial, in *Journal of Child Psychology and Psychiatry*, 50, 2009, p. 767-780.

Gevensleben, H., Holl, B., Albrecht, B., Schlamp, D., Kratz, O., Studer, P., Wangler, S., Rothenberger, A., Moll, GH., & Heinrich, H. Distinct EEG effects related to neurofeedback training in children with ADHD: a randomized controlled trial, in *International Journal of Psychophysiology*, 74, 2009b, p. 149-157.

Gevensleben, H., Holl, B., Albrecht, B., Schlamp, D., Kratz O., Studer, P., Rothenberger, A., Moll, G., & Heinrich, H. Neurofeedback training in children with ADHD: 6-month follow-up of a randomised trial, in *European Child & Adolescent Psychiatry*, 19, 2010, p. 715-724.

Ghosh, A., Rho, Y., McIntosh, AR., Kötter, R., & Jirsa, VK. Noise during rest enables the exploration of the brain's dynamic repertoire, in *PLoS Computational Biology*, 4, 2008, e1000196.

Giannitrapani, D. EEG average frequency and intelligence, in *Electroencephalography and Clinical Neurophysiology*, 27, 1969, p. 480.

Giannitrapani, D. The role of 13-Hz activity in mentation, in Giannitrapani, D., & Murri, L. (Eds.), *The EEG of Mental Activities*. Karger, Basel, 1988, p. 149-152.

Gilden, DL., Thornton, T., & Mallon, MW. 1/f noise in human cognition, in *Science*, 267, 1995, p. 1837-1839.

Gilden, DL., & Hancock, H. Response variability in attention-deficit disorders, in *Psychological Science*, 18, 2007, p. 796-802.

Gläscher, J., Hampton, AN., & O'Doherty, JP. Determining a role for ventromedial prefrontal cortex in encoding action-based value signals during reward-related decision making, in *Cerebral Cortex* 19, 2009, p. 483-495.

Goldman-Rakic, P. Topography of cognition: parallel distributed networks in primate association cortex, in *Annual Reviews Neuroscience*, 11, 1988, p. 137-156.

Gomez, C. Antizipatorische selektive Aktivierung der für die erwartete Aufgabe benötigten Hirnareale während der Contingenten Negativen Variation (CNV), CTW Congress, Berlin, 2005.

Gomez, CM., Flores, A., & Ledesma, A. Fronto-parietal networks activation during the contingent negative variation period, in *Brain Research Bulletin*, 73, 2007, p. 40-47.

Gong, G., He, Y., Concha, L., Lebel, C., Gross, DW., Evans, AC., & Beaulieu, C. Mapping anatomical connectivity patterns of human cerebral cortex using in vivo diffusion tensor imaging tractography, in *Cerebral Cortex*, 19, 2009, p. 524-536.

Gonzalez-Castro, P., Cueli, M., Rodriguez, C., Garcia, T., & Alvarez, L. Efficacy of neurofeedback versus pharmacological support in subjects with ADHD, in *Applied Psychophysiology and Biofeedback*, 41, 2016, p. 17-25.

Gorgoni, G., Ferlazzo, F., Ferrara, M., Moroni, F., D'Atri, A., Fanelli, S., Torriglia, IG., Lauri, G., Marzano, C., Rossini, PM., & De Gennaro, L. Topographic electroencephalogram changes associated with psychomotor vigilance task performance after sleep deprivation, in *Sleep Medicine*, 15, 2014, p. 1132-1139.

Grace, AA. The tonic/phasic model of dopamine system regulation: its relevance for understanding how stimulant abuse can alter basal ganglia function, in *Drug and Alcohol Dependence*, 37, 1995, p. 111-129.

Grace, AA. Psychostimulant actions on dopamine and limbic system function: relevance to the pathophysiology and treatment of ADHD. In: Solanto, M.V., Arnsten, AFT., & Castellanos, FX. (Eds.), *Stimulant Drugs and ADHD. Basic and Clinical Neuroscience*. Oxford University Press, New York, 2001, p. 134-157.

Grace, AA., Floresco, SB., Goto, Y., & Lodge, DJ. Regulation of firing of dopaminergic neurons and control of goal-directed behaviors, in *Trends in Neuroscience*, 30, 2007, p. 220-227.

Green, JJ., & McDonald, JJ. Electrical neuroimaging reveals timing of attentional control activity in human brain, in *PLoS Biology*, 6, 2008, p. 0730-0738.

Gruber, R., Sadeh, A., & Raviv, A. Instability of sleep patterns in children with attention deficit/ hyperactivity disorder, in *Journal of American Child and Adolescent Psychiatry*, 39, 2000, p. 495-501.

Gurnee, RL. QEEG based subtypes of adult ADHD and implications for treatment. 8th Annual Conference of the International Society for Neuronal Regulation, St. Paul, Minnesota, 2000.

Haenlein, M, & Caul, WF. Attention deficit disorder with hyperactivity: a specific hypothesis of reward dysfunction, in *Journal of American Academy of Child and Adolescent Psychiatry*, 26, 1987, p. 356-362.

Hajcak, G., & Simons, RF. Error-related brain activity in obsessive-compulsive undergraduates, in *Psychiatry Research*, 110, 2002, p. 63-72.

Haken, H. *Principles of Brain Functioning. A Synergetic Approach to Brain Activity, Behavior and Cognition*. Springer, Berlin, 1996.

Halpern, LE., MacLean, WE., & Baumeister, AA. Infant sleep-wake characteristics: relation to neurological status and the prediction of developmental outcome, in *Development Review*, 15, 1995, p. 255-291.

Hampshire, A., Chamberlain, SR., Monti, MM., Duncan, J., & Owen, AM. The role of the right inferior frontal gyrus: inhibition and attentional control, in *NeuroImage*, 50, 2010, p. 1313-1319.

Hansen, JC., & Hillyard, SA. Endogenous brain potentials associated with selective auditory attention, in *Electroencephalography and Clinical Neurophysiology*, 49, 1980, p. 461-475.

Hanslmayr, S., Sauseng, P., Doppelmayer, M., Schabus, M., & Klimesch, W. Increasing individual upper alpha power by neurofeedback improves cognitive performance in human subjects, in *Applied Psychophysiology and Biofeedback*, 30(1), 2005, p. 1-10.

Hare, TA., Camerer, CF. & Rangel, A. Self-control in decision-making involves modulation of the vmPFC valuation system, in Science, 324, 2009, p. 646-648.

Harmelech, T., Preminger, S., Wertman, E., & Malach, R. The day-after effect: long term, Hebbian-like restructuring of resting-state fMRI patterns induced by a single epoch of cortical activation, in *The Journal of Neuroscience*, 33, 2013, p. 9488-9497.

Harrison, Y., & Horne, JA. Performance on a complex frontal lobe oriented task with "real world" significance is impaired following sleep loss, in *Journal of Sleep Research*, 5[Suppl 1], 1996, p. 87.

Harrison, Y., & Horne, JA. The impact of sleep deprivation on decision making: a review, *in Journal of Experimental Psychology*, 6, 2000, p. 236-249.

Hart, H., Radua, J., Nakao, T., Mataix-Cols, D., & Rubia, K. Meta-analysis of functional magnetic resonance imaging studies of inhibition and attention in attention-deficit/hyperactivity disorder: exploring task-specific, stimulant medication, and age effects, in *JAMA Psychiatry*, 70, 2013, p.185-98.

Hartmann, T. *Attention deficit disorder: A different perception*. Underwoord-Miller, San Francisco, 1993.

Haschke, R., Tennigkeit, M., Lehmann, HJ., & Haschke, W. Changes of slow brain potential shifts following failure, in Haschke, W., Speckman, EJ., & Roitbak, AI. (Eds.), *Slow Potentials in the Brain, Chapter 4*, Birkhauser, Boston, 1993, p. 63-84.

Hauri, P. Treating psychophysiological insomnia with biofeedback, in *Archives of General Psychiatry*, 38, 1981, p. 752-758.

Hauri, PJ., Percy, L., Hellekson, C., Hartmann, E., & Russ, D. The treatment of psychophysiologic insomnia with biofeedback: a replication study, in *Biofeedback and Self Regulation* 7, 1982, p. 223-235.

Hauser, TU., Iannaccone, R., Stämpfli, P., Drechsler, R., Brandeis, D., Walitza, S., & Brem, S. The feedback-related negativity (FRN) revisited: new insights into the localization, meaning and network organization, in *NeuroImage*, 84, 2014, p. 159-68.

Head, H. Vigilance: a physiological state of the nervous system, in *British Journal ofPsychology*, 14, 1923, p. 126-147.

Hegerl, U., Stein, M., Mulert, C., Mergl, R., Olbrich, S., Dichgans, E., Rujescu, D., & Pogarell, O. EEG-vigilance differences between patients with borderline personality disorder, patients with obsessive-compulsive disorder and healthy controls, in *European Archives of Psychiatry and Clinical Neuroscience*, 258, 2008, p. 137-143.

Heinrich, H., Gevensleben, H., Freisleder, FJ., Moll, GH., & Rothenberger A. Training of slow cortical potentials in attention-deficit/hyperactivity disorder: evidence for positive behavioral and neurophysiological effects, in *Biological Psychiatry*, 55, 2004, p. 772-775.

Heinzel, S., Dresler, T., Baehne, CG., Heine, M., Boreatti-Hümmer, A., Jacob, CP., Renner, TJ., Reif, A., Lesch, K.-P., Fallgatter; AJ. & Ehlis, A.-C. COMT×DRD4 epistasis impacts prefrontal cortex function underlying response control, in *Cerebral Cortex*, 23, 2013, p. 1453-1462.

Hellyer, PJ., Shanahan, M., Scott, G., Wise, RJS., Sharp, DJ., & Leech, R. The control of global brain dynamics: opposing actions of frontoparietal control and fefault mode networks on attention, in *The Journal of Neuroscience*, 34, 2014, p. 451-461.

Hellyer, PJ., Jachs, B., Clopath, C., & Leech, R. Local inhibitory plasticity tunes macroscopic brain dynamics and allows the emergence of functional brain networks, in *NeuroImage*, 124, 2016, p. 85-95.

Helps, S., James, C., Debener, S., Karl, A., & Sonuga-Barke, EJS. Very low frequency EEG oscillations and the resting brain in young adults: a preliminary study of localisation, stability and association with symptoms of inattention, in *Journal of Neural Transmission*, 115, 2008, p. 279-285.

Helps, SK., Broyd, SJ., James, CJ., Karl, A., & Sonuga-Barke, EJS. The attenuation of very low frequency brain oscillations in transitions from a rest state to active attention, in *Journal of Psychophysiology*, 23, 2009, p. 191-198.

Helps, SK., Broyd, SJ., James, CJ., Karl, A., Chen, W., & Sonuga-Barke, EJ. Altered spontaneous low frequency brain activity in attention deficit/hyperactivity disorder, in *Brain Research*, 1322, 2010, p. 134-143.

Hershberger, WA. Control systems with a priori intentions register environmental disturbances a posteriori, in Jordan JS. (Ed.), *Systems theories and a priori aspects of perception*, Elsevier, Amsterdam, 1998, p. 3-24.

Herwig, U., Kaffenberger, T., Schell, C., Jäncke, L., & Brühl, AB. Neural activity associated with self-reflection, in *BMC Neuroscience*, 13, 2012, p. 52.

Hess, WR. *Diencephalon: Autonomic and Extrapyramidal Functions*. Grune & Stratton, New York, 1954.

Hinterberger, T., Veit, R., Strehl, U., Trevorrow, T., Erb, M., Kotchoubey, B., & Birbaumer, N. Brain areas activated in fMRI during self-regulation of slow cortical potentials (SCP), in *Experimental Brain Research*, 152, 2003, p. 113-122.

Ho, NF., Chong, JS., Koh, HL., Koukouna, E., Lee, TS., Fung, D., Lim, CG., & Zhou, J. Intrinsic affective network is impaired in children with attention-deficit/hyperactivity disorder, in *PLoS One*, in press.

Hodgson, K., Hutchinson, AD., & Denson, L. Nonpharmacological treatments for ADHD: a meta-analytic review, in *Journal of Attention Disorders*, 18, 2014, p. 275-282.

Hoedlmoser, K., Pecherstorfer, T., Gruber, G., Anderer, P., Doppelmayr, M., Klimesch, W., & Schabus, M. Instrumental conditioning of human sensorimotor rhythm (12-15 Hz) and its impact on sleep as well as declarative learning, in *Sleep*, 31, 2008, p. 1401-1418.

Holroyd, CB., & Coles, MGH. The neural basis of human error processing: reinforcement learning, dopamine, and the error-related negativity, in *Psychological Review*, 109, 2002, p. 679-709.

Holroyd, CB. A note on the oddball N200 and the feedback ERN, in Ullsperger, M., & Falkenstein, M. (Eds.), *Errors, Conflicts, and the Brain: Current Opinions on Performance Monitoring*, MPI of Cognitive Neuroscience, Leipzig, 2004.

Holroyd, CB., & Yeung, N. An integrative theory of anterior cingulate function: option selection in hierarchical reinforcement learning, in *Neural Basis of Motivational and Cognitive Control*, Mars, RB., Sallet, J., Rushworth, MFS., & Yeung, N. (Eds.), The MIT Press, Cambridge, Massachussets, 2011.

Holroyd, CB., & Yeung, N. Motivation of extended behaviors by anterior cingulate cortex, in *Trends in Cognitive Sciences*, 16, 2012, p. 122-128.

Holtmann, M., Grasmann, D., Cionek-Szpak, E., Hager, V., Panzer, N., & Beyer, A. Spezifische Wirksamkeit von Neurofeedback auf die Impulsivität bei ADHS - Literaturüberblick und Ergebnisse einer prospective, kontrollierten Studie [Specific effects of neurofeedback on impulsivity in ADHD], in *Kindheit und Entwicklung*, 18, 2009, p. 95-104.

Horne, JA. Human sleep, sleep loss, and behaviour. Implications for the prefrontal cortex and psychiatric disorder, in *British Journal of Psychiatry*, 162, 1993, p. 413-419.

Howe, RC., & Sterman, MB. Cortical-subcortical EEG correlates of suppressed motor behavior during sleep and waking in the cat, in *Electroencephalography and Clinical Neurophysiology*, 32, 1972, p. 681-695.

Hsu, D., & Beggs, JM. Neuronal avalanches and criticality: a dynamical model for homeostasis, in *Neurocomputing*, 69, 2006, p. 1134-1136.

Hulvershorn, LA., Mennes, M., Castellanos, FX., Di Martino, A., Milham, MP., Hummer, TA., & Roy, AK. Abnormal amygdala functional connectivity associated with emotional lability in children with attention-deficit/hyperactivity disorder, in *Journal of the American Academy of Child and Adolescent Psychiatry*, 53, 2014, p. 351-361.

Hummel, F., Celnik, P., Giraux, P., Floel, A., Wu, WH., Gerloff, C., & Cohen, LG. Effects of non-invasive cortical stimulation on skilled motor function in chronic stroke, in *Brain*, 128, 2005, p. 490-499.

Hunt, LT., Woolrich, MW., Rushworth, MF., & Behrens, TE. Trial-type dependent frames of reference for value comparison, in *PloS Computational Biology*, 9, 2013, p. 1-14.

Intriligator, J., & Polich, J. On the relationship between background EEG and the P300 event related potential, in *Biological Psychiatry*, 37, 1994, p. 207-218.

Iramina, K., Ueno, S., & Matsuoka, S. MEG and EEG topography of frontal midline theta rhythm and source localization, in *Brain Topography*, 8, 1996, p. 329-331.

Ishihara, T., & Yoshii, N. Multivariate analytic study of EEG and mental activity in juvenile delinquents, in *Electroencephalography and Clinical Neurophysiology*, 33, 1972, p. 71-80.

Iturria-Medina, Y., Sotero, RC., Canales-Rodríguez, EJ., Alemán-Gómez, Y., & Melie-García, L. Studying the human brain anatomical network via diffusion-weighted MRI and graph theory, in *NeuroImage*, 40, 2008, p. 1064-1076.

Iyer, MB., Mattu, U., Grafman, J., Lomarev, M., Sato, S., & Wassermann, EM. Safety and cognitive effect of frontal DC brain polarization in healthy individuals, in *Neurology*, 64, 2005, p. 872-875.

James, W. *The Principles of Psychology*. Henry Holt and Company, New York, 1890.

Janssen, TWP., Bink, M., Gelad, K., van Mourik, R., Maras, A., & Oosterlaan, J. A randomized controlled trial into the effects of neurofeedback, methylphenidate, and physical activity on EEG power spectra in children with ADHD, in *Journal of Child Psychology and Psychiatry*, in press, 2016.

Jasper, H., Solomon, P., & Bradley, C. Electroencephalographic analyses of behavior problem children, in *American Journal of Psychiatry*, 95, 1938, p. 641-658.

Jensen, O., & Tesche, CD. Frontal theta activity in humans increases with memory load in a working memory task, in *European Journal of Neuroscience*, 15, 2002, p. 1395-1399.

Johannes, S., Wieringa, BM., Nager, W., Rada, D., Dengler, R., & Emrich, HM. Discrepant target detection and action monitoring in obsessive-compulsive disorder, in *Psychiatry Research*, 108, 2001, p. 101-110.

John, ER. The neurophysics of consciousness, in *Brain Research Review*, 39(1), 2002, p. 1-28.

Kahn, A. & Rechtschaffen A. Sleep patterns and sleep spindles in hyperkinetic children, in *Sleep Research*, 7, 1978, p. 137.

Kahnt, T., Chang, LJ., Park, SQ., Heinzle, J., & Haynes, JD. Connectivity-based parcellation of the human orbitofrontal cortex, in *The Journal of Neuroscience*, 32, 2012, p. 6240-6250.

Kaiser, DA., & Sterman, MB. Periodicity of standardized EEG spectral measures across the waking day. 7th Annual Summer Sleep Waking Multi-Site Training for Basic Sleep Research, September 16-21, 1994, Lake Arrowhead, California.

Kaiser, D. Efficacy of neurofeedback on adults with attentional deficit and related disorders. EEG Spectrum International Inc., Encino, California, 1997.

Kaiser, D. A little ditty about functional conformity, in *What's New in Neurofeedback (web journal, EEG Spectrum International, Inc.)*, 4, 2001.

Kamiya, J. Conscious control of brain waves, in *Psychology Today*, 1, 1968, p. 57-60.

Kaufman, AS. *Intelligent Testing with the WISC-R*. Wiley, New York, 1979.

Kelso, JAS. *Dynamic Patterns: The Self-Organization of Brain and Behavior*. MIT Press, Cambridge, Massachusetts, 1995.

Kelso, JAS., & Tognoli, E. Toward a complementary neuroscience: metastable coordination dynamics of the brain, in Kozma, R., & Perlovsky, L. (Eds.), *Neurodynamics of Cognition and Consciousness*, Springer, Heidelberg, 2007.

Kelso, JAS. The dynamic brain in action: coordinative structures, criticality, and coordination dynamics, in Plenz, D., Niebur, E., & Schuster, HG. (Eds.), *Criticality in Neural Systems*, Wiley, New York, 2014.

Kencses, TZ., Antal, A., Nitsche, MA., Bartfai, O., & Paulus, W. Facilitation of probabilistic classification learning by transcranial direct current stimulation of the prefrontal cortex in the human, in *Neuropsychologia*, 42, 2003, p. 113-117.

Kerns, JG., Cohen, JD., MacDonald, AW., Cho, RY., Stenger, VA., & Carter, CS. Anterior cingulate conflict monitoring and adjustments in control, in *Science*, 303, 2004, p. 1023-1026.

Killam, KF., & Killam, EK. Rhinencephalic activity during acquisition and performance of conditional behavior and its modification by pharmacological agents, in Adey, WR., & Killgore, WDS., Schwab, ZJ. & Weiner, MR. Self-reported nocturnal sleep duration is associated with next-day resting state functional connectivity, in *NeuroReport*, 23, 2012, p. 741-745.

Tokizane, T. (Eds.), *Progress in Brain Research* vol. 27, *Structure and Function of the Limbic System*, Elsevier, New York, 1967, p. 338.

Kim, JN., & Shadlen, MN. Neural correlates of a decision in the dorsolateral prefrontal cortex of the macaque. in *Nature Neuroscience*, 2, 1999, p. 176-185.

Kim, S., Hwang, J., & Lee, D. Prefrontal coding of temporally discounted values during intertemporal choice, in *Neuron*, 59, 2008, p. 161-172.

Kingshott, RN., Cosway, RJ., Deary, IJ., & Douglas, NJ. The effect of sleep fragmentation on cognitive processing using computerized topographic brain mapping, in *Journal of Sleep Research*, 9, 2000, p. 353-357.

Kirlangic, ME. *EEG-biofeedback and epilepsy: concept, methodology and tools for (neuro)therapy planning and objective evaluation.* Dissertation, Illmenau, 2005.

Kiyatkin, EA. Functional significance of mesolimbic dopamine, in *Neuroscience Biobehavioral Reviews*, 19, 1995, p. 578-598.

Kleitman, D. *Sleep and Wakefulness (2nd Ed.).* University of Chicago Press, Chicago, 1963.

Klimesch, W. EEG alpha and theta oscillations reflect cognitive and memory performance: a review and analysis, in *Brain Research Reviews*, 29, 1999, p. 169-195.

Klimesch, W., Doppelmayr, M., Yonelinas, A., Kroll, NE., Lazzara, M., Röhm, D., & Gruber, W. Theta synchronization during episodic retrieval: neural correlates of conscious awareness, in *Brain Research Cognition*, 12, 2001, p. 33-38.

Knyazev, GG. EEG delta oscillations as a correlate of basic homeostatic and motivational Processes, in *Neuroscience and Biobehavioral Reviews*, 36, 2012, p. 677-695.

Kobayashi, S., Schultz, W., & Sakagami, M. Operant conditioning of primate prefrontal neurons, in *The Journal of Neurophysiology*, 103, 2010, p. 1843-1855.

Kober, SE., Witte, M., Ninaus, M., Neuper, C., & Wood, G. Learning to modulate one's own brain activity: the effect of spontaneous mental strategies, in *Frontiers of Human Neuroscience*, 7, 2013, p. 695.

Koechlin, E., Basso, G., Pietrini, P., Panzer, S, & Grafman, J. The role of the anterior prefrontal cortex in human cognition, in *Nature*, 399, 1999, p. 148-151.

Koechlin, E., & Hyafil, A. Anterior prefrontal function and the limits of human decision making, in *Science*, 318, 2007, p. 594-598.

Kok, A. Effects of degradation of visual stimulation on components of the event-related potential (ERP) in Go/No-Go reaction tasks, in *Biological Psychology*, 23, 1986, p. 21-38.

Kok, A. Varieties of inhibition: manifestations in cognition, event-related potentials and aging, in *Acta Psychologica*, 101, 1999, p. 129-158.

Konova, AB., Moeller, SJ., Tomasi, D., Volkow, ND., & Goldstein, RZ. Effects of methylphenidate on resting-state functional connectivity of the mesocorticolimbic dopamine pathways in cocaine addiction, in *JAMA Psychiatry*, 70, 2013, p. 857-68.

Kotchoubey, B., Kübler, A., Strehl, U., Flor, H., & Birbaumer N. Can humans perceive their brain states?, in *Consciousness and Cognition*, 11, 2002, p. 98-113.

Kotchoubey, B. Event-related potentials, cognition, behavior: a biological approach, in *Neuroscience and Behavioral Reviews*, 30, 2006, p. 42-65.

Kozma, R., & Freeman, WJ. The KIV model of intentional dynamics and decision making, in *Neural Networks*, 22, 2009, p. 277-285.

Kozma, R., & Puljic, M. Random graph theory and neuropercolation for modeling brain oscillations at criticality, in *Current Opinions in Neuroscience*, 31, 2015, p. 181-188.

Kripke, DF., & Sonnenschein, D. A biologic rhythm in waking fantasy, in Pope, D., & Songer, JL. (Eds.), *The Stream of Consciousness*, Plenum Pub, New York, 1978, p. 321-332.

Kropotov, JD., Grin-Yatsenko, V., Ponomarev, AV., Chutko, SL., Yakovenko, AE., & Nikishena, SI. ERPs correlates of EEG relative beta training in ADHD children, in *International Journal of Psychophysiology*, 55, 2005, p. 23-34.

Kropotov, JD., Grin-Yatsenko, VA., Ponomarev, VA., Chutko, LS., Yakovenko, EA., & Nikishena, IS. Changes in EEG spectrograms, event-related potentials and event-related desynchronization induced by relative beta training in ADHD children, in *Journal of Neurotherapy*, 11, 2007, p. 3-11.

Kropotov, JD., Ponomarev, VA., Hollup, S., & Mueller, A. Dissociating action inhibition, conflict monitoring and sensory mismatch into independent components of event related potentials in GO/NOGO task, in *NeuroImage* 57, 2011, p. 565-575.

Lancaster, JL., Rainey, LH., Summerlin, JL., Freitas, CS., Fox, PT., Evans, AC., Toga, AW., & Mazziotta, JC. Automated labeling of the human brain: a preliminary report on the development and evaluation of a forward-transform method, in *Human Brain Mapping*, 5, 1997, p. 238-242.

Lancaster, JL., Woldorff, MG., Parsons, LM., Liotti, M., Freitas, CS., Rainey, L., Kochunov, PV., Nickerson, D., Mikiten, SA., & Fox, PT. Automated Talairach Atlas labels for functional brain mapping, in *Human Brain Mapping*, 10, 2000, p. 120-131.

Lansing, RW., Schwartz, E. & Lindsley, DB. Reaction time and EEG activation under alerted and nonalerted conditions, in *Journal of Experimental Psychology*, 58, 1959, p. 1-7.

LaVaque, TJ., Hammond, DC., Trudeau, D., Monastra, VJ., Perry, J. & Lehrer, P. Template for developing guidelines for the evaluation of the clinical efficacy of psychophysiological interventions, in *Applied Psychophysiology and Biofeedback*, 27, 2002, p. 273-281.

Lavie, P. Ultradian rhythms in human sleep and wakefulness, in Webb, WB. (Ed.), *Biological Rhythms, Sleep, and Performance*, John Wiley & Sons, Chichester, 1982, p. 239-272.

Lavric, A., Pizzagali, DA., & Forstmeier, S. When 'go' and 'nogo' are equally frequent: ERP components and cortical tomography, in *European Journal of Neuroscience*, 20, 2004, p. 2483-2488.

Leech, R., & Sharp, DJ. The role of the posterior cingulate cortex in cognition and disease, in *Brain*, 137, 2014, p. 12-32.

Lehmann, D., Strik, WK., Henggeler, B., Koenig, T., & Koukkou, M. Brain electrical microstates and momentary conscious mind states as building blocks of spontaneous thinking: I. Visual imagery and abstract thoughts, in *International Journal of Psychophysiology*, 29, 1998, p. 1-11.

Lehmann, D., Faber, PL., Achermann, P., Jeanmonod, D., Gianotti, LRR., & Pizzagali, D. Brain sources of EEG gamma frequency during volitionally meditation-induced, altered states of consciousness, and experience of the self, in *Psychiatry Research*, 108, 2001, p. 111-121.

Leins, U. *Neurofeedback für Kinder mit einer Aufmerksamkeitsdefizit-/Hyperaktivitätsstörung*. Dissertation, Tübingen, 2004.

Leins, U., Goth, G., Hinterberger, T., Klinger, C., Rumpf, N., & Strehl, U. Neurofeedback for children with ADHD: a comparison of SCP and theta/beta protocols, in *Applied Psychophysiology and Biofeedback*, 32, 2007, p. 33-88.

Lenz, D. *Behavioural and cognitive relevance of evoked gamma-band responses in ADHD patients and healthy children*. Dissertation, Magdeburg, 2009.

Leung, LS., & Yim, CY. Rythmic delta-frequency activities in the nucleus accumbens of anesthetized and freely moving rats, in *Canadian Journal of Physiology and Pharmacology*,71, 1993, p. 311-320.

Li, L., Yanga, L. Zhuoa, CJ., & Wanga, YF. A randomised controlled trial of combined EEGfeedback and methylphenidate therapy for the treatment of ADHD, in *Swiss Medical Weekly*, 143, 2013, p. 1-4.

Liang, H., Bressler, SL., Ding, M. Truccolo, WA., & Nakamura, R. Synchronized activity in prefrontal cortex during anticipation of visuomotor processing, in *Neuroreport*, 13, 2002, p. 2011-2015.

Liddle, EB., Hollis, C., Batty, MJ., Groom, MJ., Totman, JJ., Liotti, M., Scerif, G., & Liddle, PF. Task-related default mode network modulation and inhibitory control in ADHD: effects of motivation and methylphenidate, in *The Journal of Child Psychology and Psychiatry*, 52, 2011, p. 761-771.

Liechti, MD., Maurizio, S., Heinrich, H., Jäncke, L., Meier, L., Steinhausen, HC., Walitza, S., Drechsler, R., & Brandeis, D. First clinical trial of tomographic neurofeedback in attention-deficit/hyperactivity disorder: evaluation of voluntary cortical control, in *Clinical Neurophysiology*, 123, 2012, p. 1989-2005.

Lin, HY., Tseng, WY., Lai, MC., Matsuo, K., & Gau, SS. Altered resting-state frontoparietal control network in children with attention-deficit/hyperactivity disorder, in *Journal of the International Neuropsychology Society*, 21, 2015, p. 271-84.

Linden, M., Habib, T., & Radojevic, V. A controlled study of the effects of EEG biofeedback on cognition and behavior of children with attention deficit disorder and learning disabilities, in *Biofeedback and Self-Regulation*, 21, 1996, p. 35-49.

Linkenkaer-Hansen, K., Nikulin, V., Palva JM., Kaila, K., & Limoniemi, R. Stimulus-induced change in long-range temporal correlations and scaling behaviour of sensorimotor oscillations. *European Journal of Neuroscience*, 19, 2004, p. 203-211.

Liotti, M., Pliszka, SR., Perez, R., Kothmann, D., & Woldorff, MG. Abnormal brain activity related to performance monitoring and error detection in children with ADHD, in *Cortex*, 41, 2005, p. 377-388.

Lisman, JE., & Idiart, MA. Storage of 7 ± 2 short-term memories in oscillatory subcycles, in*Science*, 267, 1995, p. 1512-1515.

Llinas, RR., & Ribary, U. Temporal conjunction in thalamocortical transactions. Consciousness: at the frontiers of neuroscience, in *Advances in Neurology*, 77, 1998, p. 95-103.

Llinas, RR., Ribary, U., Jeanmonod, D., Kronberg, E., & Mitra, PP. Thalamocortical dysrhythmia: a neurological and neuropsychiatric syndrome characterized by magnetoencephalography, in *Proceedings of the National Academy of Sciences USA*, 96, 1999, p. 15222-15227.

Lofthouse, N., Arnold, LE., Hersch, S., Hurt, E., & DeBeus, R. A review of neurofeedback treatment for pediatric ADHD, in *Journal of Attention Disorders*, 16, 2012, p. 351-372.

Logemann, HN., Lansbergen, MM,. Os, TW., Bocker, KB., & Kenemans JL. The effectiveness of EEG-feedback on attention, impulsivity and EEG: a sham feedback controlled study, in *Neuroscience Letters*, 479, 2010, p. 49-53.

Loo, SK., Teale, PD., & Reite, ML. EEG correlates of methylphenidate response among children with ADHD: a preliminary report, in *Biological Psychiatry*, 45, 1999, p. 1657-1660.

Loo, SK., Hopfer, C., Teale, PD., & Reite, ML. EEG correlates of methylphenidate response in ADHD: association with cognitive and behavioral measures, in *Journal of Clinical Neurophysiology*, 21, 2004, p. 457-464.

Loo, SK., & Barkley, RA., Clinical utility of EEG in attention deficit hyperactivity disorder. *Applied Neuropsychology*, 12, 2005, p. 64-76.

Loo, SK., & Arns, M. Should the EEG–based theta to beta ratio be used to diagnose ADHD?, in *The ADHD Report*, 23, 2015, p. 8-13.

López, V., López, J., Ortega, R. ,Kreither, J., Carrasco, X., Rothhammer, P., Rosas, R., & Aboitiz, F. Attention-deficit hyperactivity disorder involves differential cortical processing in a visual spatial attention paradigm, in *Clinical Neurophysiology*, 117, 2006, p. 2540-2548.

Lubar, JF., & Shouse, MN. EEG and behavioral changes in a hyperkinetic child concurrent with training of the sensorimotor rhythm (SMR): a preliminary report, in *Biofeedback and Self-Regulation*, 3, 1976, p. 293-306.

Lubar, JF. Discourse on the development of EEG diagnostics and biofeedback for attention deficit/hyperactivity disorders, in *Biofeedback and Self-Regulation*, 16, 1991, p. 201-225.

Lubar, JF. Neurofeedback for the management of attention deficit disorders, in Schwartz, MS.(Ed.), *Biofeedback: A Practitioner's Guide*, Guilford Press, New York, 1995a, p. 493-522.

Lubar, JF. Neocortical dynamics; implications for understanding the role of neurofeedback and related techniques for the enhancement of attention, in *Applied Psychophysiology and Biofeedback*, 22, 1997, p. 111-126.

Lubar, JF., & Lubar O. Neurofeedback assessment and treatment for attention deficit/ hyperactivity disorders, in Evans, JR., & Abarbanel, A. (Eds.), *Introduction to Quantitative EEG and Neurofeedback*, Academic Press, San Diego, California, 1999, p. 103-143.

Lubar, JF. Clinical corner, in *Journal of Neurotherapy*, 4, 2000, p. 83-93.

Lubar, JF. Rationale for choosing bipolar versus referential training, in *Journal of Neurotherapy*, 4, 2001, p. 94-97.

Lubar, JF. Neurofeedback treatment of attention deficit disorders, in Schwartz, MS (Ed.), *Biofeedback: a Practitioner's Guide*, Guilford, New York, 2005, p. 493-522.

Lubar, JF., Shabsin, HS., Natelson, SE., Holder, GS., Whitsett, SF., Pamplin, WE., & Krulikowski, DI. EEG operant conditioning in intractable epileptics, in *Archives of Neurology*, 38, 1981, p. 700-704.

Lubar, JF., Swartwood, MO., Swartwood, JN., & O'Donnell, P. Evaluation of the effectiveness of EEG neurofeedback training for ADHD in a clinical setting as measured by changes in T.O.V.A. scores, behavioral ratings, and WISC-R performance, in *Biofeedback and Self-Regulation*, 20, 1995, p. 83-99.

Luman, M., Oosterlaan, J., & Sergeant, JA. Modulation of response timing in ADHD, effects of reinforcement valence and magnitude, in *Journal of Abnormal Child Psychology*, 36, 2008, p. 445-456.

Lutzenberger, W., Birbaumer, N., Elbert, T., Rockstroh, B., Bippus, W., & Breidt, R. Selfregulation of slow cortical potentials in normal subjects and patients with frontal lobe lesions, in Kornhuber, HH., & Deecke, L. (Eds.), *Motivation, motor and sensory processes of the brain. Electrical potentials, behavior and clinical use*, Elsevier, Amsterdam, 1980.

Lutzenberger, W., Pulvermüller, F., & Birbaumer, N. Words and pseudowords elicit distinct patterns of 30-Hz EEG responses in humans, in *Neuroscience Letters*, 176, 1994, p. 115-118.

Lutzenberger, W., Preissl, H., Birbaumer, N., & Pulvermüller, F. High-frequency cortical responses: do they not exist if they are small?, in *Electroencephalography and Clinical Neurophysiology*, 102, 1997, p. 64-66.

Luu, P., & Tucker, MD. Self-regulation by the medial frontal cortex: limbic representation of motive set-points, in Beauregard, M. (Ed.), *Consciousness, Emotional Self-Regulation and the Brain*, John Benjamin Publishing Company, Philadelphia, 2004, p. 123-161.

MacDonald, AW., Cohen, JD., & Stenger, VA. & Carter, CS. Dissociating the role of the dorsolateral prefrontal and anterior cingulate cortex in cognitive control, in *Science*, 288, 2000, p. 1835-1838.

Mackworth, NH. Researches on the measurement of human performance (Special Report Series No. 268). Medical Research Council, H.M. Stationery Office, London, 1950.

Maclin, EL., Mathewson, KE., Low, KA., Boot, WR., Kramer, AF., Fabiani, M., & Gratton,

G. Learning to multitask: effects of video game practice on electrophysiological indices of attention and resource allocation, in *Psychophysiology*, 48, 2011, p. 1173-1183

Maquet, P., Degueldre, C., Delfiore, G., Aerts, J., Péters, J.-M., Luxen, A. & Franck, G. Functional neuroanatomy of human slow wave sleep, in *The Journal of Neuroscience*, 17, 1997, p. 2807-2812.

Margulies, DS., Vincent, JL., Kelly, C., Lohmann, G., Uddin, LQ., Biswal, BB., Villringer A., Castellanos, FX., Milhame, MP., & Petrides, M. Precuneus shares intrinsic functional architecture in humans and monkeys, in *Proceedings of the National Academy of Sciences USA*, 106, 2009, p. 20069-20074.

Mathalon, DH., & Sohal, VS. Neural oscillations and synchrony in brain dysfunction and neuropsychiatric disorders: it's about time, in *JAMA Psychiatry*, 72, 2015, p. 840-844.

Mayer, K., Wyckoff, S., Strehl, U., Keune, P., Schönenberg, M., & Hautzinger, M. Neurofeedback for adult ADHD: investigation of theta/beta training. Presentation at Annual Meeting of Society of Applied Neuroscience, Thessaloniki, 2011.

McLoughlin, G., Albrecht, B., Banaschewski, T., Rothenberger, A., Brandeis, D., Asherson, P., & Kuntsi, J. Electrophysiological evidence for abnormal preparatory states and inhibitory processing in adult ADHD, in *Behavioral and Brain Functions*, 6, 2010, p. 66.

Makeig, S., Westerfield, M., Jung, TP., Enghoff, S., Townsend, J. Courchesne, E., & Sejnowski, TJ. Dynamic brain sources of visual evoked responses, in *Science*, 295, 2002, p. 690-694.

Makeig, S. Mining event-related brain dynamics, in *TRENDS in Cognitive Sciences*, 8, 2004, p. 204-210.

Malone, MA., Kershner, JR., & Swanson, JM. Hemispheric processing and methylphenidate effects in attention-deficit hyperactivity disorder, in *Journal of Child Neurology*, 9, 1994, p. 181-189.

Mandelbrot, B. *The Fractal Geometry of Nature*. Freeman, San Francisco, 1982.

Mann, CA., Sterman, MB., & Kaiser, DA. Suppression of EEG rhythmic frequencies during somato-motor and visuo-motor behavior, in *International Journal of Psychophysiology*, 23, 1996, p. 1-7.

Maquet, P., Schwartz, S., Passingham, R., & Frith C. Sleep-related consolidation of a visuomotor skill: brain mechanisms as assessed by functional magnetic resonance imaging, in *Journal of Neuroscience*, 23, 2003, p. 1432-1440.

Margulies, DS., Vincent, JL., Kellye, C., Lohmann, G., Uddin, LQ., Biswalg, BB., Villringer, A., Castellanos, FX., Milhame, MP., & Petrides, M. Precuneus shares intrinsic functional architecture in humans and monkeys, in *Proceedings of the Academy of Sciences USA*, 106, 2009, p. 20069-20074.

Markela-Lerenc, J., Ille, N., Kaiser, S., Fiedler, P., Mundt, C., & Weisbrod, M. Prefrontal cingulate activation during executive control: which comes first, in *Cognitive Brain Research*, 18, 2004, p. 278-287.

Massar, SAA., Rossi, V., Schutter, DJLG. & Kenemans, JL. Baseline EEG theta/beta ratio and punishment sensitivity as biomarkers for feedback-related negativity (FRN) and risk-taking, in *Clinical Neurophysiology*, 123, 2012, p. 1958-65.

Mathewson, KE., Beck, DM., Ro, T., Maclin, EL., Low, KA., Fabiani, M., & Gratton, G. Dynamics of alpha control: Preparatory suppression of posterior alpha oscillations by frontal modulators revealed with combined EEG and event-related optical signal (EROS), in *Journal of Cognitive Neuroscience*, 26, 2014, p. 2400-2415.

Matsumoto, M., Matsumoto, K., Abe, H., & Tanaka, K. Medial prefrontal cell activity signaling prediction errors of action values, in *Nature Neuroscience*, 10, 2007, p. 647-656.

Mattfeld, AT., Gabrieli, JDE., Biederman, J., Spencer T., Brown, A., Kotte, A., Kagan, E., & Whitfield-Gabrieli, S. Brain differences between persistent and remitted attention deficit hyperactivity disorder, in *Brain*, 137, 2014, p. 2423-2428.

Mattson, AJ., Sheer DE., & Fletcher, JM. 40 Hertz EEG activity in LD and normal children, in *Journal of Clinical and Experimental Neuropsychology*, 11, 1989, p. 32.

Mattson, AJ., Sheer DE., & Fletcher, JM. Electrophysiological evidence of lateralized disturbances in children with learning disabilities, in *Journal of Clinical and Experimental Neuropsychology*, 14, 1992, p. 707-716.

Maurizio, S., Liechti, MD., Heinrich, H., Jäncke, L., Steinhausen, HC., Walitza, S., Brandeis, D., & Drechsler, R. Comparing tomographic EEG neurofeedback and EMG biofeedback in children with attention-deficit/hyperactivity disorder, in *Biological Psychology*, 95, 2014, p. 31-44.

Mayer, K., Wyckoff, S., & Keune P. Neurofeedback for adult AD/HD: investigation of theta/ beta training. Annual Meeting Society of Applied Neuroscience Thessaloniki, 2011.

Mayer, K., Blume, F ., Wyckoff, SN., Brokmeier, LL., & Strehl U. Neurofeedback of slow cortical potentials as a treatment for adults with attention deficit-/hyperactivity disorder, in *Clinical Neurophysiology*, 127, 2016, p. 1374-86.

Mazaheri, A., Nieuwenhuis, ILC., van Dijk,, H., & Jensen, O. Prestimulus alpha and mu activity predicts failure to inhibit motor responses, in *Human Brain Mapping*, 30, 2009, p. 1791-1800.

Mazaheri, A., Coffey-Corina, S., Mangun, GR., Bekker, EM., Berry, AS., & Corbett, BA. Functional disconnection of frontal cortex and visual cortex in attention-deficit/hyperactivity disorder, in *Biological Psychiatry*, 67, 2010, p. 617-623.

Mazaheri, A., Fassbender, C., Coffey-Corina, S., Hartanto, TA., Schweitzer, JB., & Mangun, GR. Differential oscillatory electroencephalogram between attention-deficit/hyperactivity disorder subtypes and typically developing adolescents, in *Biological Psychiatry*, 76, 2014, p. 422-429.

McCarthy, H., Skokauskas, N., Mulligan, A., Donohoe, G., Mullins, D., Kelly, J., Johnson, K., Fagan, A., Gill, M., Meaney, J., & Frodl, T. Attention network hypoconnectivity with default and affective network hyperconnectivity in adults diagnosed with attention-deficit/hyperactivity disorder in childhood, in *JAMA Psychiatry*, 70, 2013, p.1329-37.

McEwen, BS. The neurobiology of stress: from serendipity to clinical relevance, in *Brain Research*, 886, 2000, p. 172-189.

Meisel, C., Olbrich, E., Shriki, O. & Achermann, P. Fading signatures of critical brain dynamics during sustained wakefulness in humans, in *The Journal of Neuroscience*, 33, 2013, p. 17363-17372.

Meisel, V., Servera, M., Garcia-Banda, G., Cardo, E., & Moreno, I. Neurofeedback and standard pharmacological intervention in ADHD: a randomized controlled trial with six month follow-up, in *Biological Psychology*, 95, 2014, p. 116-125.

Menon, V., & Uddin, LQ. Saliency, switching, attention and control: a network model of insula function, in *Brain Structure and Function*, 214, 2010, p. 655-667.

Menon, V. Large-scale brain networks and psychopathology: a unifying triple network model, in *Trends in Cognitive Sciences*, 15, 2011, p. 483-506.

Miano, S. NREM sleep instability is reduced in children with attention-deficit/hyperactivity disorder, in *Sleep*, 29, 2006, p. 797-803.

Michel, AM., Lehmann, D., Henggeler, B., & Brandeis, D. Localization of the sources of EEG delta, theta, alpha and beta frequency bands using the FFT dipole approximation, in *EEG and Clinical Neurophysiology*, 82, 1992, p. 38-44.

Michel, AM., Henggeler, B., Brandeis, D., & Lehmann, D. Localization of sources of brain alpha/theta/delta activity and the influence of the mode of spontaneous mentation, in *Physiology Measures*, 14, 1993, p. 21-26.

Micoulaud-Franchi, JA., Geoffroy, PA., Fond, G., Lopez, R., Bioulac, S., & Philip, P. EEG neurofeedback treatments in children with ADHD: an updated meta-analysis of randomized controlled trials, in *Frontiers in Human Neuroscience,* 8, 2014, p. 1-7.

Mizuki, Y., Tanaka, M., Isozaki, H., Nishijima, H., & Inanaga, K. Periodic appearance of theta rhythm in the frontal midline area during performance of a mental task, in *Electroencephalography and Clinical Neurophysiology*, 49, 1980, p. 45-51.

Mo, J., Schroeder, CE., & Ding, M. Attentional modulation of alpha oscillations in macaque inferotemporal cortex, in *The Journal of Neuroscience*, 31, 2011, p. 878-882.

Moll, J., Weingartner, JH., Bado, P., Basilio, R., Sato, JR., Melo, BR., Bramati, IE., de Oliveira-Souza, R., & Zahn, R. Voluntary enhancement of neural Signatures of affiliative emotion using fMRI neurofeedback, in *PLoS ONE*, 9, e97343, 2014.

Monastra, VJ., Linden, M., Green, G., Phillips, A., Lubar, JF., VanDeusen, P., Wing, W., & Fenger, TN. Assessing attention deficit hyperactivity disorder via quantitative electroencephalography: an initial validation study, in *Neuropsychology*, 13, 1999, p. 424-433.

Monastra, VJ., Lubar, JF., & Linden, M. The development of a quantitative electroencephalographic scanning process for attention deficit-hyperactivity disorder: reliability and validity studies, in *Neuropsychology*, 15, 2001, p. 136-144.

Monastra, VJ., Monastra, DM., & George, S. The effects of stimulant therapy, EEG biofeedback, and parenting style on the primary symptoms of attention-deficit/hyperactivity disorder, in *Applied Psychophysiology and Biofeedback*, 27, 2002, p. 231-249.

Monastra, VJ. Overcoming the barriers to effective treatment for attention-deficit/

hyperactivity disorder: a neuro-educational approach, in *International Journal of Psychophysiology*, 58, 2005, p. 71-80.

Morrell, F., & Jasper, HH. Electrographic studies of the formation of temporary connections in the brain, in *Electroencephalography and Clinical Neurophysiology*, 8, 1956, p. 201.

Moruzzi ,G., & Magoun, HW. Brain stem reticular formation and activation of the EEG, in *Electroencephalography and Clinical Neurophysiology*, 1, 1949, p. 455-473.

Muraven, M., Shmueli, D., & Burkley, E. Conserving self-control strength, in *Journal of Personality and Social Psychology*, 91, 2006, p. 524-537.

Nagai, Y., Critchley, HD., Featherstone, E., Fenwick, PBC, Trimble, MR., & Dolan, RJ. Brain activity relating to the contingent negative variation: an fMRI investigation, in *NeuroImage*, 21, 2004, p. 1232-1241.

Näätänen, R. Processing negativity, in *Psychology Bulletin*, 92, 1982, p. 605-640.

Nakashima, K., & Sato, H. The effects of various mental tasks on appearance of frontal midline theta activity in EEG, in *Journal of Human Ergology (Tokyo)*, 21, 1992, p. 201-206.

Nakashima, K., & Sato, H. Relationship between frontal midline theta activity in EEG and concentration, in *Journal of Human Ergology (Tokyo)*, 22, 1993, p. 63-67.

Nauta, WJH. The problem of the frontal lobe: a reinterpretation, in *Journal of Psychiatric Research*, 8, 1971, p. 167-187.

Naylor, E., Penev, PD., Orbeta, L., Janssen, I., Ortiz, R., Colecchia, EF., Keng, M., Finkel, S., & Zee, PC. Daily social and physical activity increases slow-wave sleep and daytime neuropsychological performance in the elderly, in *Sleep*, 23, 2000, p. 87-95.

Neuper, C., & Pfurtscheller, G. Event-related dynamics of cortical rhythms: frequency-specific features and functional correlates, in *International Journal of Psychophysiology*, 43, 2001, p. 41-58.

Niendam, TA., Laird, AR., Ray, KL., Dean, YM., Glahn, DC., & Carter, CS. Meta-analytic evidence for a superordinate cognitive control network subserving diverse executive functions, in *Cognitive, and Affective and Behavioral Neuroscience*, 12, 2012, p. 241-268.

Nieuwenhuis, S., Yeung, N., van den Wildenberg, W., & Ridderinkhof, KR., Electrophysiological correlates of anterior cingulate function in a go/no-go task: effects of response conflict and trial type frequency, in *Cognitive, Affective and Behavioral Neuroscience*, 3, 2003, p. 17-26.

Nigam, S., Shimono, M., Ito, S., Yeh, FC., Timme, N., Myroshnychenko, M., Lapish, CC., Tosi, Z., Hottowy, P., Smith, WC., Masmanidis, SC., Litke, AM., Sporns, O., & Beggs, JM. Rich-club organization in effective connectivity among cortical neurons, in *The Journal of Neuroscience*, 36, 2016, p. 670-684.

Nigbur, R., Ivanova, G., & Stürmer, B. Theta power as a marker for cognitive interference, in *Clinical Neurophysiology*, 122, 2011, p. 2185-2194.

Nikulin, VV., & Brismar, T. Long-range temporal correlations in alpha and beta oscillations:effect of arousal level and test-retest reliability, in *Clinical Neurophysiology*, 115, 2004, p. 1896-1908.

Ninaus, M., Kober, SE., Witte, M., Koschutnig, K., Stangl, M., Neuper, C., & Wood, G. Neural substrates of cognitive control under the belief of getting neurofeedback training, in *Frontiers in Neuroscience*, 7, 2013, p. 1-10.

Nitschen MA., & Paulus, W. Sustained excitability elevations induced by transcranial DC motor cortex stimulation in humans, in *Neurology*, 57, 2001, p. 1899-1901.

Nitsche, MA., Fricke, K., Henschke, U., Schlitterlau, D., Liebetanz, D., Lang, N., Henning, S., Tergau, F., & Paulus, W. Pharmacological modulation of cortical excitability shifts induced by transcranial direct current stimulation in humans, in *The Journal of Physiology*, 533.1, 2003, p. 293-301.

Norman, DA., & Shallice, T. Attention to action: willed and automatic control of behavior, in Davidson, RJ., Schwartz, GE., & Shapiro, D. (Eds.), *Consciousness and Self-Regulation*, Plenum, New York, 1986, p. 1-18.

Nowak, A., Vallacher, RR., Tesser, A., & Borkowski, W. Society of self: the emergence of collective properties in self-structure, in *Psychological Review*, 107, 2000, p. 39-61.

Nunez, P. *Neocortical Dynamics and Human EEG Rhythms.* Oxford University Press, Oxford, 1995.

Nymberg, C., Jia, T., Lubbe, S., Ruggeri, B., Desrivieres, S., Barker, G., Büchel, C., Fauth-Buehler, M., Cattrell, A., Conrod, P., Flor, H., Gallinat, J., Garavan, H., Heinz, A., Ittermann, B., Lawrence, C., Mann, K., Nees, F., Salatino-Oliveira, A., Paillère Martinot, M.-L., Paus, T.,

Rietschel, M., Robbins, T., Smolka, M., Banaschewski, T., Rubia, K., Loth, E., Schumann, G. and the IMAGEN Consortium. Neural mechanisms of attention-deficit/hyperactivity disorder symptoms are stratified by MAOA genotype, in *Biological Psychiatry*, 74, 2013, p. 607-614.

Oehrn, CR., Hanslmayr, S., Fell, J., Deuker, L., Kremers, NA., Do Lam, AT., Elger, CE., & Axmacher, N. Neural communication patterns underlying conflict detection, resolution and adaptation, in *The Journal of Neuroscience*, 34, 2014, p. 10438-10452.

Ogrim, G., Kropotov, J., Brunner, JF., Candrian, G., Sandvik, L., & Hestad, KA. Predicting the clinical outcome of stimulant medication in pediatric attention-deficit/hyperactivity disorder: data from quantitative electroencephalography, event-related potentials, and a go/no-go test, in *Neuropsychiatric Disease and Treatment*, 10, 2014, p. 231-242.

Olesen, PJ., Macoveanu, J., Tegnér, J., & Klingberg, T. Brain activity related to working memory and distraction in children and adults, in *Cerebral Cortex*, 17, 2007, p. 1047-1054.

Orlandi, MA., & Greco, D. A randomized, double-blind clinical trial of EEG neurofeedback treatment for attention-deficit/hyperactivity disorder. Paper presented at the meeting of the International Society for Neuronal Regulation, Fort Lauderdale, Florida, 2004.

Othmer, S., & Othmer, SF. EEG biofeedback training for attention deficit disorder, specific learning disabilities, and associated conduct problems, in *EEG Biofeedback Training for Attention Deficit Disorder and Specific Learning Disabilities*, EEG Spectrum, Encino, California, 1991.

Othmer, S., Othmer, SF., & Kaiser, DA. EEG biofeedback: an emerging model for its global efficacy, in Evans, JR., & Abarbanel, A. (Eds.), *Introduction to Quantitative EEG and Neurofeedback*, Academic Press, San Diego, California, 1999, p. 244-310.

Ozisik, HI., Karlidag, R., Hazneci, E., Kizkin, S., & Ozcan, C. Cognitive event-related potential and neuropsychological findings in Behçet's disease without neurological manifestations, in *Tohoku Journal of Experimental Medicine*, 206, 2005, p. 15-22.

Palva, JM., Palva, S., & Kaila, K. Phase synchrony among neuronal oscillations in the human cortex, in *Journal of Neuroscience*, 25, 2005, p. 3962-3972.

Palva, JM., Montoa, S., Kulashekhara, S., & Palva, S. Neuronal synchrony reveals working memory networks and predicts individual memory capacity, in *Proceedings of the National Academy of Neuroscience USA*, 107, 2010, p. 7580-7585.

Palva, JM., & Palva, S. Functional roles of alpha-band phase synchronization in local and large-scale cortical networks, in *Frontiers in Psychology*, 2, 2011, p. 1-15

Palva, JM., & Palva, S. Roles of multi-scale brain activity fluctuations in shaping the variability and dynamics of psychophysical performance, in *Progress in Brain Research*, 193, 2011, p. 335-350.

Palva, JM., & Palva, S. Infra-slow fluctuations in electrophysiological recordings, blood-oxygenation-level-dependent signals, and psychophysical time series, in *NeuroImage*, 62, 2012, p. 2201-2211.

Parmelee, AH. Jr., & Stern, E. Developments of states in infants, in Clemente, C., Purpura, D., & Mayers, FE. (Eds.), *Sleep and the Maturing Nervous System*, Academic Press, New York, 1972, p. 199-228.

Parry, PA, & Douglas, VI. Effects of reinforcement on concept identification in hyperactive children, in *Journal of Abnormal Child Psychology*, 11, 1983, p. 327-340.

Pascual-Marqui., RD., Michel, CM., & Lehmann, D. Low resolution electromagnetic tomography: a new method for localizing electrical activity in the brain, in *International Journal of Psychophysiology*, 18, 1994, p. 49-65.

Pascual-Marqui, RD. Standardized low-resolution brain electromagnetic tomography (sLORETA): technical details, in *Methods and Findings in Experimental and Clinical Pharmacology*, 24(Suppl D), 2002, p. 5-12.

Patterson, MB., Gluck, H., & Mack, JL. EEG activity in the 13-15 Hz band correlates with intelligence in healthy elderly women, in *International Journal of Neuroscience*, 20, 1983, p. 161-172.

Paus, T. Primate anterior cingulate cortex where motor control, drive and cognition interface, in *Nature Reviews of Neuroscience*, 2, 2001, p. 417-424.

Pennington, BF. Toward a new neuropsychological model of attention-deficit/hyperactivity disorder: subtypes and multiple deficits, in *Biological Psychiatry*, 57, 2005, p. 1221-1223.

Petersen, SE., & Posner, MI. The attention system of the human brain: 20 years after, in *Annual Review of Neuroscience*, 35, 2012, p. 73-89.

Peterson, BS., Potenza, MN., Wang, Z., Zhu, H., Martin, A., Marsh, R., Plessen, KJ., & Yu, S. An fMRI study of the effects of psychostimulants on default-mode processing during Stroop task performance in youths with ADHD, in *American Journal of Psychiatry*, 166, 2009, p. 1286-1294.

Pfurtscheller, G., & Aranibar, A. Voluntary movement ERD: normative studies, in Pfurtscheller, G., Buser, P., Lopes da Silva FH., & Petsche, H. (Eds.), *Rhythmic EEG Activities and Cortical Functioning*. Elsevier, Amsterdam, 1980, p. 151-177.

Picard, C. Double blind sham study of neurofeedback treatment in children with ADHD, 14th Annual Conference of the International Society for Neuronal Regulation, Atlanta, 2006.

Pineda, JA., Brang, D., Hecht, E., Edwards, L., Carey, S., Bacon, M., Futagaki, C., Suk, D., Toma, J., Birnbaum, C., & Rork, A. Positive behavioral and electrophysiological changes following neurofeedback training in children with autism, in *Research in Autism Spectrum Disorders*, 2, 2008, p. 557-581.

Plichta, MM., Vasic, N., Wolf, RC., Lesch, KP., Brummer, D., Jacob, C., Falgätter, AJ., & Grön, G. Neural hyporesponsiveness and hyperresponsiveness during immediate and delayed reward processing in adult attention-deficit/hyperactivity disorder, in *Biological Psychiatry*, 65, 2009, p. 7-14.

Plichta, MM., & Scheres, A. Ventral-striatal responsiveness during reward anticipation in ADHD and its relation to trait impulsivity in the healthy population: a meta-analytic review of the fMRI literature, in *Neuroscience & Biobehavioral Reviews*, 38, 2014, p. 125-134.

Pliszka, SR., Liotti, M., & Woldorff, MG. Inhibitory control in children with attention deficit/ hyperactivity disorder: event-related potentials identify the processing component and timing of an impaired right-frontal response-inhibition mechanism, in *Biological Psychiatry*, 48, 2000, p. 238-246.

Polich, J. Updating P300: an integrative theory of P3a and P3b, in *Clinical Neurophysiology*, 118, 2007, p. 2128-2148.

Posner, J., Rauh, V., Gruber, A., Gat, I., Wang, Z, & Peterson, BS. Dissociable attentional and affective circuits in medication-naive children with attention-deficit/hyperactivity disorder, in *Psychiatry Research*, 213, 2013, p. 24-30.

Posner, MI., & Petersen, SE. The attention system of the human brain, in *Annual Review of Neuroscience*, 13, 1990, p. 25-42.

Posner, MI., & Dehaene, S. Attentional networks, in *Trends in Neuroscience*, 17, 1994, p. 75-79.

Pribram, KH. A review of theory in physiological psychology, in *Annual Review of Psychology*, 11, 1960, p. 1-40.

Pribram, KH., Spinelli, DN., & Kamback, MC. Electrocortical correlates of stimulus response and reinforcement, in *Science*, 157, 1967, p. 94.

Prigogine, I., & Stengers I. *Order out of Chaos*, Bantam Books, New York, 1984.

Prihidova, I., Paclt, I., D. Kemlink, & Nevsimalova, S. Sleep microstructure is not altered in children with attention-deficit/hyperactivity disorder (ADHD), in *Physiological Research*, 61, 2012, p. 125-133.

Priori, A. Brain polarization in humans: a reappraisal of an old tool for prolonged noninvasive modulation of brain excitability, in *Clinical Neurophysiology*, 114, 2003, p. 589-595.

Putman, JA. Technical issues involving bipolar EEG training protocols, in *Journal of Neurotherapy*, 5, 2001, p. 51-58.

Putman, JA., Othmer, SF., Othmer, S., & Pollock, VE. TOVA results following interhemispheric bipolar EEG training, in *Journal of Neurotherapy*, 9, 2005, p. 37-52.

Putman, P., van Peer, J., Maimari, I., & van der Werff, S. EEG theta/beta ratio in relation to fear-modulated response-inhibition, attentional control, and affective traits, in *Biological Psychology*, 83, 2010, p. 73-78.

Quartz, SR. Reason, emotion and decision-making: risk and reward computation with feeling, in *Trends in Cognitive Science*, 13, 2009, p. 209-215.

Raichle, ME., MacLeod, AM., Snyder, AZ., Powers, WJ., Gusnard, DA., & Shulman, GL. A default mode of brain function, in *Proceedings of the National Academy of Sciences USA*, 98, 2001, p. 676-682.

Ramnani, N., & Owen, AM. Anterior prefrontal cortex: insights into function from anatomy and neuroimaging, in *National Review Neuroscience*, 5, 2004, p. 184-194.

Ramot, M., Grossman, S., Friedman, D., & Malacha, R. Covert neurofeedback without awareness shapes cortical network spontaneous connectivity, in *Proceedings of the National Academy of Sciences USA*, 2016 (in press).

Rappelsberger, P., Pfurtscheller, G., & Filz O. Calculation of event-related coherence - a new method to study short lasting coupling between brain areas, in *Brain Topography*, 7, 1994, p. 121-127.

Rapport, MD., Orban, SA., Kofler, MJ., & Friedman, LM. Do programs designed to train working memory, other executive functions, and attention benefit children with ADHD? A meta-analytic review of cognitive, academic, and behavioral outcomes, in *Clinical Psychology Review*, 33, 2013, p. 1237-1252.

Reinhart, RMG., & Woodman, GF. Causal control of medial–frontal cortex governselectrophysiological and behavioral indices of performance monitoring and learning, in *The Journal of Neuroscience*, 34, 2014, p. 4214-4227.

Renn, R. *Sleep Deprivation and Performance Monitoring*. Dissertation, Brock University, St. Catharines, Ontario, 2012.

Ridderinkhof, KR., Ullsperger, M., Crone, EA., & Nieuwenhuis, S. The role of the medial frontal cortex in cognitive control, in *Science*, 306, 2004, p. 443-447.

Rizzuto, DS., Madsen, JR., Bromfield, EB., Schulze-Bonhage, A., Seelig, D., Aschenbrenner-Scheibe, R., & Kahana, MJ. Reset of human neocortical oscillations during a working memory task, in *Proceedings of National Academy of Sciences USA*, 100, 2003, p. 7931-7936.

Robinson, DL. The neurophysiological bases of high IQ, in *International Journal of Neuroscience*, 46, 1989, p. 209-234.

Rockstroh, B., Elbert, T., Lutzenberger, W., & Birbaumer, N. Operant control of slow brain potentials: a tool in the investigation of the potential's meaning and its relation to attentional dysfunction, in Elbert, T., Rockstroh, B., Lutzenberger, W., & Birbaumer, N. (Eds.), *Self-Regulation of the Brain and Behavior*, Springer, Berlin, 1984, p. 227-239.

Rockstroh, B., Elbert , T., Lutzenberger, W. & Birbaumer, N. Biofeedback: evaluation and therapy in children with attentional dysfunctions, in Rothenberger, A. (Ed.), *Brain and Behavior in Child Psychiatry*, Springer, Berlin, 1990, p. 345-357.

Ros, T., Théberge, J., Frewen, PA., Kluetsch, R., Densmore, M., Calhoun, VD., & Lanius, RA. Mind over chatter: plastic up-regulation of the fMRI salience network directly after EEG neurofeedback, in *NeuroImage*, 65, 2013, p. 324-335.

Ros, T., Baars, BJ., Lanius, RA., & Vuilleumier, P. Tuning pathological brain oscillations with neurofeedback: a systems neuroscience framework, in *Frontiers in Human Neuroscience*, 8, 2014, p. 1-22.

Ros, T., Frewen, PA., Théberge, J., Kluetsch, R., Mueller, A., Candrian, G., Jetly, R., Vuillemier,

P., & Lanius, RA. Neurofeedback tunes long-range temporal correlations in spontaneous brain activity, in *Cerebral Cortex*, 2016.

Rosenfeld, JP., Cha, G., Blair, T., & Gotlib, IH. Operant (biofeedback) control of left-right frontal alpha power differences: potential neurotherapy for affective disorders, in *Biofeedback and Self-Regulation*, 20, 1995, p. 241-258.

Rosenfeld, JP. EEG biofeedback of frontal alpha asymmetry in affective disorders, in *Biofeedback*, 25, 1997, p. 8-9; p. 25-26.

Rossiter, TR., & La Vaque, TJ. A comparison of EEG biofeedback and psychostimulants in treating attention deficit/hyperactivity disorder. *Journal of Neurotherapy*, 1, 1995, p. 48-59.

Rossiter, TR. Neurofeedback for AD/HD: a ratio feedback case study and tutorial, in *Journal of Neurotherapy*, 6, 2002, p. 9-35.

Rossiter, TR. The effectiveness of neurofeedback and stimulant drugs in treating AD/HD: part II. Replication, in *Applied Psychophysiology and Biofeedback*, 29, 2004, p. 233-243.

Roth, SR., Sterman, MB., & Clemente, CD. Comparison of EEG correlates of reinforcement, internal inhibition, and sleep, in *Electroencephalography and clinical Neurophysiology*, 1967, 23, p. 509-520.

Rougeul-Buser, A., Bouyer, JJ., Montaron, MF. & Buser, P. Patterns of activities in the ventrobasal thalamus and somatic cortex SI during behavioral immobility in the awake cat: focal waking rhythms, in *Experimental Brain Research*, suppl. 7, 1983, p. 69-87.

Rougeul-Buser, A. Electrocortical rhythms in the 40 Hz band in cat: in search of their behavioural correlates, in Buzsaki, G., Llinas, R., Singer, W., Berthoz, A., & Christen, Y. (Eds.), *Temporal Coding in the Brain*, Springer, Berlin, 1994, p. 103-114.

Rowland, V. Discussion under electroencephalographic studies of conditioned learning, in Brazier, M. (Ed.), *The Central Nervous System and Behavior*, Josiah Macy, Jr Foundation, New York, 1958, p. 347.

Rubia, K., Halari, R., Cubillo, A., Mohammad, AM., Brammer, M., & Taylor, E. Methylphenidate normalises activation and functional connectivity deficits in attention and motivation networks in medication-naive children with ADHD during a rewarded continuous performance task, in *Neuropharmacology*, 57, 2009, p. 640-652.

Rubia, K., Alegria, AA., Cubillo, A., Smith, AB., Brammer MJ., & Radua, J. Effects of stimulants on brain function in attention-deficit/hyperactivity disorder: a systematic review and meta-analysis, in *Biological Psychiatry*, 76, 2014, p. 616-628.

Ruiz, S., Buyukturkoglu, K., Rana, M., Birbaumer, N., & Sitaram, R. Real-time fMRI brain computer interfaces: self-regulation of single brain regions to networks, in *Biological Psychology*, 95, 2014, p. 4-20.

Russell-Chapin, L., Kemmerly, T., Liu, WC., Zagardo, MT., Chapin, T., Dailey, D., & Dinh, D.

The effects of neurofeedback in the default mode network: pilot study results of medicated children with ADHD, in *Journal of Neurotherapy*, 17, 2013, p. 35-42.

Russo, R., Herrmann, H J., & de Arcangelis, L. Brain modularity controls the critical behavior of spontaneous activity, in *Scientific Reports*, 4, 2014, p. 4312.

Sadaghiani, S., Scheeringa, R., Lehongre, K., Morillon, B., Giraud, AL., & Kleinschmidt, A. Intrinsic connectivity networks, alpha oscillations, and tonic alertness: a simultaneous electroencephalography/functional magnetic resonance imaging study, in *The Journal of Neuroscience*, 30, 2010, p. 10243-10250.

Sadaghiani, S., Scheeringa, R., Lehongre, K., Morillon, B., Giraud, A.-L., D'Esposito, M., &

Kleinschmidt, A. Alpha-band phase synchrony is related to activity in the fronto-parietal adaptive control network, in *The Journal of Neuroscience*, 32, 2012, p. 14305-14310.

Sagvolden, T., Russell, VA., Aase, H., Johansen, EB., & Farshbaf, M. Rodent models of attention-deficit/hyperactivity disorder, in *Biological Psychiatry*, 57, 2005, p. 1239-1247.

Sakhiulina, GT. EEG manifestations of tonic cortical activity accompanying conditioned

reflexes, in *Pavlov Journal of Higher Nervous Activity*, 11, 1961, p. 48.

Sakurai, Y., Song, K., Tachibana, S., & Takahashi, S. Volitional enhancement of firing synchrony and oscillation by neuronal operant conditioning: interaction with neurorehabilitation and brain-machine interface, in *Frontiers in Systems Neuroscience*, 8, 2014, p. 1-11.

Saraev, SY., Kropotov, YD., & Ponomarev, VA. The possibilities of using direct transcranial polarization for treatment of children with attention deficit disorder, unpublished, 2002.

Sartory, G., Heine, A., Müller, BX., & Elvermann-Hallner, A. Event- and motor-related potentials during the CPT in AD/HD, in *Journal of Psychophysiology*, 16, 2002, p. 97-106.

Sauseng, P., Klimesch, W., Doppelmayr, M., Hanslmayr, S., Schabus, M, & Gruber, WR. Theta coupling in the human electroencephalogram during a working memory task, in *Neuroscience Letters*, 354, 2004, p. 123-126.

Schabus, M., Gruber, G., Parapatics, S., Sauter, C., Klösch, G., Anderer, P., Klimesch, W., Saletu, B., & Zeitlhofer, J. Sleep spindles and their significance for declarative memory consolidation, in *Sleep*, 27, 2004, p. 1479-1485.

Schabus, M., Heib, DPJ., Lechinger, J., Griessenberger, H., Klimesch, W., Pawlizkia, A., Kunzd,

AB., Sterman, BM., & Hoedlmoser, K. Enhancing sleep quality and memory in insomnia using instrumental sensorimotor rhythm conditioning, in *Biological Psychology*, 95, 2014, p. 126-134.

Shackman, AJ. ,Salomons, TV., Slagter, HA., Fox, AS., Winter, JJ. & Davidson, RJ. The integration of negative affect, pain and cognitive control in the cingulate cortex, in *Nature Reviews Neuroscience*, 12, 2011, p. 154-167.

Scheibel, AB. Anatomical and physiological substrates of arousal; a view from the bridge, in Hobson, JA., & Brazier, MAB. (Eds.), *The Reticular Formation Revisited*, Raven Press, New York, 1980, p. 55-66.

Scheinbaum, S., Zecker, S., Newton, CJ., & Rosenfeld, P. A controlled study of EEG biofeedback as a treatment for attention-deficit disorders, in *Proceedings of the Association of Applied Psychophysiology and Biofeedback*, 1995, p. 131-134.

Scheres, A., Milham, MP., Knutson, B., & Castellanos, FX. Ventral striatal hyporesponsiveness during reward anticipation in attention-deficit/hyperactivity disorder, in *Biological Psychiatry*, 61, 2007, p. 720-724.

Schiller, B., Gianotti, LRR., Nash, K. & Knoch, D. Individual differences in inhibitory control—relationship between baseline activation in lateral PFC and an electrophysiological index of response inhibition, in *Cerebral Cortex*, 24, 2014, p. 2430-2435.

Schultz, W., Dayan, P., & Montague, PR. A neural substrate of prediction and reward, in *Science*, 275, 1997, p. 1593-1599.

Seeley, WW., Menon, V., Schatzberg, AF., Keller, J., Glover, GH., Kenna, H., Reiss, AL. & Greicius, MD. Dissociable intrinsic connectivity networks for salience processing and executive control, in *The Journal of Neuroscience*, 27, 2007, p. 2349-2356

Seo, H., & Lee, D. Temporal filtering of reward signals in the dorsal anterior cingulate cortex during a mixed-*strategy* game, in *The Journal of Neuroscience*, 27, 2007, p. 8366-8377.

Sergeant, JA. The cognitive-energetic model: an empirical approach to attention-deficit hyperactivity disorder, in *Neuroscience and Behavioral Review*, 24, 2000, p. 7-12.

Shaw, P., Eckstrand, K., Sharp, W., Blumenthal, J., Lerch, J., Greenstein, D., Clasen, L., Evans, A., Giedd, J., & Rapoport, JL. Attention-deficit/hyperactivity disorder is characterized by a delay in cortical maturation, in *Proceedings of the National Academy of Sciences USA*, 104, 2007, p. 19649-19654.

Sheer, DE. Electrophysiological correlates of memory consolidation, in Ingar, G. (Ed.), *Molecular Mechanisms in Memory and Learning*, Plenum, New York, 1970.

Sheer, DE. Biofeedback training of 40 Hz EEG and behavior, in Burch, N., & Altschuler, HL. (Eds.), *Behavior and Brain Electrical Activity*, Plenum Press, New York, 1975, p. 325 362.

Sheer, DE. Focused arousal and 40 Hz EEG, in Knights, RM., & Bakker, DJ. (Eds.), *The Neurophysiology of Learning Disorders*, University Park Press, Baltimore, 1976, p. 71-87.

Sheer, DE. Biofeedback training of 40 Hz EEG and behavior, in Kamiya, J. (Ed.), *Biofeedback and self control, 1976/77*, Aldine, Chicago, 1977.

Sheer, DE. Focused arousal and the cognitive 40 Hz event-related potentials: differential diagnosis of Alzheimer's disease, in *Progress in Clinical and Biological Research*, 317, 1989, p. 79-94.

Shibagaki, M., Kiyono, S., & Watanabe, K. Nocturnal sleep in severe mentally retarded children: abnormal EEG patterns in sleep cycle, in *Electroencephalography and Clinical Electroencephalography*, 49, 1980, p. 337-344.

Sidlauskaite, J., Sonuga-Barke, E., Roeyers, H., & Wiersema, JR. Altered intrinsic organisation of brain networks implicated in attentional processes in adult attention-deficit/hyperactivity disorder: a resting-state study of attention, default mode and salience network connectivity, in *European Archives of Psychiatry and Clinical Neuroscience*, 266, 2016, p. 349-357.

Silberman, J. *Using source-localized EEG operant conditioning to up-regulate neural mechanisms underlying self-control and improve self-control ability.* Dissertation University of Rochester, Rochester, New York, 2013.

Simon, H., Scatton, B., & Le Moal, M. Dopaminergic A10 neurons are involved in cognitive function, in *Nature*, 286, 1980, p. 150-151.

Siniatchkin, M., Kropp, P., & Gerber, WD. Neurofeedback - the significance of reinforcement and the search for an appropriate strategy for the success of self-regulation, in *Applied Psychophysiology and Biofeedback*, 25, 2000, p. 167-175.

Sitaram, R., Lee, S., Ruiz, S., Rana, M., Veit, R., & Birbaumer, N. Real-time support vector classification and feedback of multiple emotional brain states, in *NeuroImage*, 56, 2011, p. 753-765.

Skinner, JE., & Yingling, CD. Central gating mechanisms that regulate event-related potentials and behavior, in Desmedt, JE (Ed.), *Attention, Voluntary Contraction and Event-Related Cerebral Potentials: Progress in Clinical Neurophysiology. Vol. 1*, Karger, Basel, 1977, p. 30-69.

Smallwood, J. Beach, E., Schooler, JW., & Handy, TC. Going AWOL in the brain: mind wandering reduces cortical analysis of external events, in *Journal of Cognitive Neuroscience*, 20, 2008, p. 458-469.

Song, DH., Shin, DW., Jon, DI., & Ha, EH. Effects of methylphenidate on quantitative EEG of boys with attention-deficit hyperactivity disorder in continuous performance test, in *Yonsei Medical Journal*, 46, 2005, p. 34-41.

Sonuga-Barke, EJS. Interval length and time-use by children with AD/HD: a comparison of four models, in *Journal of Abnormal Child Psychology*, 30, 2002, p. 257-264.

Sonuga-Barke, EJ. The dual pathway model of AD/HD: an elaboration of neuro-developmental characteristics, in *Neuroscience and Biobehavioral Reviews*, 27, 2003, p. 593-604.

Sonuga-Barke, EJ., & Castellanos, FX. Spontaneous attentional fluctuations in impaired states and pathological conditions: a neurobiological hypothesis, in *Neuroscience and Biobehavioral Reviews*, 31, 2007, p. 977-86.

Sonuga-Barke, EJ., Brandeis, D., Cortese, S., Daley, D., Ferrin, M., Holtmann, M., Stevenson, J., Danckaerts, M., van der Oord, S., Döpfner, M., Dittmann, RW., Simonoff, E., Zuddas, A., Banaschewski, T., Buitelaar, J., Coghill, D., Hollis, C., Konofal, E., Lecendreux, M., Wong, ICK., & Sergeant, J. Non-pharmacological interventions for ADHD: systematic review and meta-analyses of randomized controlled trials of dietary and psychological treatments, in *American Journal of Psychiatry*, 170, 2013, p. 275-289.

Sporns, O., Tononi, G., & Edelman, GM. Theoretical neuroanatomy: relating anatomical and functional connectivity in graphs and cortical connection matrices, in *Cerebral Cortex*, 10, 2000, p. 127-141.

Sporns, O., Tononi, G., & Edelman, GM. Theoretical neuroanatomy and the connectivity of the cerebral cortex, in *Behavioural Brain Research*, 135, 2002, p. 69-74.

Sporns, O. Network attributes for segregation and integration in the human brain, in *Current Opinion in Neurobiology*, 23, 2013, p. 162-171.

Spydell, JD., & Sheer, DE. Effect of problem solving on right and left hemisphere 40 Hz EEG activity, in *Psychophysiology*, 19, 1982, p. 420-425.

Sripada, CS., Kessler, D., Welsh, R., Angstadt, M., Liberzon, I., Phan, KL., & Scott, C. Distributed effects of methylphenidate on the network structure of the resting brain: a connectomic pattern classification analysis, in *NeuroImage*, 81, 2013, p. 213-221.

Sripada, CS., Kessler, D., & Angstadt, M. Lag in maturation of the brain's intrinsic functional architecture in attention-deficit/hyperactivity disorder, in *Proceedings of the National Academy of Sciences USA*, 111, 2014, p. 14259-14264.

Steiner, NJ., Frenette, EC., Kirsten, MR., Brennan, RT., & Perrin, EC. Neurofeedback and cognitive attention training for children with attention-deficit hyperactivity disorder in schools, in *Journal of Developmental & Behavioral Pediatrics*, 38, 2014, p. 18-27.

Steiner, NJ., Frenette, EC., Kirsten, MR., Brennan, RT., & Perrin, EC. In-school neurofeedback training for ADHD: sustained improvements from a randomized control trial, in *Pediatrics*, 133, 2014, p. 483-492.

Steriade, M., Nunez, A., & Amzica, F. A novel slow (<1Hz) oscillation of neocortical neurons in vivo: depolarizing and hyperpolarizing components, in *Journal of Neuroscience*, 13, 1993, p. 3252-3265.

Steriade, M., McCormick, DA., & Sejnowski, TJ. Thalamocortical oscillations in the sleeping and aroused brain, in *Science*, 262, 1993b, p. 679-685.

Steriade, M., & Amzica, F. Intracortical and corticothalamic coherency of fast spontaneous oscillations, in *Proceedings of the National Academy of Sciences USA*, 93, 1996, p. 2533-2538.

Sterman, MB. Ontogeny of sleep: implications for function, in Drucker-Colin, R., Shkurovich, M., & Sterman, MB. (Eds.), *The Functions of Sleep*, Academic Press, New York, 1979, p. 207-232.

Sterman, MB., & Shouse, MN. Quantitative analysis of training, sleep EEG and clinical response to EEG operant conditioning in epileptics, in *Electroencephalography and Clinical Neurophysiology*, 49, 1980, p. 558-576.

Sterman, MB., & Bowersox, SS. Sensorimotor EEG rhythmic activity: a functional gate mechanism, in *Sleep*, 4, 1981, p. 408-422.

Sterman, MB. Physiological origins and functional correlates of EEG rhythmic activities: implications for self-regulation, in *Biofeedback and Self-Regulation*, 21, 1996, p. 3-26.

Sterman, MB., Kaiser, DA., & Veigel, B. Spectral analysis of event-related EEG responses during short-term memory performance, in *Brain Topography*, 9, 1996, p. 21-30.

Stewart, CV., & Plenz, D. Inverted-U profile of dopamine-NMDA-mediated spontaneous avalanche recurrence in superficial layers of rat prefrontal cortex, in *The Journal of Neuroscience*, 26, 2006, p. 8148-8159.

Strehl, U., Leins, U., Goth, G., Klinger, C., Hinterberger, T., & Birbaumer, N. Self-regulation of slow cortical potentials: a new treatment for children with attention-deficit/hyperactivity disorder, in *Pediatrics*, 118(5), 2006, p. 1530-1540.

Ströhle, A., Stoy, M., Wrase, J., Schwarzer, S., Schlagenhauf, F., Huss, M., Hein, J., Nedderhut, A., Neumann, B., Gregor, A., Juckel, G., Knutson, B., Lehmkuhl, U., Bauer, M., & Heinz, A.

Reward anticipation and outcomes in adult males with attention-deficit/hyperactivity disorder, in *NeuroImage*, 39, 2008, p. 966-972.

Suffin, SC., & Emory, WH. Neurometric subgroups in attentional and affective disorders and their association with pharmacotherapeutic outcome, in *Clinical Electroencephalography*, 25, 1995, p. 1-8.

Sun, L., Cao, Q., Long, X., Sui, M., Cao, X., Zhu, C., Zuo, X., An, L., Song, Y., Zang, Y., & Wang, Y. Abnormal functional connectivity between the anterior cingulate and the default mode network in drug-naïve boys with attention deficit hyperactivity disorder, in *Psychiatry Research*, 201, 2012, p.120-127.

Swartwood, MO., Swartwood, JN., Lubar, JF., Timmermann, DL., Zimmerman, AW., & Muenchen, RA. Methylphenidate effects on EEG, behavior, and performance in boys with ADHD, in *Pediatric Neurology*, 18, 1998, p. 244-250.

Tallon, C., Bertrand, O., Bouchet, P., & Pernier, J. Gamma-range activity evoked by coherent visual stimuli in humans, in *European Journal of Neuroscience*, 7, 1995, p. 1285-1291.

Tallon-Baudry, C., Bertrand, O., Delpuech, C., & Pernier, J. Stimulus specificity of phase-locked

and non-phase-locked 40 Hz visual responses in humans, in *Journal of Neuroscience*, 16, 1996, p. 4240-4249.

Talmi, D., Atkinson, R., & El-Deredy, W. The feedback-related negativity signals salience prediction errors, not reward prediction errors, in *The Journal of Neuroscience*, 33, 2013, p. 8264-8269.

Tanaka, SC., Balleine, BW., & O'Doherty, JP. Calculating consequences: brain systems that encode the causal effects of actions, in *The Journal of Neuroscience*, 28, 2008, p. 6750-6755.

Tansey, MA. Brainwave signatures – an index reflective of the brain's functional neuroanatomy: further findings on the effect of EEG sensorimotor rhythm biofeedback training on the neurologic precursors of learning disabilities, in *International Journal of Psychophysiology*, 3, 1985, p. 85-99.

Tansey, MA. Righting the rhythms of reason: EEG biofeedback training as a therapeutic modality in a clinical office setting, in *Medical Psychotherapy*, 3, 1991, p. 57-68.

Tansey, MA. Wechsler (WISC-R) changes following treatment of learning disabilities via EEG biofeedback training in a private practice setting, in *Australian Journal of Psychology*, 43, 1991a, p. 147-153.

Terzano, MG., Parrino, L., & Spaggiari, MC. The cyclic alternating pattern sequences in the dynamic organization of sleep, in *Electroencephalography and Clinical Neurophysiology*, 69, 1988, p. 437-447.

Terzano, MG., Parrino, L., Smerieri, A., Chervin, R., Chokrovertry, S., Guilleminault, C., Hishkowitz, M., Mahowald, M., Moldofsky, H., Rosa, A., Thomas, R., & Walters, A.

Atlas, rules and recording techniques for the scoring of cyclic alternating patterns (CAP) in human sleep, in *Sleep Medicine*, 2, 2001, p. 537-553.

Tesche, CD., & Karhu, J. Theta oscillations index human hippocampal activation during a working memory task, in *Proceedings of the National Academy of Sciences USA*, 97, 2000, p. 919-924.

Thatcher, RW., Krause, PJ., & Hrybyk, M. Cortico-cortical associations and EEG coherence: a two-compartmental model, in *Electroencephalography and Clinical Neurophysiology*, 64, 1986, p. 123-143.

Thatcher, RW. A predator-prey model of human cerebral development, in Newell, K., & Molenaar, P. (Eds.), *Applications of Nonlinear Dynamics to Developmental Process Modeling*, Lawrence Erlbaum Associates, Mahway, New Jersey, 1998, p. 87-128.

Thatcher, RW., North, D., & Biver, C. EEG and intelligence: relations between EEG coherence, EEG phase delay and power, in *Clinical Neurophysiology*, 116, 2005, p. 2129-2141.

Thatcher, RW., North, D., & Biver, C. Intelligence and EEG phase reset: A two compartmental model of phase shift and lock, in *NeuroImage*, 42, 2008, p. 1639-1653.

Thelen, E. Self-organization in developmental processes: can systems approaches work?, in Johnson, MH. (Ed.), *Brain Development and Cognition*, Blackwell, Oxford, 1993, p. 555-592.

Thoman, E. Regulation of stimulation by prematures with a breathing blue bear, in *The Malleability of Children*, Gallagher, JJ., & Ramey, CT. (Eds.), Brooks Publishing, Baltimore, 1987, p. 51-70.

Thomas, M, Sing, H., Belenky, G., Holcomb, H., Mayberg, H., Dannals, R., Wagner; H., Thorne, D., Popp, K., Rowland, L., Welsh, A., Balwinski, S., & Redmond, D. Neural basis of alertness and cognitive performance impairments during sleepiness. I. Effects of 24 h of sleep deprivation on waking human regional brain activity, in *Journal of Sleep Research*, 9, 2000, p. 335-352.

Thompson, L., & Thompson, M. Neurofeedback combined with training in metacognitive strategies: effectiveness in students with ADD, in *Applied Psychophysiology and Biofeedback*, 23, 1998, p. 243-263.

Thompson, L., & Thompson, M. *The Neurofeedback Book: an Introduction to Basic Concepts in Applied Psychophysiology*. Association for Applied Psychophysiology and Biofeedback, Wheat Ridge, Colorado, 2003.

Thompson, L., & Thompson, M. Neurofeedback intervention for adults with ADHD, in *Journal of Adult Development*, 12, 2005, p. 123-130.

Tinius, T., & Tinius, KA. Changes after EEG biofeedback and cognitive retraining in adults with mild traumatic brain injury and attention deficit hyperactivity disorder, in *Journal of Neurotherapy*, 4, 2000, p. 27-44.

Tirsch, WS., Keidel, M., & Sommer, G. Time order in brain chaos, in Croon, MA., & van de Vijver, FJR. (Eds.), *Viability of Mathematical Models in the Social and Behavioral Sciences*, Swets & Zeitlinger, Lisse, 1995, p. 55-77.

Tirsch, WS., Keidel, M., Perz, S., Scherb, H., & Sommer, G. Inverse covariation of spectral density and correlation dimension in cyclic EEG dynamics of the human brain, in *Biological Cybernetics*, 82, 2000, p. 1-14.

Tirsch, WS., Stude, P., Scherb, H., & Keidel, M. Temporal order of nonlinear dynamics in

human brain, in *Brain Research Reviews*, 45, 2004, p. 79-95.

Tomasi, D., & Volkow, ND. Abnormal functional connectivity in children with attention deficit/hyperactivity disorder, in *Biological Psychiatry*, 71, 2012, p. 443-450.

Townsend, RE., & Johnson, LC. Relation of frequency-analyzed EEG to monitoring behavior, in *Electroencephalography and Clinical Neurophysiology*, 47, 1979, p. 272-279.

Tricomi, EM., Delgado, MR., & Fiez, JA. Modulation of caudate activity by action contingency, in *Neuron*, 41, 2004, p. 281-292.

Tripp, G., & Wickens, JR. Research review: dopamine transfer deficit: a neurobiological theory of altered reinforcement mechanisms in ADHD, in *Journal of Child Psychology and Psychiatry*, 49, 2008, p. 691-704.

Tripp, G., & Wickens, JR. Neurobiology of ADHD, in *Neuropharmacology*, 57, 2009, p. 579-589.

Tripp., G. & Wickens, J. Reinforcement, dopamine and rodent models in drug development for ADHD, in *Neurotherapeutics*, 9, 2012, p. 622-634.

Tsai, LL., Young, HY., Hsieh, S., & Lee, CS., Impairment of error monitoring following sleep deprivation, in *Sleep*, 28, 2005, p. 707-713.

Tucker, DM., & Williamson, PA. Asymmetric neural control system in human self-regulation, in *Psychological Review*, 91, 1984, p. 185-215.

Uddin, LQ., Kelly, AM., Biswal, BB., Margulies, DS., Shehzad, Z., Shaw, D., Ghaffari, M., Rotrosen, J., Adler, LA., Castellanos, FX., & Milham, MP. Network homogeneity reveals decreased integrity of default-mode network in ADHD, in *Journal of Neuroscience Methods*, 169, 2008, p. 249-54.

Ulrich, G. *Psychiatrische Elektro-Enzephalographie*. Fischer, Jena, 1994.

Ulrich, G. *The Theoretical Interpretation of Electroencephalography: The important role of spontaneous resting EEG and vigilance*. BMED Press LLC, Corpus Christi, Texas, 2013. (http://www.bmedpress.com/shop/theoretical-interpretation-of-electroencephalography-eeg)

Vaidya, CJ., Austin, G., Krikorian G., Ridlehuber HW., Desmond GE., Glover GH., & Gabrieli, JD. Selective effects of methylphenidate in attention deficit hyperactivity disorder: a functional magnetic resonance study, in *Proceedings of the National Academy of Sciences USA*, 95, 1998, p. 14494-14499.

Valko, L., Doehnert, M., Müller, UC., Schneider, G., Albrecht, B., Drechsler, R., Maechler, M., Steinhausen, H.-C., & Brandeis, D. Differences in neurophysiological markers of inhibitory and temporal processing deficits in children and adults with ADHD, in *Journal of Psychophysiology*, 23, 2009, p. 235-246.

Van der Meere, J. ADHD en toestandregulatie, in *Neuropraxis*, 5, 2001, p. 185-190.

van Dongen-Boomsma, M., Vollebregt, MA., Slaats-Willemse, D., & Buitelaar, JK. A randomized placebo-controlled trial of electroencephalographic (EEG) neurofeedback in children with attention-deficit/hyperactivity disorder, in *Journal of Clinical Psychiatry*, 74, 2013, p. 821-827.

Vanhatalo, S., Palva, JM., Holmes, MD., Miller, JW., Voipio, J., & Kaila, K. Infraslow oscillations modulate excitability and interictal epileptic activity in the human cortex during sleep, in *Proceedings of the National Academy of Sciences USA*, 101, 2004, p. 5053-5057.

Vanhatalo, S., Voipio, J., & Kaila, K. Full-band EEG (FbEEG): a new standard for clinical electroencephalography, in *Clinical EEG and Neuroscience*, 36, 2005, p. 311-317.

Van Orden, G., & Holden, JG., Intentional contents and self-control, in *Ecological Psychology*, 14, 2002, p. 87–109.

Vanrullen, R., & Dubois, J. The psychophysics of brain rhythms, in *Frontiers in Psychology*, 2, 2011, p. 203.

Varela, FJ., Thompson, E., & Rosch, E. *The Embodied Mind*. MIT Press, Cambridge, MA, 1991.

Venkatraman, V., Chuah, YML., Huettel, SA., & Chee, MWL. Sleep deprivation elevates expectation of gains and attenuates response to losses following risky decisions, in *Sleep*, 30, 2007, p. 603-609.

Venkatraman, V., Huettel, SA., Chuah, LYM., Payne, JW. & Chee, MWL. Sleep deprivation biases the neural mechanisms underlying economic preferences, in *The Journal of Neuroscience*, 31, 2011, p. 3712-3718.

Vincent, JL., Kahn, I., Snyder, AZ., Raichle, ME., & Buckner, RL. Evidence for a frontoparietal control system revealed by intrinsic functional connectivity, in *Journal of Neurophysiology*, 100, 2008, p. 3328-3342.

Volkow, ND., & Swanson, JM. Variables that affect the clinical use and abuse of methylphenidate in the treatment of ADHD, in *American Journal of Psychiatry*, 160, 2003, p. 1909-1918.

Volkow, ND., Wang, GJ., Kollins, SH., Wigal, TL., Newcorn, JH., Telang, F., Fowler, JS., Zhu, W., Logan, J., Ma, Y., Pradhan, K., Wong, C., & Swanson, JM. Evaluating dopamine reward pathway in ADHD: clinical implications, in *JAMA*, 302, 2009, p. 1084-1091.

Volkow, ND., Wang, G.-J., Newcorn, JH., Kollins, SH., Wigal, TL., Telang, F., Fowler, JS., Goldstein, RZ., Klein, N., Logan, J., Wong, C., & Swanson, JM. Motivation deficit in ADHD is associated with dysfunction of the dopamine reward pathway, in *Molecular Psychiatry*, 16, 2011, p. 1147-1154.

Volkow, ND., Tomasi, D., Wang, G.-J., Telang, F., Fowler, JS., Logan, J., Benveniste, H., Kim, R., Thanos, PK., & Ferré, S. Evidence that sleep deprivation downregulates dopamine D2R in ventral striatum in the human brain, in *The Journal of Neuroscience*, 32, 2012, p. 6711-6717.

Volkow, ND., & Baler, RD. Now versus later brain circuits: implications for obesity and addiction, in *Trends in Neurosciences*, 38, 2015, p. 345-352.

Vollebregt, MA., van Dongen-Boomsma, M., Buitelaar, JK., & Slaats-Willemse, D. Does EEG-neurofeedback improve neurocognitive functioning in children with attention deficit/hyperactivity disorder? A systematic review and a double-blind placebo-controlled study, in *Journal of Child Psychology and Psychiatry*, 55, 2014, p. 460-472.

von Stein, A., Chiang, C., & Konig, P. Top-down processing mediated by interareal synchronization, in *Proceedings of the National Academy of Sciences USA*, 97, 2000, p. 14748-14753.

Wallis, JD., & Miller, EK. Neuronal activity in primate dorsolateral and orbital prefrontal cortex during performance of a reward preference task, in *European Journal of Neuroscience*, 18, 2003, p. 2069–2081.

Wang, J.-R., & Hsieh, S. Neurofeedback training improves attention and working memory performance, in *Clinical Neurophysiology*, 124, 2013, p. 2406-2420.

Wang, L., Zhu, C., He, Y., Zang, Y., Cao, QJ., Zhang, H., Zhong, Q., & Wang, Y. Altered small-world brain functional networks in children with attention-deficit/hyperactivity disorder, in *Human Brain Mapping*, 30, 2009, p. 638-649.

Wang, Q., Sourina, O., & Nguyen, MK. Fractal dimension based neurofeedback in serious games, In *Visual Computer*, 27, 2011, p. 299-309.

Watson, JB, How animals find their way home, in *Harper's Monthly Magazine*, 119, 1909, p. 685-689.

Watts, DJ., & Strogatz, SH. Collective dynamics of "small-world" networks, in *Nature*, 393, 1998, p. 440-442.

Wauquier, A. La microstructure du sommeil au cours du vieillissement. Founding Congress of the World Federation of Sleep Research Societies. Cannes, 1991.

Weber, E., Köberl, A., Frank, S., & Doppelmayr, M. Predicting successful learning of SMR neurofeedback in healthy participants: methodological considerations, in *Applied Psychophysiology and Biofeedback*, 36, 2011, p. 37-45.

Weiss, V. The relationship between short-term memory capacity and EEG power spectral density, in *Biological Cybernetics*, 68, 1992, p. 165-172.

Weissman, DH., Warner, LM., & Woldorff, MG. Momentary reductions of attention permit greater processing of irrelevant stimuli, in *NeuroImage*, 48, 2009, p. 609-615.

Wender, PH. *Minimal brain dysfunction syndrome in children*. Wiley, New York, 1971.

Wender, PH. The minimal brain dysfunction syndrome in children, in *Journal of Nervous and Mental Disorders*, 155, 1972, p. 55-71.

Wender, PH. Some speculations concerning a possible biochemical basis of minimal brain dysfunction, in *Life Science*, 14, 1974, p. 1605-1621.

Wender, PH., Wolf, LE., & Wasserstein, J. Adults with ADHD. An overview, in *Annals of the New York Academy of Sciences USA*, 931, 2001, p.1-16.

Werner, J., Weisbrod, M., Resch, F., Roessner, V., & Bender, S. Increased performance uncertainty in children with ADHD? - Elevated post-imperative negative variation (PINV) over the ventrolateral prefrontal cortex, in *Behavioral and Brain Functions*, 7:38, 2011.

Wiener, N. *Cybernetics, or control and communication in the animal and the machine*. MIT Press, New York, 1948.

Wilbertz, G., van Elst, LT., Delgado, MR., Maier, S., Feige, B., Philipsen, A., & Blechert J. Orbitofrontal reward sensitivity and impulsivity in adult attention deficit hyperactivity disorder, in *NeuroImage*, 60, 2012, p. 353-361.

Willcutt, EG., Doyle, AE., Nigg, JT., Faraone, SV., & Pennington, BF. Validity of the executive function theory of attention-deficit/hyperactivity disorder: a meta-analytic review, in *Biological Psychiatry*, 57, 2005, p. 1336-1346.

Wilson, TW., Franzen, JD., Heinrichs-Graham, E., White, ML., Knott, NL., & Wetzel, MW. Broadband neurophysiological abnormalities in the medial prefrontal region of the default-mode network in adults with ADHD, in *Human Brain Mapping*, 34, 2013, p. 566-574.

Winson, J. *Brain and Psyche: the Biology of the Unconscious*. Vintage Books, New York, 1986.

Winstanley, CA., Theobald, DE., Cardinal, RN., & Robbins, TW. Contrasting roles of basolateral amygdala and orbitofrontal cortex in impulsive choice, in *The Journal of Neuroscience*, 24, 2004, p. 4718-4722.

Witte, M., Kober, SE., Ninaus, M., Neuper, C., & Wood, G. Control beliefs can predict the ability to up-regulate sensorimotor rhythm during neurofeedback training, in *Frontiers in Human Neuroscience*, 7, 2013, p. 1-8.

Woltering, S., Jung, J., Liu, Z., & Tannock R. Resting state EEG oscillatory power differences in ADHD college students and their peers, in *Behavioral and Brain Functions*, 8, 2012, p. 1-9.

Wunderlich, K., Rangel, A., & O'Doherty, JP. Neural computations underlying action-based decision making in the human brain, in *Proceedings of the National Academy of Sciences USA*, 106, 2009, p. 17199-17204.

Wyrwicka, W. & Sterman, MB. Instrumental conditioning of sensorimotor cortex EEG spindles in the waking cat, in *Physiology and Behavior*, 3, 1968, p. 703-707.

Yan-ling, R., & Xuan, D. Effects of methylphenidate in children with attention deficit hyperactivity disorder: a comparison of behavioral results and event-related potentials, in Banerjee, S. (Ed.), *Attention Deficit Hyperactivity Disorder in Children and Adolescents*, Intech, 2013.

Yeung, N. Relating cognitive and affective theories of the error-related negativity, in Ullsperger, M., & Falkenstein, M. (Eds.), *Errors, Conflicts, and the Brain. Current Opinions on Performance Monitoring*, MPI of Cognitive Neuroscience, Leipzig, 2004.

Yeung, N. Conflict monitoring and cognitive control, in Ochsner, KN. & Kosslyn, S. (Eds.), *The Oxford Handbook of Cognitive Neuroscience: Volume 2: The Cutting Edges*, Oxford University Press, Oxford, 2013.

Young, ES., Perros, P., Price, GW., & Sadler, T. Acute challenge ERP as a prognostic of stimulant therapy outcome in attention-deficit/hyperactivity disorder, in *Biological Psychiatry*, 37, 1995, p. 25-33.